MOYLISH

ELEMENTARY MECHANICS

D. A. QUADLING, M.A., F.I.M.A.
Mathematics Tutor, Cambridge Institute of Education
Formerly Senior Mathematical Master, Marlborough College

and

A. R. D. RAMSAY, M.A.
Formerly Head of the Mathematics Department, Christ's College
Christchurch, New Zealand
Formerly Senior Mathematical Master, Marlborough College

Volume 1

SECOND EDITION

(*METRICATED*)

BELL & HYMAN
LONDON

Published by
BELL & HYMAN LIMITED
Denmark House
37–39 Queen Elizabeth Street
London SE1 2QB

First published in 1959 by
G. Bell & Sons Limited
Reprinted 1960, 1962, 1963, 1965, 1966

Second edition (metricated) published 1971
Reprinted 1971, 1972, 1975, 1978, 1979 (twice), 1981, 1983

ISBN 0 7135 1690 9

Printed in Great Britain by
Richard Clay (The Chaucer Press) Ltd,
Bungay, Suffolk

PREFACE TO THE SECOND EDITION

THE widespread adoption of the International System of Units (SI) has made necessary a revision of this book. The authors would like to express their appreciation to the publishers for inviting the preparation of this new edition and for their helpfulness at all stages of its production.

Since the first edition was published, there have been some changes in the importance attached to the teaching of various topics at this level. Vector methods, still regarded as an innovation fifteen years ago, are now widely used by quite young pupils at the school; vectors and vector algebra provide the ideal mathematical model for much of newtonian mechanics, and the opportunity has been taken to make more use of them, particularly in the chapter on the motion of projectiles. Space travel has acquainted pupils with a new range of experiences which the teacher can call upon to strengthen understanding of the fundamental laws of motion. Some teachers have begun to make considerable use of mechanisms as a means of enriching spatial experience, leading to a freer treatment of geometry by transformation methods, and it is hoped that the chapter on machines (no longer so popular as an examination topic) may be seen as a natural and interesting extension of this approach.

Certain changes in notation have been made in line with the report on SI units by the Education Committee of the Association for Science Education (1969); it is hoped that the use of a common language may help to strengthen cooperation between teachers of mathematics, science and technical subjects. In a few cases, however, the authors have felt it necessary to deviate from the letter of these recommendations. In particular, the abbreviation for gramme has been taken as gm rather than g, since experience has shown that otherwise there can be considerable confusion (especially in manuscript) with g, the acceleration due to gravity. Furthermore, the authors consider the proposal that letters in formulae should always represent physical quantities to be unnecessarily rigid and have felt free to use algebraic symbols in whatever manner has seemed most appropriate to each particular situation.

The authors are especially indebted to Mr. J. A. L. Clark, of Merchant Taylors School, Northwood, who undertook the preliminary revision of all the exercises in this volume, and in the process contributed many useful ideas which are reflected in the revised text.

D. A. Q.
A. R. D. R.

PREFACE TO THE FIRST EDITION

THIS is the first of three volumes whose purpose is to provide a continuous course in mechanics leading from the beginnings of the subject up to the threshold of university work. It is hoped that the course will be suitable not only for the scientist and mathematical specialist but also for the future engineer. In the first volume most of the basic ideas of the subject are introduced and their consequences worked out in simple applications; these have been kept as far as possible within the immediate experience of the student.

The authors feel that, although the early treatment of mechanics must not be too rigorous, it is important that pupils should from the start understand the basic principles. If the theoretical treatment during the first year is too cursory, much of the work has to be repeated at a later stage. With this in mind, the authors have given proofs of results which are within the scope of a beginner; but if a proof is too difficult to be appreciated by an inexperienced student, the result has been quoted, with a brief explanation on practical lines, and a full proof deferred until a later volume.

In writing this first volume the authors have not felt themselves to be tied to the requirements of any particular examination, since they regard a sound understanding of the subject as of greater importance than the acquisition of techniques for solving particular problems. Nevertheless, it will be found that the book contains all that is needed for the papers set in Mechanics at Ordinary level for the General Certificate of Education. The second volume will continue the work as far as the Advanced level, and will also be suitable for those preparing for certain other examinations, such as the Qualifying Examination for the Mechanical Sciences Tripos at Cambridge[1] and Part I of the examination for B.Sc. (Engineering) at London University.

There is much to be said in favour of developing statics and dynamics side by side from the very beginning, rather than confining the first term's work to one or other branch of the subject, and this policy has been adopted in deciding the order of the topics dealt with in this book. This order, which aims at a logical yet didactic development of the subject, has been found successful in the classroom, but teachers using the book will easily find variations to suit their own wishes. For example, the chapters on large bodies, relative velocity and the triangle of forces could be taken earlier in the course if desired, and the chapter on

---

[1] This examination has since been discontinued.

vii

projectiles could come earlier or later without upsetting the logical development. Some teachers whose pupils are taking a parallel course in physics like to introduce the idea of energy at an early stage; they could use Chapter 16 at any time after Chapter 4 has been read.

Absolute units of force, with the equation of motion in the form $F = ma$; are used from the very beginning of the work in dynamics. The authors have found in their experience that this is the surest way of avoiding confusion about units later on, and they have been encouraged by the weight of opinion in favour of this policy which they have encountered in discussion with other teachers of the subject. If none but gravitational units are used at the outset, the pupils have to use an equation which they will later have to unlearn, and this is most undesirable. Another feature of the book is that more use is made of vectors than is customary in a work of this standard. In this first volume, only the simplest operations with vectors—addition, subtraction and multiplication by a scalar—are introduced, and they are accompanied by worked examples and exercises in order that the notation may become thoroughly familiar.

Nearly all of the book can be read by a student with no knowledge of calculus, although the authors have not hesitated to use calculus when it has seemed appropriate. Sections and exercises which require its use have been marked with an asterisk. The only chapter into which a substantial amount of calculus has been introduced is that on centres of gravity; the authors believe that it is impossible otherwise to give a satisfactory treatment of this branch of the subject.

A large number of exercises is provided in the text. These are carefully designed to give the student practice in all branches of the work, and the questions are graded according to difficulty. Some of the questions involve the use of metric systems of units (both c.g.s. and m.k.s.). Most exercises contain a few questions marked with daggers (†); these questions are of a harder nature than the rest, and are designed for the abler or more mature student. Teachers may also find them useful for a second reading. Four sets of miscellaneous exercises are included, the questions in these being taken largely from papers set by various examining bodies.

The authors wish to thank the examining bodies concerned for permission to reprint these questions. They are also indebted to Mr. W. M. Dain, who read the whole manuscript and made numerous criticisms and suggestions, and to a number of other colleagues whose advice they sought on particular matters.

D. A. Q.
A. R. D. R.

CONTENTS
VOLUME 1

ix

Questions have been used, with permission, from examination papers set by the Department of Engineering, University of Cambridge, and from G.C.E. Examinations of the following Boards:

Joint Matriculation Board
London University
Oxford and Cambridge Joint Board
Southern Universities Joint Board

In many of these questions data have been changed to approximate SI equivalents.

INTRODUCTION

ABBREVIATIONS, CONVENTIONS, TRIGONOMETRY

Abbreviations

0.1 Abbreviations for basic and named derived units in SI used in this book are:

m	metre
kg	kilogramme
s	second
N	newton
J	joule
W	watt
l	litre

Any of these (except for the kilogramme) may be modified by the use of prefixes to give multiple and submultiple units as follows:

m	milli-	$(\times 10^{-3})$
k	kilo-	$(\times 10^{3})$
M	mega-	$(\times 10^{6})$

Abbreviations for other units used in this book are:

gm	gramme	$(= 10^{-3} \text{ kg})$
cm	centimetre	$(= 10^{-2} \text{ m})$
h	hour	
min	minute	

The megagramme $(= 10^{3} \text{ kg})$ is often known as a *tonne*.

The following abbreviations are also used:

N, S, E, W	north, south, east, west
C.G.	centre of gravity
K.E.	kinetic energy
P.E.	potential energy
$\tilde{\omega}$	$\tan^{-1}\left(\frac{3}{4}\right)$ (see § 0.3)

Conventions

0.2 In elementary mechanics it is customary to make a number of approximations to reality, for the sake of simplicity.

By a *particle* is meant a body possessing some mass but with linear dimensions so small that the body may be regarded as located at a single point. By a *lamina* is meant a body with some mass having an appreciable plane area but negligible thickness.

Unless the contrary is specifically stated it will be supposed that all strings are light (i.e. of negligible mass) and inextensible. It will also be supposed that the Earth's surface is flat, and that the acceleration due to gravity does not vary with height. The effect of air resistance is ignored unless specific mention is made of it.

A *rigid body* is one for which the distance between every pair of particles of matter composing it remains constant.

The following letters are reserved for special purposes:

g	acceleration due to gravity
μ	(Greek 'mu') coefficient of friction
λ	(Greek 'lambda') angle of friction.

The acceleration due to gravity (g) is approximately 9·8 m s⁻², often conveniently taken to a sufficient degree of accuracy as 10 m s⁻².

By a *slope of angle* α is meant a slope inclined at an angle α to the horizontal. A hill of slope 1 in n (or $100/n$ per cent) is one which rises 1 metre for every n metres measured along the slope; that is, a slope of angle $\sin^{-1}(1/n)$.

The symbol * preceding a piece of work or a question in an exercise means that a knowledge of calculus is necessary to understand it. The symbol † designates a piece of work of a rather harder nature, which may be omitted at a first reading.

Mathematical symbols in heavy type (**a, b, c,** etc) always denote vector quantities.

Trigonometry

0.3 Some knowledge of trigonometry is required for the solution of many problems in mechanics.

In Chapter 4 we use the results:

$$\cos(90° - \theta) = \sin\theta, \qquad \cos(180° - \theta) = -\cos\theta,$$

$$\cos^2\theta + \sin^2\theta = 1, \qquad \tan\theta = \frac{\sin\theta}{\cos\theta}.$$

It is often helpful to make use of the simple values for the sin, cos, tan, etc. of 30°, 45°, 60°, which are given by Figs. 1 and 2. Thus

$$\sin 45° = \frac{1}{\sqrt{2}}, \qquad \cos 60° = \tfrac{1}{2}, \text{ etc.}$$

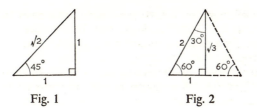

Fig. 1   Fig. 2

It is also useful to denote by the symbol $\tilde{\omega}$ (which may conveniently be pronounced 'pomega') the smallest angle of the 3, 4, 5 right-angled triangle (Fig. 3). Thus

$$\sin \tilde{\omega} = \tfrac{3}{5} = 0 \cdot 6, \quad \cos \tilde{\omega} = \tfrac{4}{5} = 0 \cdot 8, \quad \tan \tilde{\omega} = \tfrac{3}{4} = 0 \cdot 75.$$

$\tilde{\omega}$ is approximately $36° 52'$.

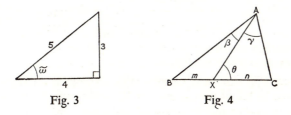

Fig. 3   Fig. 4

In solving vector triangles (Chapters 7 and 9) the following formulae are useful:

$$\frac{a}{\sin A} = \frac{b}{\sin B} = \frac{c}{\sin C},$$

$$a^2 = b^2 + c^2 - 2bc \cos A,$$

$$\tan \frac{B - C}{2} = \frac{b - c}{b + c} \cot \frac{A}{2}.$$

In problems on large bodies using the concurrency principle (Chapter 10) Fig. 4 is often encountered. The desired relations between the lengths and angles in this figure may be obtained by applying the sine formula in turn to two of the three triangles ABX, ACX, ABC, or by use of one or other of the following formulae:

$$n \cot B - m \cot C = (m + n) \cot \theta,$$

$$m \cot \beta - n \cot \gamma = (m + n) \cot \theta.$$

CHAPTER 1

VELOCITY AND ACCELERATION

Velocity

1.1 *EXAMPLE 1. An aircraft flies for 50 seconds in a straight line at a speed of 0·6 km per second. Represent this on a graph.*
On the axis across the page we represent time, and on the axis up the page the distance gone. The aircraft is covering equal distances in equal intervals of time; in each second it goes 0·6 km. The table shows the distances from the starting point at various times:

Time (s)	0	10	20	30	40	50
Distance (km)	0	6	12	18	24	30

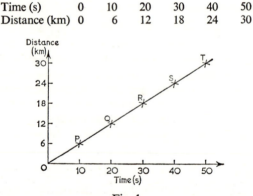

Fig. 1

The points *P, Q, R, S, T* have been plotted from this table. It will be seen that the graph representing the progress of the aircraft is a straight line.

A body moving in a straight line, and covering equal distances in equal periods of time, is said to have a CONSTANT VELOCITY, or UNIFORM VELOCITY. The aircraft in Example 1 has a uniform velocity of 0·6 km per second.

1.2 The units in which velocity is measured are determined by the units of distance and time. Thus a velocity may be given in metres per second (m s⁻¹), kilometres per hour (km h⁻¹), etc.

4

An alternative form of abbreviation uses the solidus (/) rather than the negative index, in forms such as m/s, km/h. Either notation is consistent with the familiar usage for arithmetic fractions: a velocity measured in m s⁻¹, or m/s, is found by dividing the number of metres travelled by the number of seconds taken.

When using the abbreviation m s⁻¹, care should be taken to make a small space between the letters m and s. This is to avoid confusion with ms⁻¹, which could be an abbreviation for 'per millisecond'.

EXAMPLE 2. A car's speedometer registers 72 km h⁻¹. Express this velocity in m s⁻¹.

If the car goes 72 km in 1 h, then in 1 s it goes 72/3600 km. Since 1 km = 1000 m, the number of metres travelled in each second is

$$\frac{72}{3600} \times 1000 = 20.$$

The speed of the car is therefore 20 m s⁻¹.

We sometimes find it convenient to write calculations of this kind in a somewhat different way, as follows:

$$\text{speed} = \frac{72 \text{ km}}{1 \text{ h}} = \frac{72\,000 \text{ m}}{3600 \text{ s}} = 20 \text{ m s}^{-1}.$$

What has been done here is to extend the idea of division to allow the operation to be performed on the physical quantities themselves rather than the numbers with which they are measured. Students are sometimes uneasy about this, and it is a practice which can always be avoided if desired; but it is in fact possible to justify this algebra of physical quantities, and labour can sometimes be saved by using it.

1.3 *EXAMPLE 3. A motorist is driving along a motorway which runs due N and S from a junction known as Roman's Cross. He starts 20 km N of the junction at 9 a.m., drives for ¾ h N at 80 km h⁻¹, waits for ¾ h at a service centre and then drives S a distance of 120 km at 60 km h⁻¹. After another ½ h wait he returns to Roman's Cross, arriving there at 2 p.m. Represent his journey on a graph.*

The graph used is of the type known as a DISPLACEMENT–TIME GRAPH. On the axis across the page we represent time, and on the other the displacement of the car from some convenient origin, in this example the Roman's Cross junction. It is necessary to establish a positive and a negative sense in which displacements are measured; we shall choose this so that points to the north of the junction have a positive displacement from the origin, and points to the south a negative displacement. It is important to notice that we now use the idea of displacement rather than distance. During the journey the car actually goes 220 km, but this distance is not directly represented on the graph. It is customary to use the letter *s* to stand for displacements.

We have supposed that the car travels at a uniform velocity on each leg of its journey. It follows that, as in § 1.1, the corresponding portions of the graph will be straight lines (see Fig. 2). The velocity of the car is shown in the following way.

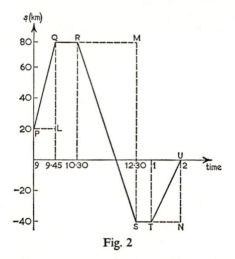

Fig. 2

Consider the motion between the points P and Q on the graph. The time for this leg is $\frac{3}{4}$ h, represented by the line PL. In this time the car goes 60 km N, represented by the line LQ. The velocity of the car is shown by the fraction LQ/PL, and is

$$60 \text{ km} \div \tfrac{3}{4} \text{ h} = 80 \text{ km h}^{-1}.$$

This fraction is called the SLOPE, or the GRADIENT, of the graph.

It should be noted that the displacement from P to Q can be calculated as (displacement at Q)−(displacement at P)=(+80 km)−(+20 km)= +60 km.

Similarly over the leg TU the displacement is 40 km, since

(displacement at U) − (displacement at T) = 0 − (−40 km) = +40 km.

This time represented by TN is 1 h, so that the velocity for this leg is shown by NU/TN, giving

$$40 \text{ km} \div 1 \text{ h} = 40 \text{ km h}^{-1}.$$

For the leg RS the time is represented by RM and is 2 h. The displacement MS is

(displacement at S)−(displacement at R)=(−40 km)−(+80 km)= −120 km.

The minus sign indicates that the displacement is 120 km *south*. The velocity is given by MS/RM, and equals

$$(-120 \text{ km}) \div 2 \text{ h} = -60 \text{ km h}^{-1}.$$

The negative sign in the velocity is interpreted as meaning that the car is moving southwards and not northwards. Velocity is a quantity that has direction; the value of a velocity is positive when that velocity is in the direction of positive displacements.

1.4 When the velocity of a body is not uniform (for example, if we consider the complete motion of the car in Example 3 from 9 a.m. to 2 p.m.) we define the AVERAGE VELOCITY as

$$\frac{\text{total displacement}}{\text{total time}}.$$

In Example 3 the total displacement of the car between 9 a.m. and 2 p.m. is

(displacement at U) $-$ (displacement at P)
$$= 0 - (+20 \text{ km}) = -20 \text{ km}.$$

The time interval is 5 h, so that the average velocity is
$$(-20 \text{ km}) \div 5 \text{ h} = -4 \text{ km h}^{-1},$$

i.e. 4 km h^{-1} south. This velocity would be represented by the slope of the line PU.

The average velocity should be distinguished from the average speed, which is obtained by dividing the total distance covered by the total time. In Example 3 the car travels $(60 + 120 + 40)$ km $= 220$ km in the 5 h, so that the average speed is 220 km $\div$ 5 h $= 44$ km h^{-1}.

1.5 *EXAMPLE 4. Fig. 3 shows the displacement–time graph for a train between two stops. Find (i) the average velocity between the two stops, (ii) the average velocity between 9.50 and 10.10, (iii) the velocity at 9.30.*

(i) Between 9 and 10.30 the displacement from the first stop increases from 0 to 114 km. The average velocity is therefore
$$114 \text{ km} \div 1\tfrac{1}{2} \text{ h} = 76 \text{ km h}^{-1}.$$

(ii) Between 9.50 and 10.10 the displacement increases from 60 to 82 km. The average velocity is
$$(82 - 60) \text{ km} \div \tfrac{1}{3} \text{ h} = 66 \text{ km h}^{-1}.$$

This is represented by the slope of the chord PQ, i.e. by the fraction LQ/PL. It is often more accurate to make this measurement by producing the chord PQ and observing that $LQ/PL = YZ/XY$.

(iii) The velocity of the train *at the particular instant* 9.30 cannot be calculated as the slope of any chord, but the following argument shows how it can be evaluated. Let R be the point on the curve corresponding to the time 9.30, and let points S_1, S_2, S_3, . . . be taken corresponding to 9.50, 9.40, 9.35, . . . (See Fig. 3b, which is an enlargement of the relevant part of Fig. 3a.) The slopes of the chords RS_1, RS_2, RS_3 are 36, 60, 76 km h^{-1}, and these are the average velocities over periods starting at 9.30 and ending at 9.50, 9.40, 9.35 respectively. In this way we can find the average velocities over shorter and shorter intervals of time starting at 9.30. As points S are taken on the curve closer to R, so the slope of the chord RS approaches the actual velocity at the instant 9.30; on the graph this velocity is represented by the slope of the tangent at R. This tangent can be drawn by eye with reasonable accuracy. It is shown as RT in Fig. 3b, and its slope can be calculated by finding the displacement indicated by the tangent over any convenient time-interval. For example, between 9.30 and 10 the tangent indicates an increase in the displacement from 48 km to 92 km; if the train continued at a steady speed for $\frac{1}{2}$ h beyond 9.30, it would travel $(92 - 48)$ km. The velocity at 9.30 is thus

$$(92 - 48) \text{ km} \div \tfrac{1}{2} \text{ h} = 88 \text{ km h}^{-1}.$$

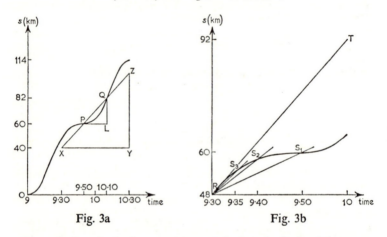

Fig. 3a   Fig. 3b

The velocity of a body at an instant is in fact the limit of the average velocity over a short period of time as this period tends to the value zero. The student familiar with the notation of calculus will see that this velocity is given by the formula

$$v = \lim_{\delta t \to 0} \frac{\delta s}{\delta t} = \frac{ds}{dt}.$$

DEFINITION. *The* VELOCITY *of a body is the rate at which its displacement is increasing with respect to the time.*

EXERCISE 1(a)

1. Express a speed of 3000 m s^{-1} in km h^{-1}.

2. The speed of sound is 330 m s^{-1}. How long will it take an aircraft to fly 990 km at a speed of Mach 0·9 ($\frac{9}{10}$ of the speed of sound)?

3. Given that 1 m = 39·4 inches, and that there are 63 360 inches in a mile, express a speed of 30 miles per hour in km h^{-1}.

4. The speed of light is 3×10^8 m s^{-1}. How long does light take to travel the 1.5×10^8 km from the sun to the earth?

5. A toy electric train runs successively 4 m forwards, 2 m backwards and 3 m forwards along a straight track. The times for the three phases are 6 s, 4 s and 5 s. Draw a displacement–time graph for the motion and find (i) the average speed, and (ii) the average velocity.

6. Between A and B is a hill whose summit is C. A cyclist going from A to B climbs from A to C at 10 km h^{-1} and descends from C to B at 25 km h^{-1}, taking 40 min for the ascent and 20 min for the descent. He spends an hour at B and then returns, climbing from B to C at 5 km h^{-1} and descending from C to A at 20 km h^{-1}. Draw a displacement–time graph, and find his average velocities for the outward and return journeys.

7. In the following table, for a racing car starting from rest, t stands for the time in seconds after the start and s for the distance in metres travelled up to that time.

t	1	2	4	5	6	8	9	10	12	13	14	15
s	1	5	15	23	31	49	61	75	110	142	174	215

Find the average velocity (i) in the first 5 s, (ii) in the first 10 s, (iii) in the first 15 s, (iv) in the 15th second, (v) between $t = 5$ and $t = 10$. Draw the displacement–time graph, and use it to estimate (vi) the average velocity between $t = 7$ and $t = 11$, (vii) the actual velocities when $t = 5, 8, 11$ and 15. What is happening between $t = 4$ and $t = 6$, and between $t = 12$ and $t = 14$?

8. In travelling between two stations a tube train has the following average speeds in successive intervals of 10 s: 3, 7, 13, 13, 9, 4, 1 m s^{-1}. Draw a displacement–time graph, and estimate the actual speeds of the train 10 seconds and 50 seconds after starting.

9. A sandbag is dropped out of a balloon 2000 m above the ground. Its heights above the ground (h metres) at different times (t seconds) after being dropped are given by the following table:

t	2·5	5	7·5	10	15	20	25	30	35	40
h	1970	1880	1750	1610	1290	950	620	290	0	0

Draw a displacement–time graph, and estimate (i) when it hits the ground, (ii) the velocities when $t = 5, 10$ and 20.

*10. A bead running in a groove under the influence of a magnet has its motion described by the equation
$$s = 2t^3 - 15t^2 + 24t,$$
where s is the displacement in millimetres from a point O of the groove and t is the time in seconds after it passes through O. Find (i) the velocities when $t = 0, 3, 6$; (ii) the values of t when the bead is stationary, and its positions at those times. Sketch the displacement–time graph, and describe the motion of the bead.

*11. A ball is thrown vertically upwards from the edge of a cliff, and falls to the beach below. The height above the beach t seconds after it is thrown is given by the formula $(100 + 5t - 5t^2)$ metres. Find the height of the cliff, the speed with which the ball is thrown, how long it is in the air, and the greatest height reached by the ball.

*12. During the first minute after a signal check a train has its speed given by the formula $t^2 (90 - t)/4320$ m s^{-1}, where t is the time in seconds after it starts. Find the speed at the end of the minute and the distance travelled during the first minute.

*13. The upward velocity of a balloon t seconds after ballast has been thrown out is given by the formula $(t - 3)$ m s^{-1}. If it was 60 m above the ground when the ballast was discarded, find the time which must elapse before it is 200 m above the ground. By how much does it miss hitting the ground?

14. The displacement–time table for a train slowing down is:

t (seconds)	0	5	9	11	15	17
s (metres)	0	65	105	121	145	153

Draw a graph, and estimate (i) the velocity when $t = 0$, (ii) the time when the velocity is 7 m s^{-1}, (iii) the time when the train comes to rest.

* Questions marked with an asterisk require the use of calculus.

Acceleration

1.6 When the velocity of a body is not uniform, we introduce a quantity which measures the rate at which the velocity is changing. This is called the *acceleration* of the body.

If a train is moving at 18 km h^{-1} at one instant, and at 90 km h^{-1} two minutes later, its velocity has increased by 72 km h^{-1} in 2 min. If we suppose that it is gaining speed at a steady rate, we say that it has an acceleration of 36 km h^{-1} per minute.

This could also be regarded as an increase of 72 km h^{-1} in $\frac{1}{30}$ h, i.e. as a rate of 2160 km h^{-1} per hour; or as an increase of 20 m s^{-1} (see § 1.2, Ex. 2) in 120 s, a rate of $\frac{1}{6}$ m s^{-1} per second. The units km h^{-1} per hour, m s^{-1} per second, are usually abbreviated to km h^{-2}, m s^{-2} respectively (or sometimes km/h^2, m/s^2).

We shall use the letter a to denote acceleration. Acceleration, like displacement and velocity, is a quantity which has a direction associated with it. If the velocity of a body is decreasing, the body is said to have a negative acceleration (usually called a *retardation*).

1.7. It is frequently useful to draw a graph of the velocity of a body plotted against the time. When the velocity is uniform, this graph is simply a straight line parallel to the time-axis. Velocity–time graphs for Ex. 3 (see § 1.3) and Ex. 4 (see § 1.5) are shown in Fig. 4 and Fig. 5.

If the velocity increases by equal amounts in equal times, so that the graph is a straight line inclined at an angle to the time-axis, the body is said to have UNIFORM ACCELERATION. The value of this acceleration is represented by the slope of the line.

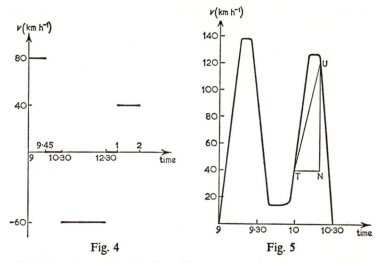

Fig. 4   Fig. 5

Whether the acceleration is uniform or not, the *average acceleration* over a period of time is measured by dividing the increase in velocity during that period by the time. For example, the train for whose motion Fig. 5 is the velocity–time graph has a velocity of 40 km h⁻¹ at 10 o'clock and one of 120 km h⁻¹ at 10.20. The average acceleration between 10 and 10.20 is therefore

$$(120-40) \text{ km h}^{-1} \div \tfrac{1}{3}\text{h} = 240 \text{ km h}^{-2}$$

This is represented on the graph by NU/TN, i.e. the slope of the line TU. (Notice how, using the operation of division with physical quantites, (km h⁻¹) ÷ h is replaced by km h⁻² according to the usual laws of algebra.)

*1.8 The acceleration of a body *at a particular instant* is represented on the velocity–time graph by the slope of the tangent. Using the notation of calculus,

$$a = \frac{dv}{dt}.$$

DEFINITION. *The* ACCELERATION *of a body is the rate at which its velocity is increasing with respect to the time.*

Since
$$v = \frac{ds}{dt},$$

it follows also that
$$a = \frac{d^2s}{dt^2}.$$

* Sections marked with an asterisk require the use of calculus.

Moreover, because $$\frac{dv}{dt} = \frac{dv}{ds} \times \frac{ds}{dt},$$

we may deduce that $$a = v\frac{dv}{ds}.$$

This last formula is important when the velocity or the acceleration are given as functions of the displacement rather than as functions of the time.

EXAMPLE 5. A particle moves along a straight line in such a way that when it has moved s metres from its starting point its velocity in m s^{-1} is $10\sqrt{s}$. Prove that its acceleration is uniform.

Since $$v = 10\sqrt{s},$$

$$\frac{dv}{ds} = \frac{5}{\sqrt{s}},$$

so that $$a = v\frac{dv}{ds} = 10\sqrt{s} \times \frac{5}{\sqrt{s}} = 50.$$

The particle therefore has a uniform acceleration of 50 m s^{-2}.

EXAMPLE 6. A train passes a signal box at 120 km h^{-2}, and gains speed during the next minute in such a way that t hours after passing the signal box its acceleration in km h^{-2} is $1800-108\,000t$. Find its acceleration, speed and position at the end of the minute.

If all quantities are measured in kilometre-hour units,

$$a = 1800 - 108\,000t.$$

Putting $t = \frac{1}{60}$, $$a = 1800 - 1800 = 0.$$

The train has therefore stopped accelerating by the end of the minute.

Since $$a = \frac{dv}{dt},$$

we can write $$\frac{dv}{dt} = 1800 - 108\,000t,$$

whence by integration $v = 1800t - 54\,000t^2 + b,$

where b is a constant. Now it is given that when $t = 0$, $v = 120$; therefore $b = 120$, and

$$v = 1800t - 54\,000t^2 + 120.$$

Putting $t = \frac{1}{60}$, $$v = 30 - 15 + 120 = 135.$$

The speed of the train at the end of the minute is 135 km h^{-2}.

If s denotes the displacement of the train from the signal box in km,

$$v = \frac{ds}{dt},$$

so that $$\frac{ds}{dt} = 1800t - 54\,000t^2 + 120.$$

A further integration gives

$$s = 900t^2 - 18\,000t^3 + 120t + c$$

where c is a constant. We are given that when $t = 0$, $s = 0$; therefore $c = 0$, and

$$s = 900t^2 - 18\,000t^3 + 120t.$$

Putting $t = \frac{1}{60}$, $\qquad s = \frac{1}{4} - \frac{1}{12} + 2 = 2\frac{1}{6}$.

The train is $2\frac{1}{6}$ km from the signal box at the end of the minute.

Area under the velocity–time graph

1.9 *EXAMPLE 7. In catching a train a man runs for* 80 *s at* 2·5 *m s^{-1}, then walks for* 100 *s at* 2 *m s^{-1}, and finally runs for* 20 *s at* 3 *m s^{-1}. Sketch the velocity–time graph and find the total distance that he covers.*

The velocity–time graph consists of three straight lines parallel to the time-axis (Fig. 6).

Since the velocity over each leg is uniform, the total distance the man goes is

$$(2\cdot5 \times 80 + 2 \times 100 + 3 \times 20)\text{m} = 460 \text{ m.}$$

It will be noticed that this quantity is measured by the area of the three rectangles which make up the space between the velocity–time graph and the time-axis.

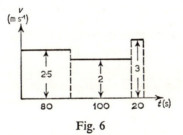

Fig. 6

This is a special case of an important general result, which holds not only when the graph is of the type shown in Fig. 6 but also when it has a more irregular shape such as Fig. 5 or Fig. 7:

The displacement of a moving body in a certain period of time is represented by the area under the velocity–time graph over the appropriate interval of time.

It is, of course, necessary in interpreting this to take account of scale. For example, in Fig. 6, 1 mm on the vertical axis represents a speed of 0·2 m s^{-1}, and 1 mm on the horizontal axis a time of 5 s. Therefore an area of 1 mm^2 in the diagram represents a displacement of

$$(0\cdot2 \text{ m s}^{-1}) \times (5 \text{ s}) = 1 \text{ m.}$$

The whole figure has an actual area of 460 mm², representing a displacement of 460 m.

The student who is familiar with calculus will see that the relation between displacement and area can be proved in the following way. Since

$$v = \frac{ds}{dt},$$

$$s = \int v dt,$$

and this integral, between appropriate limits, measures the area under the velocity–time graph. For a curve of irregular shape whose equation is not known, the area must be found by some approximate method, e.g. by counting squares, by Simpson's rule or the trapezium rule.

If during a part of the motion the velocity is negative, the corresponding displacement during this time is also negative. For this period the velocity–time graph lies below the time-axis. It follows that, when using the rule given above, areas must be counted as negative when they are below the time-axis.

EXAMPLE 8. *An electric train starts from a station and maintains an acceleration of* 0·9 *m s*⁻² *for* 20 *seconds. It then travels for* 80 *seconds with uniform velocity, and finally has a uniform retardation which brings it to rest in a further* 10 *seconds. Find the retardation and the total distance gone.*

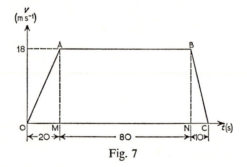

Fig. 7

The velocity–time graph consists of the three lines OA, AB and BC (Fig. 7). The slope of the line OA represents the original acceleration; since $MA/OM = 0·9$, and $OM = 20$, it follows that $MA = 18$. This means that the maximum velocity attained is 18 m s⁻¹. $MN = 80$, the time in seconds for which the train has a uniform velocity. $NC = 10$, the time in seconds during which there is a retardation.

The slope of the line BC is BN/NC, representing an acceleration of

$$\frac{-18 \text{ m s}^{-1}}{10 \text{ s}} = -1·8 \text{ m s}^{-2}.$$

The fact that this is negative indicates that the train is slowing down, and the retardation is $1 \cdot 8$ m s^{-2}.

The distance gone is represented by the area of the trapezium $OABC$, which is

$$\tfrac{1}{2}(110 + 80) \times 18 = 1710.$$

The distance between the two stops is therefore 1710 m, or $1 \cdot 71$ km.

EXERCISE 1(b)

1. Express an acceleration of $9 \cdot 8$ m s^{-2} in km h^{-2}.

2. What multiplying factor converts an acceleration measured in km h^{-2} to cm s^{-2}?

3. A train increases its speed from 25 km h^{-1} to 100 km h^{-1} in 2 min. Find the average acceleration in km h^{-2} and in m s^{-2}.

4. A car is travelling at 72 km h^{-1} when the brakes are applied, producing a retardation of 4 m s^{-2}. How long does it take to stop?

5. An electric train starts from a station and reaches a speed of 14 m s^{-1} in 25 s with uniform acceleration. Sketch the velocity–time graph and find how far it has gone by the time it reaches this speed.

6. An aircraft can take off when it reaches a speed of 180 km h^{-1}. If it attains this speed in $\tfrac{1}{2}$ min with uniform acceleration, what distance does it require for taking off?

7. An express train is travelling at 144 km h^{-1} when its brakes are applied. If these produce a retardation of 2 m s^{-2}, how long will it take to stop and what distance will it cover in doing so?

8. A goods train starts from rest and attains a speed of 50 km h^{-1} in 4 min with uniform acceleration. It runs at that speed for 5 min and then slows down at a uniform rate, coming to rest in a further 2 min. Draw the velocity–time graph and find the total distance travelled.

9. A train starts from rest at a station; it moves at first with a constant acceleration of 30 km h^{-1} per minute, then with a constant velocity of 70 km h^{-1} for 6 minutes, and then with a constant retardation until it comes to rest at the next station 10 minutes after the start. Find the distance between the stations and the retardation.

10. A train starts from rest and travels 8 km in 12 minutes, ending at rest. The acceleration is half the retardation, both are uniform, and there is a period when the train runs at its maximum speed of 50 km h^{-1}. Find the time taken to reach full speed.

11. A 100 m sprinter starts with a speed of 6 m s^{-1}, accelerates uniformly to 10 m s^{-1} and finishes the race at this speed. If his total time is $10 \cdot 4$ s, find his uniform acceleration and after what distance he is going at full speed.

12. A car takes 2 min to travel between two sets of traffic lights 2145 m apart. It has uniform acceleration for 30 s, then uniform velocity, and then uniform retardation for the last 15 s. Find the maximum velocity and the acceleration.

13. A train travels the 15 km between two stations at an average speed of 50 km h^{-1}. Its acceleration is half the retardation, and both are uniform. If the maximum speed is 72 km h^{-1}, find the acceleration in m s^{-2}. Sketch roughly the displacement–time graph.

14. A car accelerates at 2 m s^{-2} in bottom gear, $1\frac{1}{2}$ m s^{-2} in second gear and 1 m s^{-2} in top gear. Each gear change takes $1\frac{1}{2}$ s, during which time the car travels at constant speed. If a motorist changes gear when his speeds are 3 m s^{-1} and 9 m s^{-1}, find how long he will take to reach 15 m s^{-1} from rest and how far he will go in doing so. Sketch the velocity–time and distance–time graphs.

15. The velocities of a car at intervals of 2 s are given in the following table:

t (s)	0	2	4	6	8	10	12
v (m s^{-1})	0	3·9	6·4	8·1	9·2	9·5	9·2

Plot a graph and find (i) the acceleration when $t = 6$, (ii) the average acceleration between $t = 6$ and $t = 12$, (iii) the distance travelled between $t = 4$ and $t = 12$.

16. The table gives the corresponding values of v and t, where the speed at the end of t seconds is v m s^{-1}, for an electrically propelled vehicle:

t	0	2	4	6	8	10
v	0	3·07	5·6	7·6	9·07	10

Draw the speed–time graph, and estimate (i) the acceleration after 5 seconds, and (ii) the whole distance travelled.

17. The table gives values of velocity in m s^{-1} at time t seconds. Plot the velocity–time graph, and find the accelerations at times $t = 3$ and $t = 10$, and the distance covered in the first 10 s.

t	0	2	4	5	7	9	11
v	0	9·5	18	21·6	28·4	34	38·6

18. The table gives corresponding values of the velocity (v in m s^{-2}) and the time (t in seconds) for a car starting from rest:

t	0	1	2	3	4	5	6	7	8	9	10
v	0	5	8·4	11	13·2	15	16·3	17·5	18·5	19·4	20

Find the average velocity over the 10 s.

*19. A point of light travels along a straight line, its displacement in metres from a point O of the line after t seconds being given by the formula $t^3 - 6t^2 + 9t$. Find the velocity and the acceleration for each of the times when the point is at O, and the displacement, velocity and acceleration when $t = 2$.

*20. The velocity of a bus in m s^{-2} between two stops is given by the formula

$$\tfrac{1}{750}t(30 - t)(10 + t),$$

where t is the time in seconds after leaving the first stop. Find how far apart the two stops are, the acceleration of the bus at the instant of starting and the retardation at the instant of stopping.

*21. The velocity (v cm s^{-1}) and the time after it starts (t seconds) of a body moving in a straight line are connected by the equation $v = 12t - 4t^3$. Find the distance travelled in the 10th second, and the acceleration of the body when it is 8 cm from its starting place in the positive direction.

*22. A car travelling at 12 m s^{-1} starts to accelerate 40 m before quitting a built-up area, so that t seconds later its acceleration in m s^{-2} is $\frac{1}{9}(18 - 2t)$. How long will it be before the speed is 20 m s^{-1} and how far outside the built-up area will the car be then?

*23. A sprinter starts with a speed of 6 m s^{-1}, and his acceleration in m s^{-2} at a time t seconds after the start is $(1 - \frac{1}{6}t)$ until he reaches his maximum speed, after which he runs with uniform speed. How long will he take to run 200 m?

*24. Prove that if the velocity of a body is given by the formula $a + bs$, the acceleration is proportional to the velocity; but if it is given by the formula $c\sqrt{s}$, the acceleration is constant. (a, b and c are constant.)

†25. Between two stations a train travels for the first $\dfrac{1}{n}$ of the distance with uniform acceleration, then with uniform speed v, then for the last $\dfrac{1}{n}$ of the distance with uniform retardation. What is the average speed?

†26. What would be the average speed in Question 25 if the acceleration and retardation each occupied $\dfrac{1}{n}$ of the total time?

†*27. A body moves in a straight line so that when its displacement from a fixed point of the line is s metres, its velocity in m s^{-1} is $\dfrac{2}{s}$. Prove that its retardation is then $\dfrac{4}{s^3}$ in m s^{-2}. If it starts when $s = 2$, find where it is after 8 s.

Formulae for uniform acceleration

1.10 Motion with uniform acceleration in a straight line is particularly important, and in this section we derive a number of formulae for calculating velocities, distances, etc, when the acceleration is uniform.

We use the notation:

$u =$ velocity at the start of the period under consideration;
$v =$ velocity at the end of the period;
$a =$ acceleration (now supposed constant throughout the period);
$s =$ displacement from the initial position to the final position;
$t =$ time taken.

† More difficult questions are indicated by a dagger.

It will appear that if any three of these quantities are known, then the other two can be calculated. It is important that all the quantities be measured in a coherent system of units; for example, if s is the displacement in metres and t the time in seconds, then u and v must be in m s^{-1} and a in m s^{-2}.

Since the velocity changes from u to v in time t,

$$a = \frac{\text{change in velocity}}{\text{time}} = \frac{v - u}{t},$$

so that
$$v = u + at \tag{1}$$

The velocity–time graph is a straight line, and the area between the graph and the time-axis is that of a trapezium with parallel vertical sides u and v at a distance t apart (Fig. 8).

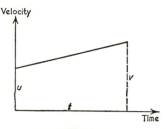

Fig. 8

Since the area of this trapezium measures the displacement s,

$$s = \tfrac{1}{2}(u + v)t. \tag{2}$$

If we eliminate v from equations (1) and (2), we obtain

$$s = \tfrac{1}{2}\{u + (u + at)\}t,$$

so that
$$s = ut + \tfrac{1}{2}at^2. \tag{3}$$

A similar equation may be derived by eliminating u from (1) and (2), which gives

$$s = \tfrac{1}{2}\{(v - at) + v\}t,$$
$$s = vt - \tfrac{1}{2}at^2,$$

but this equation is seldom needed.

If we eliminate t from equations (1) and (2), we obtain

$$s = \tfrac{1}{2}(u + v) \times \frac{v - u}{a},$$

whence
$$v^2 = u^2 + 2as. \tag{4}$$

The equations (1) to (4) should be memorized.

*1.11. The equations derived in the last section can also be obtained with the help of calculus. It is now convenient to use the letters v, s and t

to stand not just for the velocity, displacement and time at the end of the motion, but for the values of these quantities at any stage of the motion. They are therefore variables, but the equations obtained for them can be taken to hold in particular for the values at the end of the motion.

Since $$\frac{dv}{dt} = a, \text{ a constant number,}$$

$$v = at + b,$$

where b is a constant. We know that when $t = 0$, $v = u$, so that $b = u$. Therefore

$$v = u + at. \tag{1}$$

Writing this in the form

$$\frac{ds}{dt} = u + at,$$

a further integration gives

$$s = ut + \tfrac{1}{2}at^2 + c,$$

where c is a constant. Since when $t = 0$, $s = 0$, it follows that $c = 0$. Therefore

$$s = ut + \tfrac{1}{2}at^2. \tag{3}$$

Moreover, using the alternative expression $v \times dv/ds$ for the acceleration (see § 1.8),

$$v\frac{dv}{ds} = a.$$

Now $v \times dv/ds$ is the formula which is obtained when the function $\tfrac{1}{2}v^2$ is differentiated with respect to s. We may therefore integrate this last equation, and deduce

$$\tfrac{1}{2}v^2 = as + k.$$

Since $v = u$ when $s = 0$, $k = \tfrac{1}{2}u^2$. Therefore

$$\tfrac{1}{2}v^2 = as + \tfrac{1}{2}u^2,$$

$$v^2 = u^2 + 2as. \tag{4}$$

Equation (2) can be obtained by eliminating a between two of the equations already derived.

1.12 EXAMPLE 9. *A marble is rolled down a gentle slope. It has a constant acceleration, and its velocity increases from 10 cm s⁻¹ to 32 cm s⁻¹ in a distance of 77 cm. Find the acceleration.*

We are given that $u = 10$, $v = 32$ and $s = 77$, and we are required to find a. We use equation (4):

$$v^2 = u^2 + 2as,$$

so that $$32^2 = 10^2 + 2a \times 77,$$
$$a = \frac{32^2 - 10^2}{2 \times 77} = \frac{924}{154} = 6.$$

In this calculation all quantities are measured in centimetre-second units. The acceleration is therefore 6 cm s^{-2}.

EXAMPLE 10. A train starts from rest and, moving with constant accelera-tion, passes through a station 9 km away after 5 minutes. Find the accelera-tion.

Using metre-second units, we are given that $u = 0$, $s = 9000$ and $t = 300$. From equation (3):

$$s = ut + \tfrac{1}{2}at^2,$$

we have $$9000 = 0 + \tfrac{1}{2}a \times 300^2,$$

$$a = \frac{2 \times 9000}{90\,000} = 0.2.$$

The acceleration is therefore 0·2 m s^{-2}.

This example could, if preferred, have been worked in some other coherent system of units, such as the kilometre-hour system. We should then have $u = 0$, $s = 9$ and $t = \frac{1}{12}$; equation (3) would then give $a = 2592$, the acceleration in km h^{-2}.

†**1.13** Equation (2) of § 1.10 can be written in the form

$$\frac{s}{t} = \frac{u + v}{2}.$$

The quantity on the left side of this equation, the total distance moved divided by the time taken, is the average velocity (see § 1.4). It follows that, for motion with uniform acceleration, the two quantities

(i) the average velocity, and

(ii) the average of the velocities at the beginning and the end,

are equal. Moreover, since the velocity increases by equal amounts in equal times, (ii) is also equal to

(iii) the velocity at half-time.

When the acceleration is not uniform throughout the period of time, these three quantities are not in general equal. For example, for the motion of the train discussed in Example 8 (§ 1.9), the values are (i) (1710 m) ÷ (110 s) = 15·6 m s^{-1}, (ii) 0, and (iii) 18 m s^{-1}.

The equality of (i) and (iii) for uniformly accelerated motion is sometimes useful in solving problems.

† More difficult sections, which may be omitted if desired, are indicated by a dagger.

EXAMPLE 11. A car approaching a speed limit applies its brakes. It takes 4 s to cover the next 100 m, and 5 s to cover the succeeding 100 m. Find the retardation, and the speed at which it was moving when the brakes were applied.

The average speeds while covering the two stretches of 100 m are 25 m s⁻¹ and 20 m s⁻¹. Assuming the retardation to be uniform, these are the speeds of the car half-way through the corresponding periods of time; that is to say, it is moving at 25 m s⁻¹ at a time 2 seconds after the brakes are applied, and at 20 m s⁻¹ 6·5 seconds after they are applied. The speed decreases by 5 m s⁻¹ in 4·5 s, so that the retardation is (5 m s⁻¹) ÷ (4·5 s) = 1·1 m s⁻². In the first two seconds after the brakes are applied the speed therefore decreases by 2·2 m s⁻¹, and at the end of this time the speed is 25 m s⁻¹. The car was therefore moving at 27·2 m s⁻¹ initially.

†**1.14** If a slow train travelling on the up line at 15 m s⁻¹ is overtaken by an express travelling at 40 m s⁻¹ at night (so that only the lights of the other train are visible), a passenger in the slow train would be unaware of his own speed but could observe that the express was approaching the destination at a speed 25 m s⁻¹ greater than his own. We say that the express has a velocity of 25 m s⁻¹ *relative to the slow train.*

If the slow train now overtakes a goods train moving at 5 m s⁻¹, the latter seems to be falling behind at a rate of 10 m s⁻¹; we say that it has a velocity of −10 m s⁻¹ relative to the slow train. A down train coming in the opposite direction at 20 m s⁻¹ would be said to have a velocity of −35 m s⁻¹ relative to the slow train, since in each second it gets 35 m further behind the slow train.

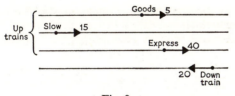

Fig. 9

It is also possible to measure displacements and accelerations relative to a moving origin rather than with reference to some fixed object. The position of a shunting engine at a particular time could be described as '1 km in front of the slow train' rather than as '5 km beyond the station'. If the express were retarding at 0·6 m s⁻², and the slow train accelerating at 0·4 m s⁻², we could say that the express has a retardation of 1 m s⁻² relative to the slow train, since the velocity of the express relative to the slow train is decreasing by 1 m s⁻¹ in each second.

In solving problems, it is sometimes more convenient to use the formulae of § 1.10 with the letters standing for the displacements, velocities and accelerations relative to some moving object rather than a fixed point.

EXAMPLE 12. A reckless driver travelling at 40 m s⁻¹ *and accelerating at* 0·2 m s⁻² *overtakes a police car at the instant when the police car starts up in pursuit. If the police car maintains a uniform acceleration of* 1 m s⁻², *how far behind the other car is it* 20 *seconds later?*

Initially the reckless driver has a speed of 40 m s⁻¹ relative to the police car, but its acceleration is 0·8 m s⁻² less than that of the pursuers. We therefore substitute the values $u = 40$, $a = -0.8$, $t = 20$ in the formula

$$s = ut + \tfrac{1}{2}at^2,$$

and obtain $\qquad s = 40 \times 20 - \tfrac{1}{2} \times 0.8 \times 400 = 640.$

It must be remembered that s now stands for the displacement of the pursued car in front of the police car, and not for the actual distance that the car has travelled. The police car is therefore 640 m behind after 20 s.

EXERCISE 1(c)

1. A car accelerating uniformly has speeds of 8 m s⁻¹ and 19 m s⁻¹ at times separated by 10 s. How far does it go during this period, and what is its acceleration?

2. A marble running down a groove increases speed from 12 cm s⁻¹ to 15 cm s⁻¹ in 6 s. How far does it go, and what is its acceleration?

3. In accelerating uniformly from 10 km h⁻¹ to 50 km h⁻¹ a train covers 2½ km. Find the time taken and the acceleration.

4. A toboggan starting from rest reaches a speed of 7 m s⁻¹ in 7 s. How far has it gone by then?

5. A train running at 15 m s⁻¹ is brought to rest with constant retardation in 2½ min. How far does it travel during this time?

6. The brakes of a car can produce a retardation of 1½ m s⁻². How long will it take the driver to reduce speed from 35 m s⁻¹ to 20 m s⁻¹, and how far will the car go during that time?

7. An electric train starts from rest at a station and accelerates at ½ m s⁻² for 324 m. How fast is it going by then?

8. A train passes through a station at 60 km h⁻¹ and accelerates at 1300 km h⁻² (0·10 m s⁻²) for the next ½ km. How fast is it then going?

9. A car is travelling along a narrow lane at 54 km h⁻¹ when the driver sees an obstruction across the road 25 m ahead. The brakes produce a retardation of 4 m s⁻². With what speed will the car hit the obstruction?

10. A skier increases his speed from 5 m s⁻¹ to 15 m s⁻¹ in a distance of 40 m. Find his acceleration.

11. A car leaves a speed limit at 90 km h⁻¹ and accelerates at ½ m s⁻². How far does it go in the next 10 seconds?

12. A stone dropped down a well gains speed at 10 m s^{-2} approximately. It hits the bottom $2\frac{1}{2}$ s later. How deep is the well?

13. A train travels 510 m in 30 s and has an acceleration of 0·6 m s^{-2}. How fast was it going at the beginning?

14. A cyclist starts at 1 m s^{-1} and has an acceleration of 0·4 m s^{-2} for the first 100 m of his ride. How long does he take to travel the 100 m and what is then his speed?

15. An air-liner has to reach a speed of 60 m s^{-1} before it can take off. If its acceleration along the ground is 1·5 m s^{-2}, how long must the runway be?

16. A mile runner accelerates at a rate of 0·1 m s^{-2} up the final straight, and breasts the tape at a speed of 7 m s^{-1}. If he entered the final straight 20 s before breasting the tape, how long is the straight and at what speed did he enter it?

17. A brick is dropped into a lake with a speed of 3·5 m s^{-1} and falls through it with an acceleration of 5 m s^{-2}. Find the speed after 3 s and the time it takes to go 12 m.

18. A pencil point starts from O with a velocity of 12 cm s^{-1} to the right and moves in a straight line with an acceleration of 6 cm s^{-1} to the left. After what time is it stationary? When does it come back to O? Where is it and what is its velocity after 1 s, 3 s and 5 s?

19. A car is moving with increasing acceleration. Which of these statements is true: (i) $s > \frac{1}{2}(u + v)t$, (ii) $s = \frac{1}{2}(u + v)t$, (iii) $s < \frac{1}{2}(u + v)t$? Give a reason for your answer.

20. The brakes of a train are able to produce a retardation of 1·5 m s^{-2}. In order to stop at a station, how far away must the driver apply the brakes if the train is travelling at 108 km h^{-1}? If the brakes are applied 27 m too late, with what speed will the train pass through the station?

21. A car accelerates uniformly in top gear from 14 m s^{-1} to 34 m s^{-1} in 20 s. Find how far it travels while accelerating, and how long it takes to cover the first half of that distance.

22. A train passes a row of posts 400 m apart at 3·5 m s^{-1} and 6·5 m s^{-1}. If it is accelerating uniformly, with what speed does it pass the next post? How long does it take to cover the distance between each pair of posts? How far does it go in the 4 min after passing the last post?

†**23.** A cyclist reaches the top of a hill moving at 2 m s^{-1}, and accelerates uniformly so that, in the sixth second after reaching the top, he goes 13 m. Find his speed at the end of the sixth second.

†**24.** Four points A, B, C, D lie in order on a straight line, the distances AB, BC, CD being 320 cm, 448 cm, 576 cm. A mouse running along this line covers each of these distances in 8 s. Show that this is consistent with the assumption that its acceleration is uniform, and on this assumption find the acceleration, and the speed at D.

†**25.** If the distance travelled in the pth second by a body moving with constant acceleration is a metres, and in the qth second is b metres, prove that the acceleration in m s^{-2} is $(b - a)/(q - p)$.

†**26.** Two trains are standing at a station. On the up line is an electric train which accelerates to 72 km h⁻¹ in 200 m, and on the down line a diesel train which accelerates to 108 km h⁻¹ in 4·5 km. Find their separate accelerations, supposed uniform, in m s⁻². A man sitting in the electric train is opposite the engine of the diesel train. Both trains start together, and the man notices that it is 12 s before the end of the train passes him. How long is the diesel train?

†**27.** Two cars P and Q are parked by the side of a straight road, with P 27 m in front of Q. P moves off with uniform acceleration 1 m s⁻², and 6 s later Q sets off in pursuit with uniform acceleration 1·5 m s⁻². Find the greatest distance that P is in front of Q and the time that it will take Q to draw level with P.

†**28.** The driver of an express travelling at velocity u sees ahead of him a train at rest. He immediately applies the brakes, thus communicating a retardation a_1. At the same instant the other train starts with acceleration a_2. What distance must originally separate the trains if they are just to avoid a collision?

Vertical motion under gravity

1.15 Experiments have shown that, when a body is moving vertically under the influence of gravity alone (the effect of air resistance being ignored), it does so with a uniform acceleration.[1] Moreover, at any given part of the earth's surface this acceleration is the same for all bodies. These results were first observed by Galileo (1564–1642).

This acceleration is denoted by the letter g. It varies slightly at different parts of the earth, being greatest at the poles and least at the equator. Some typical values are:

North Pole	9·832 m s⁻²
Equator	9·780 m s⁻²
Greenwich	9·812 m s⁻²
Wellington (N.Z.)	9·803 m s⁻²

We also use the letter g to denote, without ambiguity, the numerical value of this acceleration in the units currently under discussion. Unless a high degree of accuracy in the answers is desired, it is sufficient to take g in m s⁻² to be 9·8, or even 10. One or other of these values will be used throughout this book unless the contrary is stated; but with a warning that it is misleading to give answers which depend on these approximate values of g to more than a small number of significant figures.

---

[1] There is in fact a very slight decrease of the acceleration due to gravity with increasing height, but this effect is quite negligible in ordinary terrestrial problems.

EXAMPLE 13. A stone is thrown vertically upwards from the edge of a cliff with an initial velocity of 15 m s⁻¹. Find the displacement and velocity after times 1, 1½, 2, 3, 4 s, and interpret the results. Draw the displacement–time and velocity–time graphs.

We shall consider the upward direction as positive and use the approximation 10 m s^{-2} for g; it is immaterial whether the stone is moving upwards or downwards. We therefore write $a = -10$ in the equations.

Using the equation

$$v = u + at,$$

we have

$$v = 15 - 10t,$$

and obtain the following values of v:

t	0	1	1·5	2	3	4
v	15	5	0	−5	−15	−25

Also, from the equation

$$s = ut + \tfrac{1}{2}at^2,$$

we deduce

$$s = 15t - 5t^2,$$

and obtain the following values of s:

t	0	1	1·5	2	3	4
s	0	10	11·25	10	0	−20

The displacement–time and velocity–time graphs are shown in Fig. 10 and Fig. 11.

The upward velocity decreases from its initial value of 15 m s⁻¹ until after 1½ seconds it becomes zero. The stone has then reached the highest point of its flight, at a height of just over 11 m. After this time the velocity is downwards, represented by negative values of v in the table. After 3 seconds the displacement is zero; the stone is now level with the top of the cliff. It should be noticed that its velocity is now 15 m s⁻¹ downwards, so that it has the same speed as that with which it was thrown up. When more than 3 seconds have elapsed

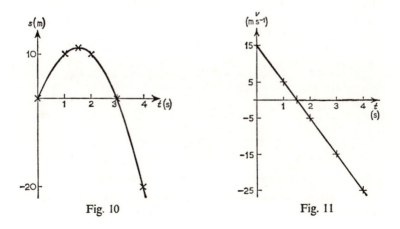

Fig. 10 Fig. 11

the displacement s has negative values. The stone has by now fallen below the top of the cliff, and its downward velocity continues to increase.

EXAMPLE 14. A stone is thrown vertically upwards at 5 m s⁻¹ from the top of a platform 10 m above the ground. After what time will it reach the ground?

We take the level of the platform as origin, and upwards as the positive direction for displacement and velocity. We therefore have, in metre-second units, $u = 5$, $a = -10$, $s = -10$. Using the equation

$$s = ut + \tfrac{1}{2}at^2,$$
$$-10 = 5t - 5t^2,$$
so that
$$t^2 - t - 2 = 0,$$
$$(t - 2)(t + 1) = 0.$$

This gives $t = 2$ or $t = -1$. The negative answer has, however, no relevance in this problem, so that the stone reaches the ground after 2 seconds.

We could equally well have solved this problem by taking the downward direction as positive. This would involve taking $u = -5$, $a = +10$, $s = +10$, but would lead to the same quadratic equation for t.

EXERCISE 1(d)

Use an approximation $g = 9.8$ or 10 m s⁻² as appropriate, and give answers to a suitable degree of accuracy. An indication is given where the work is simplified by taking a particular value for g.

1. A marble falls off a shelf 1·25 m high. How long will it take to fall, and with what speed will it hit the floor? (Take $g = 10$ m s⁻².)

2. An airgun pellet is fired vertically upwards 36 m s⁻¹. How high does it rise?

3. A shell explodes in the air, and a piece of shell-casing is projected vertically downwards at 50 m s⁻¹. If it lands 2 s later, at what height did the shell explode?

4. A tennis ball is hit vertically upwards with a speed of 12 m s⁻¹. At what times is it 4 m above its point of projection, and what are its speeds at these times? (Take $g = 10$ m s⁻².)

5. Water in a fountain rises vertically to a height of 5 m. At what speed does it leave the nozzle?

6. A stone is catapulted vertically upwards at 30 m s⁻¹. For how long does its height exceed 40 m? (Take $g = 10$ m s⁻².)

7. A stone is thrown down from the top of a well at 5 m s⁻¹ and reaches the bottom of the well in 3 seconds. Find the depth of the well.

8. A sandbag is let fall from a balloon which is 100 m above the ground and rising at 5 m s⁻¹. With what speed will it reach the ground?

9. A ball is thrown vertically upwards at 8 m s^{-1} and caught at the same height. For how long is it in the air?

10. A juggler performing on a tight-rope fails to catch one of the balls, which falls into the arena below. If the ball was thrown upwards with a speed of 2 m s^{-1} from a height of 24 m, how long afterwards does it land? If it rebounds with a speed of $\frac{7}{11}$ of that with which it strikes the floor, how high does it rise on the first bounce? (Take $g = 10$ m s^{-2}.)

11. A stone is dropped from the top of a cliff. A second later another stone is thrown downwards from the same point at 11 m s^{-1}. The two stones land at the same time. Find the height of the cliff. (Take $g = 10$ m s^{-2}.)

12. A boy throws a stone straight up from the top of a tower 20 m high. It falls past him again 3 seconds after he has thrown it. Find (i) the speed with which he throws it up, (ii) the speed with which it reaches the ground, (iii) the time when it is 10 m above the boy, (iv) the time when it is 5 m above the ground. (Take $g = 10$ m s^{-2}.)

†13. Prove by means of the formulae of § 1.10 that if an object is projected vertically upwards and returns to the same level, then the time of ascent is the same as the time of descent and that the object returns with the same speed as that with which it was projected. What modifications would you expect to have to make in these rules if air resistance were taken into account?

†14. A stone is dropped from rest at the top of a vertical cliff. In the last second of its flight before hitting the ground it covers $\frac{25}{169}$ of the total distance it drops. Find the height of the cliff.

CHAPTER 2

FORCES AND DIAGRAMS

2.1 The basic ingredients of mechanics are FORCE and MOTION. In Chapter 1 we considered motion by itself without reference to force; this part of the subject is called *kinematics*. In this chapter we shall be concerned with force, and in Chapter 3 we consider the effect which force has on motion. Those topics relating to force alone belong to *statics*; those into which velocities and accelerations also enter belong to *dynamics*.

The most obvious example of force is a push or pull applied directly to a body by hand. We know that if we push a body hard enough it will begin to move. Therefore, when we see a body starting to move under some other agency we are led to postulate that there is a force moving it. For example, when an apple falls from a tree there is no visible evidence to account for its behaviour; we therefore say that the apple is attracted to the earth by a certain force, which we call the gravitational force, or the weight of the apple.

DEFINITION. *The* WEIGHT *of a body is the force with which the earth attracts it.*

2.2 If a body remains stationary, we are led to suppose that there is no force acting on it – or rather, that any forces which do act on it cancel each other out. In this section we consider a few examples.

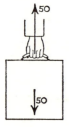

Fig. 1

EXAMPLE 1. A man holding a suitcase. (See Fig. 1.)
The suitcase does not move, but we know that there is at least one force acting upon it, namely its weight – for the earth does not cease to attract a body just because somebody is holding it. We know from experience that in order to hold the suitcase up it is necessary to exert a pull with our arm. It is reasonable to expect this pull to be exactly equal to the weight of the suitcase; if the case weighs 50 units, then we must pull upwards with a force of 50 units. (We defer until Chapter 3 a discussion of the units in which force is measured.)

EXAMPLE 2. A suitcase suspended from the ceiling by a string. (See Fig. 2.)
The string has now taken the place of the arm in Example 1, and provides
the upward force. We call this force the TENSION in the string.

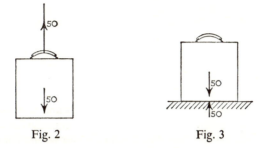

Fig. 2   Fig. 3

EXAMPLE 3. A suitcase standing on the floor. (See Fig. 3.)
The only possible source from which the compensating upward force can now
come is the floor. This push upwards is called the NORMAL CONTACT FORCE[1]
(frequently abbreviated to 'normal force'). The word 'normal' in mathematics
means perpendicular—the normal force acts at right angles to the two surfaces
in contact.

It will be noticed that although Figs. 1–3 appear to be different, the
diagrammatic representation of the forces is similar in each. From the
mechanical point of view these three examples are equivalent, and the
analysis of the forces in this way effects a simplification. It is very
important to acquire skill in analysing forces and representing them on
a diagram.

*EXAMPLE 4. A man tries to push a suitcase
along the ground, but does not succeed.* (See Fig. 4.)
The two forces which were present in Example 3
are still acting, but there are two more forces:
the push, and the friction force from the ground.
The friction force arises when there is a tendency
for one surface to move over another one; it acts
in the common tangent plane to the two surfaces in such a way as to oppose the motion.

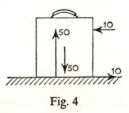

Fig. 4

It is, in fact, another kind of contact force. Since the suitcase does not move,
the friction is equal in magnitude to the push applied (shown in Fig. 4 as a
force of 10 units), but it acts in the opposite direction.

When the forces on a body cancel each other out, as in the above
examples, they are said to be in EQUILIBRIUM.

[1] Some writers call this force the 'normal reaction'.

2.3 In a particular problem it is helpful to analyse the forces acting on the chosen body under the following headings:

(i) 'Action at a distance.' By far the most important instance of this is the weight of the body itself (the gravitational force), but occasionally there may be other examples such as magnetic forces. In astronomical problems it may be necessary to consider the gravitational attraction from more than one source; a space capsule on its way to the moon is, for example, significantly affected by the forces from the earth, the moon and the sun at the same time.

(ii) Forces from agents connected with the body, such as—

    a. Normal contact force, the 'pressure' between two bodies in contact with each other.
    b. Friction force.
    c. Tension from a string attached to the body. Tension can also come from rods, springs, etc.
    d. Thrust from a rod or spring. This is similar to tension, but acts in the opposite direction.

Drawing the figure is an important part of the solution of a question in mechanics. It is essential that the figure should be clear and easily understood. The most common faults are:

  (i) making the figure too small;
 (ii) leaving out some of the forces acting upon the body;
(iii) putting the same force in twice;
(iv) confusing in the same diagram the forces acting on different bodies.

Examples 5–9 (see Figs. 5–9) illustrate the way in which these figures should be drawn. In the diagrams the letter W is used for a weight, N for a normal contact force, F for friction, T for a tension and S for a thrust. If two or more forces of the same kind occur in one example, they are distinguished by suffixes.

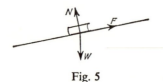

Fig. 5

EXAMPLE 5. The forces on a book on a sloping desk.
The tendency of the book is to slide down the desk, so that the friction force restraining it acts up the slope. The diagram is the same whether the book is stationary or sliding down.

*EXAMPLE 6. The forces on a tobog-
gan being pulled uphill.*
The friction now acts down the hill, since
the tendency to move is in the uphill
direction.

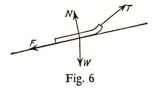

Fig. 6

EXAMPLE 7. The forces on the bob of a pendulum.
In this example the forces are not in equilibrium; we know that
the pendulum could not rest in this position.

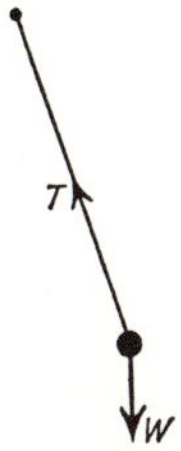

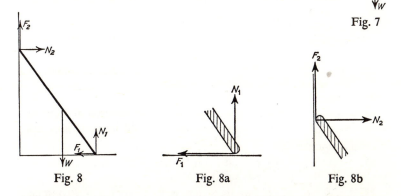

Fig. 7

Fig. 8   Fig. 8a   Fig. 8b

*EXAMPLE 8. The forces on a ladder which stands on rough ground leaning
against a rough wall.*
Notice that the normal contact forces are respectively perpendicular to the
ground and to the wall. The reason for this will be clear from the magnified
diagrams (Figs. 8a and 8b) showing in greater detail the situation at the
points of contact.

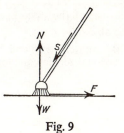

Fig. 9

EXAMPLE 9. The forces on a broomhead when the floor is swept.

EXERCISE 2

Draw diagrams to show the forces acting on the bodies in Questions 1–21. State what kind of force each one is.

1. An electric light hung from the ceiling.

2. The seat of a swing.

3. A cricket ball in the air.

4. A boy sliding across the ice.

5. A boy on skates gaining speed on the ice.

6. A car accelerating on a level road.

7. An aircraft in steady level flight.

8. An aircraft gliding with the engine off.

9. A child sliding down a chute.

10. An aircraft looping the loop at the top of its loop.

11. A planet going round the sun.

12. A toy motor boat on a lake.

13. The seat of a swing with a child on it.

14. A plank being lifted by one end from the ground.

15. A crowbar being used to raise a flagstone.

16. The seat of a swing, with a child on it, when pulled away from the vertical by another child.

17. A ladder on rough ground resting against a smooth wall, with a man standing one-third of the way up the ladder.

18. A gate with two hinges, the weight being supported by the top hinge only.

19. A gate with two hinges, the weight being supported by the bottom hinge only.

20. A horse pulling a cart along the road.

21. A boy climbing a rope.

22. An object hangs by a string from a fixed hook in the ceiling and is pulled downwards by a boy standing on the floor. Draw diagrams to show the forces acting on (i) the object, (ii) the boy.

23. Two bricks A and B have weights 30 and 20 units. B rests on a table, and A rests on B. Draw diagrams to show the forces (i) on block A, (ii) on block B.

CHAPTER 3

FORCE AND ACCELERATION

The equation of motion

3.1 We shall now consider the effect which forces have on the motion of bodies. Elementary dynamics is based on three laws, first enunciated by Newton (1642–1727) and published in his *Principia*[1], and hence known as 'Newton's laws of motion'. These laws may be treated as axioms; they cannot be proved, and our justification for accepting them is that mathematicians working from them have deduced results which agree well with experiment and with everyday experience.

For more than two centuries after these laws were first given, scientists believed that they were exactly true and that they were adequate to give a perfect description of dynamical phenomena. Research in recent years has shown, however, that this is not so, and that Newton's laws are slightly inaccurate; these inaccuracies become apparent only when we are making very large measurements, as in some problems in astronomy, or very small ones, as in nuclear physics. Nevertheless, there is no doubt that these laws will continue to be used as the basis of the work of engineers and most physicists; any discrepancies introduced through their use are usually quite insignificant when compared with the errors of observation which are inseparable from any practical work, however precise the instruments used. Even in the astronomy of the solar system it is necessary to compare very accurate observations made over long periods before any divergence can be detected on the true motion from that predicted by means of Newton's laws.

3.2 Newton's First Law. *Every body remains stationary or in uniform motion in a straight line unless it is made to change that state by external forces.* (Corpus omne perseverare in statu suo quiescendi vel movendi uniformiter in directum, nisi quatenus a viribus impressis cogitur statum illum mutare.)

This law might at first sight appear to contradict 'common sense' in its reference to uniform motion, for we know that everything within

[1] *Philosophiæ Naturalis Principia Mathematica*, 1st edition 1687.

33

our experience comes to rest sooner or later as a result of friction or air resistance. But the friction and air resistance are themselves external forces acting on the body, so that the law does not apply when these forces are present. Perhaps the example closest to our experience is that of the earth going round the sun; this maintains an almost constant speed of about 30 km s^{-1}, and has done so for millions of years. No force is needed to drive it round, for there is nothing tending to slow it down. (Admittedly the earth does experience a gravitational pull from the sun, but this simply has the effect of pulling it sideways and causing it to move in a closed path rather than in a straight line.) If one could imagine a star moving through space so far from all other bodies that their gravitational attractions on it were negligible, then it would continue to move at a constant speed in a straight line.

Within our more immediate experience, the effect of the first law of motion is seen when forces act on a body but cancel each other out. We can still deduce from the law that the body will either stay at rest or continue to move with constant velocity. Consider, for example,

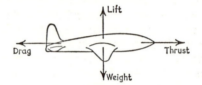

Fig. 1

an aircraft flying at constant speed on a level course. There are four forces acting on it:

    (i) its weight;
    (ii) the thrust of the engines, acting forwards;
    (iii) the aerodynamic 'lift' force, acting vertically upwards;
    (iv) the air resistance, or 'drag' force.

Since the aircraft is in level flight, we naturally expect the lift force to be equal to the weight. It is perhaps more surprising that, in accordance with Newton's first law, the thrust is equal to the air resistance. There is thus no resultant external force acting on the aircraft, so that it continues to fly at the same height with the same speed. If the thrust of the engines were greater than the air resistance, the aircraft would gain speed.

Again, if a balloon is rising at constant speed, this does not mean that the upthrust due to the enclosed gases is greater than the weight of the balloon, but that these two forces are equal. (In this statement we have ignored the effect of air resistance. Which would be the greater if air resistance were taken into account?)

3.3 Before discussing Newton's second law it is necessary to introduce another dynamical concept – the MASS of a body. A massive body is one which takes a large force to make it change its motion. A brick has a larger mass than a ping-pong ball, since it requires only a small tap with the bat to give the ball a speed of 5 m s^{-1}, whereas a much larger blow is required to produce the same effect on the brick. The alternative name 'inertia' encountered in older books describes well this fundamental property of mass, the disinclination of a body to change its motion.

In the international system (SI) the fundamental unit of mass is the kilogramme. This is established by international agreement as the mass of the 'standard kilogramme', which is kept at the Bureau International des Poids et Mesures at Sèvres, near Paris. Notice that, although this is the basic unit, its name carries the prefix kilo-; the thousandth part of a kilogramme is called a gramme, not a millikilogramme. (The gramme was originally the basic metric unit of mass, defined as the mass of a volume of 1 cm^3 of water.)

The mass of a body is associated with its weight, but it is most important that these two quantities should be clearly distinguished. The weight of a body was defined in Chapter 2 as a force – the force with which the earth attracts it. A brick of mass 1 kg, if carried to the top of Everest, would diminish in weight, since the gravitational pull of the earth decreases slightly with increasing height; but its mass would remain 1 kg, since the force needed to make it move in a horizontal direction would be the same at a height of 8·8 km as at sea-level. The word 'weight' is only applied to bodies at or near the surface of the earth; it is pointless to talk of the weight of the moon, or Neptune, and meaningless to talk of the weight of the earth itself, since the earth does not attract itself with any force at all; but it is quite reasonable to speak of the earth as having a mass of 6·0 × 10^{24} kg.

As for 'weightlessness', of which we hear nowadays in relation to space travel, this is a loose form of words describing a sensation rather than an actual situation. A traveller in a space-ship orbiting the earth has precisely the same mass as he had on earth. Since he is further from the centre of the earth, his weight is smaller than it would be on the earth's surface; but this weight is not zero, since he is still within the influence of the earth's gravitational force. The *appearance* of weightlessness is connected with the fact that the space-ship is circling round the earth, and it is not really different in kind from the sensation of a passenger in a freely falling lift (see Ex. 3(b), Question 9); a full understanding of it must wait until we are in a position to discuss the behaviour of objects moving in circular paths.

3.4 Consider a trolley on smoothly running wheels being pushed down a long corridor, starting from rest. If it is pushed by a weak boy, it will gain speed, but only slowly. If a stronger boy were to push with a force twice as large, it would gain speed more rapidly – in fact, its acceleration would be twice as great. This illustrates

Newton's Second Law. *Acceleration*[1] *is proportional to the impressed force, and acts along the same straight line.* (Mutationem motus proportionalem esse vi motrici impressae, et fieri secundum lineam rectam qua vis illa imprimitur.)

Let us now introduce a second trolley. We shall suppose that the first trolley is empty and has a mass of 20 kg, and that the other is piled with plates and has a mass of 100 kg. Then, if both trolleys are to gain speed at the same rate, it will obviously be necessary to apply a much larger force to the more massive one; in fact, the force will have to be five times as large. This illustrates another general principle:

In order to produce a given acceleration, the force needed is proportional to the mass of the body being moved.

However, if both trolleys were pushed with the same force, the more massive one would gain speed far less quickly than the other. Its acceleration would in fact be one-fifth of that of the lighter trolley, so that it would take five times as long to acquire a given speed. This illustrates yet another principle:

If a given force is applied to different bodies the resulting acceleration is inversely proportional to the mass.

These principles are all incorporated in the equation

$$F = k \times ma \tag{1}$$

where F is the force applied, m the mass moved, a the acceleration and k is a constant which is the same for all bodies. Thus, in the form

$$F = (km)a$$

we have Newton's second law, since km is constant and so $F \propto a$. On the other hand, if we write the equation

$$F = (ka)m,$$

then we see that for constant acceleration the force is proportional to the mass. Finally,

$$a = (F/k) \times \frac{1}{m}$$

shows that, for a given force, the acceleration of the body is inversely proportional to its mass.

It cannot be too strongly emphasized that the impressed force determines not the velocity with which a body moves, but the acceleration.

---

[1] More literally 'change of momentum', see Chapter 13.

To maintain a constant velocity no force is needed. A spacecraft far out in space needs no motors to keep it going at a steady speed. On the other hand, a small rocket burn is enough to change its speed – even a very small force will produce some acceleration whilst it is being applied.

3.5 As in many equations of physics, the value of the constant k in equation (1) depends on the units in which the variables are measured. The unit of acceleration has already been defined in terms of the more elementary units of length and time (see § 1.6); the unit of mass is fixed arbitrarily (see § 3.3). The choice of a unit of force is independent of these other two units, and can be made in any way that we please. What we do in practice is to select it so that the constant k in equation (1) has the value 1; that is, so that $F = 1$ when $m = 1$ and $a = 1$. In the international system this unit of force is known as the newton (N):

DEFINITION. *A* NEWTON *is the force which, when acting in isolation on a particle of mass* 1 *kg, gives it an acceleration of* 1 *m s*$^{-2}$.

The final shape of the equation epitomizing Newton's second law is then

$$F = ma,$$

where F is the force in newtons, m the mass in kilogrammes and a the acceleration in m s^{-2}. This is commonly known as the EQUATION OF MOTION.

To cope with large and small forces, multiples and sub-multiples of the newton are used. These are described by the usual prefixes kilo-, milli-, etc, exactly as with other units. For example, a millinewton (mN) is a force of 10^{-3} N.

We may if we wish express the definition of a newton symbolically in the form

$$(1 \text{ kg}) \times (1 \text{ m s}^{-2}) = (1 \text{ N});$$

that is, if we substitute m as 1 kg and a as 1 m s^{-2}, then F is equal to 1 N. This is a natural extension of the algebra of physical quantities described in §§ 1.2 and 1.7.

EXAMPLE 1. An alternative system of metric units (the cgs system) is based on the centimetre, the gramme and the second as fundamental units of length, mass and time. In this system the unit of force, the dyne, is defined as the force which, acting on a particle of mass 1 *gm, gives it an acceleration of* 1 *cm s*$^{-2}$. *Express the magnitude of a dyne in newtons.*
In the equation of motion we write m as 1 gm = 10^{-3} kg, and a as 1 cm s^{-2} = 10^{-2} m s^{-2}. This gives

$$F = ma$$
$$= (10^{-3} \text{ kg}) \times (10^{-2} \text{ m s}^{-2})$$
$$= 10^{-5} \text{ N}.$$

A dyne is therefore the equivalent of 10^{-5} newtons.

EXAMPLE 2. A man drags a dinghy of mass 200 kg across the beach with a force of 200 N. The motion is hindered by a friction force of 170 N. Find the acceleration of the dinghy.

In the equation of motion, with F measured in newtons and m in kilogrammes, we put $F = 200 - 170 = 30$ and $m = 200$. This gives

$$30 = 200a,$$
$$a = 0 \cdot 15.$$

The dinghy therefore has an acceleration of $0 \cdot 15$ m s^{-2}.

3.6 In solving problems on forces and accelerations, the student should develop the habit of drawing diagrams in which are shown:

(i) the forces acting on the body whose motion is under review;
(ii) the acceleration of that body.[1]

It is not often desirable to mark velocities on the diagram as well, but instances may occur in which this is helpful. To avoid confusion we

Fig. 2

shall in this book indicate forces by single-headed arrows, accelerations by double-headed arrows and velocities by arrows with solid heads (see Fig. 2).

EXAMPLE 3. One person pushing a 1000 kg car can accelerate it at $0 \cdot 1$ m s^{-2}. Two people pushing equally hard with the same force as before can accelerate it at $0 \cdot 3$ m s^{-2}. How large is the resistance to motion?

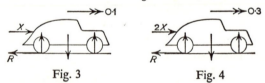

Fig. 3　　　　　　Fig. 4

Let the force with which each person pushes be X newtons, and the resistance to motion R newtons.

With one person pushing (Fig. 3), we substitute in the equation of motion $F = X - R$, $m = 1000$, $a = 0 \cdot 1$, so that

$$X - R = 1000 \times 0 \cdot 1 = 100.$$

With two people (Fig. 4), $F = 2X - R$, $m = 1000$, $a = 0 \cdot 3$, whence

$$2X - R = 1000 \times 0 \cdot 3 = 300.$$

[1] In very complicated examples it is sometimes better to have two diagrams, one reserved for the forces and the other for the accelerations.

From these two equations we deduce that $R = 100$; the resistance is 100 newtons.

3.7 Before applying the equation of motion it is sometimes necessary to use one of the formulae of kinematics from Chapter 1 to calculate the acceleration.

EXAMPLE 4. A rifle bullet of mass 10 gm has a muzzle velocity of 800 m s⁻¹. The cross-section of the barrel has area 50 mm² and the bullet travels 0·8 m in the barrel. Neglecting the resistance experienced by the bullet, find the average pressure in the barrel when a round is fired.

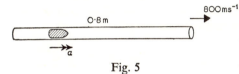

Fig. 5

By 'average pressure' we shall understand the constant pressure which, if it were to act on the bullet throughout its travel, would produce the given muzzle velocity. If the pressure were constant, so too would be the acceleration; and on this assumption we may use the formula

$$v^2 = u^2 + 2as$$

to calculate it. Working in metre-second units, we have (Fig. 5) $u = 0$, $v = 800$, $s = 0\cdot8$, so that

$$800^2 = 2 \times 0\cdot8\,a,$$
$$a = 4 \times 10^5.$$

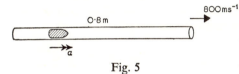

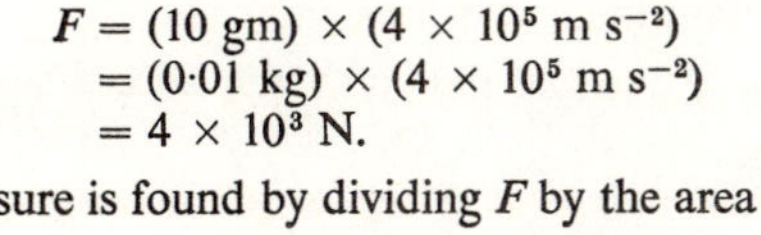

Fig. 6

We can now use the equation of motion $F = ma$ to find the force:

$$F = (10 \text{ gm}) \times (4 \times 10^5 \text{ m s}^{-2})$$
$$= (0\cdot01 \text{ kg}) \times (4 \times 10^5 \text{ m s}^{-2})$$
$$= 4 \times 10^3 \text{ N}.$$

Finally, the pressure is found by dividing F by the area of cross-section of the barrel:

$$\text{Pressure} = (4 \times 10^3 \text{ N}) \div (50 \text{ mm}^2)$$
$$= (4 \times 10^3 \text{ N}) \div (50 \times 10^{-6} \text{ m}^2)$$
$$= 8 \times 10^7 \text{ N m}^{-2}.$$

In practice the *maximum* pressure would be considerably greater than this, and would occur when the bullet has travelled a short distance along the barrel.

EXERCISE 3(a)

1. An electron of mass 9×10^{-31} kg in a magnetic field has a momentary acceleration of 6×10^{16} m s^{-2}. What is the force acting on it?

2. What force is needed to give a paper pellet of mass 0·7 gm an acceleration of 160 m s^{-2}?

3. An ice-yacht of mass 300 kg has an acceleration of 0·8 m s^{-2}. What force is needed to produce this?

4. A circus artist is shot from a gun horizontally. While he is in the barrel the force on him is 150 newtons and his acceleration is 2·5 m s^{-2}. What is his mass?

5. A cricket ball of mass 150 gm is acted on by a force of 30 N. Find its acceleration.

6. A skater of mass 75 kg is opposed by frictional resistances of 60 N. Find his retardation.

7. A force of 60 N acting on a smoothly running trolley produces an acceleration of 0·6 m s^{-2}. What is the mass of the trolley?

8. A 5-tonne (5000 kg) yacht is running before the wind. The wind produces a force of 300 N and the water a resistance of 90 N. Find the acceleration of the yacht.

9. A cabin trunk of mass 50 kg is dragged along the floor by a horizontal force of 40 N at a constant speed of 0·3 m s^{-1}. How large is the friction force?

10. A cabin trunk of mass 50 kg is dragged along the floor by a horizontal force of 40 N with an acceleration of 0·3 m s^{-2}. How large is the friction force?

11. What force is necessary to give a speedboat of mass 6000 kg an acceleration of 4 m s^{-2} if the water offers a resistance of 36 000 N?

12. A liner of displacement 20 000 tonnes (2×10^7 kg) is steaming at a steady speed of 12 m s^{-1}. The resistance of the water is $1·6 \times 10^6$ N. What force are the engines producing? If the engines were to stop, what would be the retardation of the liner, and how long would it take to stop (assuming that the resistance were to remain constant)?

13. A table is pushed across the floor with an acceleration of 0·1 m s^{-2}. It is pushed with a force of 93 N, and there is a friction resistance of 90 N. Find the mass of the table.

14. A balloon is descending with a constant speed of 3 m s^{-1} when one of its occupants falls out. Describe, with reasons, but without detailed calculations, what happens to the balloon in the next few seconds.

15. A four-engined air liner has a mass of 50 000 kg. It is flying horizontally at a steady speed of 200 m s^{-1} with each engine producing a thrust of 10 000 newtons. If one of the engines cuts out, find the retardation immediately afterwards.

16. Six dogs pulling a 1500 kg sledge over level snow keep it going at constant speed. Eight dogs give it an acceleration of 0·3 m s⁻². With what force does each dog pull?

17. In the old British system of units, one unit of force was the *poundal*, the force required to give a mass of 1 lb an acceleration of 1 ft s⁻². Given that 1 lb is the equivalent of 0·454 kg, and that 1 ft is 0·305 m, express the magnitude of a poundal in newtons.

18. A car of mass 700 kg is brought to rest in 7 seconds from a speed of 72 km h⁻¹. What constant force is necessary to produce this retardation?

19. A train of mass 360 000 kg is running into a station when its brakes fail. It hits the buffers at 6 km h⁻¹ and depresses them a distance of 1¼ m. What is the retarding force, assumed constant, provided by the buffers?

20. A twin-engined aircraft of mass 15 000 kg increases its speed from 720 km h⁻¹ to 792 km h⁻¹ in level flight while travelling 21 km. Taking the air resistance to have the constant value of 14 000 N, what constant thrust must each engine produce?

†**21.** The thrust exerted by the engines of an aircraft is inversely proportional to the speed, and the air resistance is proportional to the square of the speed. If the maximum speed of the aircraft is 720 km h⁻¹, prove that its acceleration at 360 km h⁻¹ is about 2·27 times its acceleration at 540 km h⁻¹.

†**22.** Five children each of mass 50 kg have a truck of mass 100 kg. If three children sit on the truck and two push, the acceleration is 0·2 m s⁻²; if two sit on the truck and three push, the acceleration is 0·6 m s⁻². Taking the resistance to motion to be proportional to the number of children on the truck, find how hard each child pushes.

The force of gravity

3.8 It was stated in § 1.15 that a body falling freely to the earth will have a constant acceleration which is the same for all bodies (the effect of air resistance being neglected). That the acceleration is constant agrees with the second law of motion given in § 3.4, since the only force acting on the body is its weight, which is constant throughout its fall (or, at least, very nearly so).

If the weight of a body of mass m is W, and this body falls to the earth under the action of its weight alone with an acceleration of g (about 9·8 m s⁻²), the equation $F = ma$ can be applied to give

$$W = mg.$$

This means that, *numerically*, the weight of a body in newtons is always about 9·8 times its mass in kilogrammes. This is an important result, which must be memorized. For example, a 5 kilogramme mass has a weight of $5 \times 9·8$ newtons, or 49 newtons. (Often the rougher approximation 10 m s⁻² is used for g, giving the weight of a 5 kg mass as about 50 N.)

We represent this diagrammatically by drawing

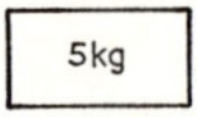

Fig. 7

when we are concerned solely with mass, and

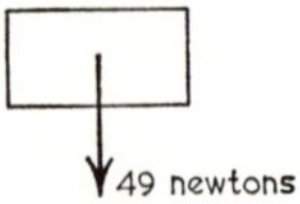

Fig. 8

when we are interested in the force of gravity. We call mass a scalar quantity, and weight a vector quantity (see Chapter 7). The two items of information may be combined in one diagram:

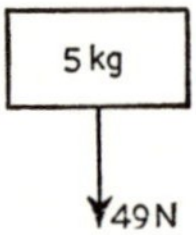

Fig. 9

This is often necessary when we are concerned with motion in a direction which is not horizontal, as in Examples 5 and 6.

It follows from the relation $W = mg$ that the weights of two bodies at the same part of the earth's surface are proportional to their masses; in fact, some of the methods used to compare masses, such as the common balance, are actually devices for comparing weights.

EXAMPLE 5. The cage in a pit shaft descends by first accelerating at 3 m s⁻² for 4 seconds, then travelling at a constant speed of 12 m s⁻¹ and finally retarding at 2 m s⁻² for 6 seconds. A miner carries a piece of equipment of mass 5 kg down in the cage with him. How much does it appear to weigh during each of the three stages of the motion?

The man judges the weight of his burden by the force needed to hold it up, i.e. the tension in his arm. Denote this tension in the successive stages by T_1, T_2 and T_3 newtons. We consider the forces acting on his load, which are the tension and the weight of $5 \times 9.8 = 49$ newtons.

(i) See Fig. 10. The total force accelerating the load is $49 - T_1$ newtons. The equation of motion is therefore

$$49 - T_1 = 5 \times 3,$$

giving $T_1 = 34.$

(ii) See Fig. 11. The cage is moving at constant speed, so that the net force on the load must be zero. It follows that the tension is 49 N.

(iii) See Fig. 12. The acceleration is now 2 m s⁻² upwards (although the

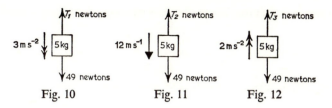

Fig. 10   Fig. 11   Fig. 12

cage is still moving downwards). If we continue to take the downward vertical as the positive direction, we must write $a = -2$, so that

$$49 - T_3 = 5 \times (-2)$$

giving $$T_3 = 59.$$

The load will therefore *appear* to weigh 34, 49 and 59 N in the three stages of the motion.

Note on Example 5

Had the upward vertical been taken as the positive direction in stage (iii), we would have written $a = +2$, so that the equation of motion would become

$$T_3 - 49 = 5 \times 2.$$

This leads to the same solution as before.

EXAMPLE 6. In falling vertically under the influence of gravity a stone of mass 0·2 kg experiences a resistance which varies with the speed of the stone, being given by the formula $R = 0.2 + 0.0005 v^2$ newtons, v being the speed of the stone in m s^{-1}. Find the downward acceleration of the stone at speeds of 0 and 20 m s^{-1}, and the greatest speed which the stone can attain in its fall.

The empirical formula for the resistance is unlikely to have very great accuracy, so we shall use the approximation $g = 10$ m s^{-2}. The weight of the stone will then be taken to be $0.2 \times 10 = 2$ newtons, so that if a is the acceleration of the stone in m s^{-2} the equation of motion is

$$2 - R = 0.2a.$$

When $v = 0$, $R = 0.2$, so that the acceleration of the stone is

$$1.8/0.2 = 9 \text{ m s}^{-2}.$$

When $v = 20$, $R = 0.2 + 0.2 = 0.4$, giving an acceleration of 8 m s^{-2}.

Fig. 13

Evidently the acceleration decreases as the speed increases; when the stone is travelling at its maximum speed it will have no acceleration. The resistance is then equal to the weight of the stone and the speed is given by the equation

$$0.2 + 0.0005 v^2 = 2$$

so that $$v = 60.$$

The maximum speed attainable by the stone in its fall is therefore 60 m s^{-1}. This is known as the *terminal speed* of the stone.

In fact, with the given law of resistance the speed of the stone would never actually reach the terminal speed, although after falling for a few seconds it would get very close indeed to this maximum value; the longer it fell, the closer its speed would approximate to the terminal value.

3.9 Gravitational units of force

The adoption of the international system (SI) is making obsolete a large number of other units. This is especially true of units of force; for these have varied not only with the system adopted, but there have been at least three different ways of defining the basic unit of force within each system. For some time yet some of these other units may be encountered, in books even if not in practice, so a brief account will be given here.

Most obviously, there have been systems based on other fundamental units than the metre, kilogramme and second which characterize SI. The two most important have been the centimetre-gramme-second (cgs) and the foot-pound-second systems. In these the units of force corresponding to the newton were the *dyne* (giving a mass of 1 gm an acceleration of 1 cm s^{-2}) and the *poundal* (giving a mass of 1 pound an acceleration of 1 foot s^{-2}). Besides the poundal there were the tondal (or tonnal) related to the ton, the ouncedal related to the ounce, and so on.

The complication does not end here. It has been common practice also to use a unit of force related not directly to the equation $F = ma$ but to the force of gravity. Thus we have the *kilogramme weight* (kg wt) as the force with which the earth attracts a body of mass 1 kg, the *pound weight* (lb wt) as the force of attraction on a body of mass 1 pound, and so on. Clearly, from the relation $W = mg$,

$$1 \text{ kg wt} \approx 9{\cdot}8 \text{ N.}$$

Similarly, $1 \text{ gm wt} \approx 980 \text{ dynes}$

and $1 \text{ lb wt} \approx 32 \text{ poundals,}$

since 980 and 32 are the numerical values of g in cm s^{-2} and foot s^{-2} respectively. These units of force are called *gravitational units.*

The appeal of gravitational units lies in the direct experience which we have of their magnitude; we have all carried objects of mass 1 kg, and know 'in our bones' how large a force this requires. The use of the sign $\approx$ above, however, points to an obvious snag: that since the force of gravity varies slightly from place to place over the earth's surface, the unit of force also varies. This is clearly unsatisfactory when any real precision is required; for example, a spring balance manufactured in Hong Kong and calibrated in lb wt would not read truly if used subsequently in Manchester.

A third kind of force unit was therefore devised which had a constant value over the earth's surface but which still resembled the gravitational unit sufficiently to retain the advantage of intuitive appreciation. The method used was to select the weight of a 1 kg (or 1 gm, or 1 pound) mass at a particular latitude and to use this as the unit of force. The latitude selected was 45°, where the value of g was measured – slightly inaccurately, as is now known – as 9·806 65 m s^{-2} (or 980·6 65 cm s^{-2}, or very nearly 32·1740 foot s^{-2}). The corresponding unit of force is called the *kilogramme force*, abbreviated to kgf (and similarly gmf, lbf), and we may write *exactly*

$$1 \text{ kgf} = 9{\cdot}806\,65 \text{ N,}$$
$$1 \text{ gmf} = 980{\cdot}665 \text{ dynes;}$$

and, correct to six significant figures,

$$1 \text{ lbf} = 32{\cdot}1740 \text{ poundals.}$$

Thus at one particular latitude the kilogramme weight is the same as the kilogramme force; at other points of the surface of the earth a mass of 1 kg weighs *approximately* 1 kgf.

With these other force units we can, of course, no longer use the equation $F = ma$. For example, to give a mass of m kilogrammes an acceleration of a m s^{-2} requires a force of ma newtons, which is the same as $(ma/9{\cdot}806\,65)$ kgf. The equation of motion with force measured in kgf, mass in kg and acceleration in m s^{-2} therefore has the form

$$F = \frac{1}{9{\cdot}806\,65}\, ma.$$

To add further to the confusion, users of these units often referred loosely to 'a force of 1 pound' when they really meant 'a force of 1 lbf', thereby confusing a unit of mass with a unit of force. For example, a tyre pressure would be described as '20 pounds per square inch' rather than the correct '20 pounds force per square inch'.

The student will learn with some relief that we do not propose to make any further reference in this book to units outside SI.[1]

EXERCISE 3(b)

1. A brick of mass 2 kg falls through water with an acceleration of 3 m s^{-2}. Find the total force of resistance and buoyancy.

2. A 1000 kg car is being lowered into the hold of a ship. Find the force in the cable if the car has (i) an acceleration of 0·4 m s^{-2} downwards, (ii) a velocity of 2 m s^{-1}, (iii) a retardation of 0·6 m s^{-2}.

[1] A very clear account of the whole question will be found in an article by H. V. Lowry in the *Mathematical Gazette*, Vol. XLVIII, No. 363, for February 1964.

3. An empty bottle of mass 0·2 kg is released from a submarine and rises to the surface with an acceleration of 0·7 m s^{-2}. If the water offers a resistance of 0·5 N, what is the force of buoyancy impelling it upwards?

4. A 50 kg boy goes up in a lift. What force does the floor exert on him when the lift has an upward acceleration of 0·6 m s^{-2}?

5. During lift-off a 100 kg astronaut experiences a contact force of 8000 N from the seat. What is the acceleration of the rocket?

6. If the contact force between the floor of a lift and an 80 kg man is 720 N, what can you say about the motion of the lift?

7. The tension in a cable raising a load with an acceleration of 1·2 m s^{-2} is 11 kN. What is the load? (Take $g = 9·8$ m s^{-2}.)

8. A man in a lift is trying to weigh a parcel with a spring balance. The lift is going down, first accelerating at 0·4 m s^{-2}, then running at a constant speed of 2 m s^{-1} and finally retarding to rest at 0·6 m s^{-2}. During the accelerating phase the dial reads 4·8 kg. What does it read during the other two phases? (Take $g = 10$ m s^{-2}.)

9. A lift is descending near the top of a skyscraper when the mechanism fails and the lift starts to fall freely with acceleration g. Describe the (mechanical) sensation experienced by a passenger during the time that the lift is falling.

†**10.** When a billiard ball and a table-tennis ball of the same diameter are dropped from the same height, the billiard ball reaches the ground first (air resistance being taken into account). Explain why this happens. If the air resistance is assumed constant and the same for both balls, and if their accelerations are f and f', find the ratio of their masses.

†**11.** A train covers successive half-kilometres in 15 s and 25 s. Express the retarding force as a fraction of the weight of the train.

The interaction principle

3.10 The first two laws of motion have concerned one body only. There is, however, a law which enables us to deal with problems in mechanics in which two or more bodies are present, each affecting the other; for example, two girders of a bridge jointed together, the earth and the moon attracting each other, two billiard balls colliding or a man sitting on a chair. In all these examples each of the partners exerts a force on the other. The earth attracts the moon, so that the moon describes an orbit round the earth; but the moon also attracts the earth, and this attraction causes perturbations in the earth's motion round the sun which can be observed. The chair exerts an upward force on the man (a normal contact force) which prevents him from falling, but the man also exerts a force on the chair (with disastrous results for the chair if the man is too heavy). A little reflection will convince the reader that the forces between bodies never occur singly, but always in pairs.

The third law of motion is concerned with these mutual forces between pairs of bodies:

The Interaction Principle. *If a body A exerts a force (of whatever kind) on a body B, then B exerts on A a force of the same magnitude acting along the same line but in the opposite direction.*

The original statement of this law was:

Newton's Third Law. *Action is always equal and in the opposite direction to reaction.* (Actioni contrariam semper et aequalem esse reactionem: sive corporum duorum actiones in se mutuo semper esse aequales et in partes contrarias dirigi.)

EXAMPLE 7. A car of mass 1200 *kg tows a trailer of mass* 300 *kg along a level road. The engine produces a thrust of* 900 *N, and the car experiences a resistance of* 150 *N. The trailer runs freely without any resistance. Investigate the motion.*

We consider separately the motion of the trailer and that of the car. In order to accelerate the trailer a horizontal force is needed, and this is provided through its contact with the car. If this force is X newtons, and the acceleration in m s^{-2} of the car and trailer is a, the equation of motion of the trailer is

$$X = 300a.$$

Now the interaction principle tells us that, since the car exerts on the trailer a force of X in the direction of motion, the trailer will exert on the car a force

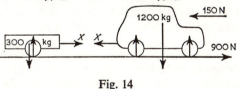

Fig. 14

of X in the reverse direction. The driver will describe this as an additional drag due to the presence of the trailer. (But this drag will disappear as soon as the car settles down to a constant speed, and when the car is braked the trailer will exert a forward force on the car. It is therefore only an apparent drag, and is quite different from the effect of air resistance or a punctured tyre.) Other forces on the car are a forward thrust of 900 N, and a resistance of 150 N, so that for the car the equation of motion is

$$900 - 150 - X = 1200a.$$

From these two equations we deduce that $a = 0.5$ and that the contact force between the car and its trailer is 150 N.

In this simple example the value of a could have been calculated by regarding the car and trailer as a single body of mass 1500 kg acted on by a thrust of 900 N and a resistance of 150 N, but the two motions must be considered separately to find the value of X. This method cannot always be used, but the student should be on the look-out for short cuts of this kind.

3.11 In Chapter 2 we introduced the notion of the tension in a string as a force acting on the body to which it is attached. A string, however, has two ends; and if it is connecting two bodies, it will exert a force on each. Suppose that, in Example 7 above, the car were towing the trailer by means of a rope. This rope is now the means by which the forward force acts on the trailer; we will suppose that this force is Y newtons. The rope also exerts a backward force of Z newtons on the car. By the interaction principle, the towing rope has two forces acting

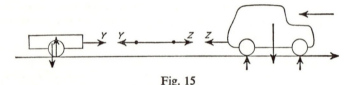

Fig. 15

on it – a forward force of Z newtons from the car, and a backward force of Y newtons from the trailer (see Fig. 15).

Let us suppose now that the mass of this rope is negligible in comparison with the other masses in the problem; we refer to this as a 'light rope', and the assumption is a reasonable one for most purposes. It then requires no force to accelerate it, so that we can deduce that $Y = Z$. (Since the mass is neglected, so also is the weight of the rope; Y and Z therefore act along the same line, and the rope is straight.)

The force which a rope exerts on the bodies to which it is attached is called the TENSION in the rope (and similarly for strings, cables, etc). The previous paragraph shows that the tension in a light rope which is in contact with other bodies only at its two ends is the same at either end. (If the rope is regarded as divided at any point into two parts, this tension is also the force which one part exerts on the other, and it is the same throughout the length of the rope; but this need not concern us now.)

A rope in tension is represented diagrammatically thus:

$$\longrightarrow \quad \longleftarrow$$

Fig. 16

The directions of the arrows indicate the directions of the forces which the rope exerts on the attached bodies at the respective ends.

The disadvantage of using a rope to tow a trailer is that in slowing down it is necessary to exert a backward force on the trailer, and this cannot be done with a rope. To obviate this a rod could be used for towing. When the car is accelerating, the rod will have a tension in the same way as the rope, but a rod can also exert a force in the other direction, i.e. outwards from its ends. This is referred to as the THRUST in the rod; provided that the mass of the rod is negligible, the thrust in the rod is the same at each end. A rod in thrust is represented diagrammatically as in Fig. 17:

Fig. 17

Another property frequently ascribed to strings, ropes, etc, is that of being 'inextensible'. No real string possesses this property, but in many practical instances the stretching of the string is so small that no appreciable error arises from ignoring it. When a string is inextensible, the velocities along the line of the string of the two bodies attached to it are the same, and for one-dimensional motion the accelerations are the same also.

Thus if the towing rope in our example were both light and inextensible, we should have $Y = Z$ and the accelerations of the car and the trailer equal; this brings us back to precisely the same conditions as in Example 7.

3.12 In many examples a string is not straight throughout its length, but passes over a peg. The result of this, in general, is that the tensions in the string are different on the two sides of the peg, because of the friction where it runs over the peg; but if the peg were smooth (a condition impossible to achieve completely in practice) the tension would be the same on either side of the peg.

The tension also remains constant along a string which runs over a pulley whose mass is negligible and which rotates smoothly on its bearings; in this case the pulley turns round with the string, but the force required to make it do this is so small that it may be neglected.

EXAMPLE 8. A truck of mass 40 kg can run smoothly on horizontal rails. A light, inextensible rope is attached to the front of the truck, and this runs parallel to the rails until it passes over a light, smoothly running pulley; the rest of the rope hangs down a vertical shaft, and carries a 10 kg load attached at the other end. Find the tension in the rope and the acceleration with which the truck and the load move. (See Fig. 18, p. 50.)

Since the string is inextensible, both the truck and the hanging load have the same acceleration; we denote this by a. The conditions of the problem also ensure that the tension in the rope is the same at either end; let this be T newtons.

The problem is solved by considering the forces on the two bodies separately. On the 10 kg mass the forces are its weight and the tension in the rope. Using the approximation $g = 10$ m s^{-2}, the weight is 100 N, so that the equation of motion is

$$100 - T = 10a,$$

a being in m s^{-2}.

The forces on the truck are the tension in the rope, its weight and the contact forces from the ground on the wheels – but of these only the tension

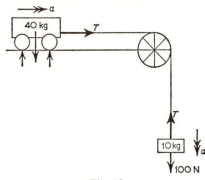

Fig. 18

affects the horizontal motion of the truck, so that the equation of motion is simply

$$T = 40a.$$

Adding the two equations gives

$$100 = 50a,$$

whence $a = 2$ and $T = 80$.

The tension in the rope is therefore 80 newtons. It will be noticed that the tension must be less than the weight of the hanging load; if it were not so the load could not accelerate.

3.13 Problems in mechanics frequently refer to 'particles'. A particle is really another convenient fiction, like a light rod, an inextensible string or a smooth peg. We suppose that a finite mass can be concentrated at a single point.

Equations such as the equation of motion ($P = mf$) should in the first place be applied only to particles, although we shall frequently apply them to large bodies and suppose that cricket balls, motor cars or even the earth itself (in astronomical problems) can be regarded as particles. The justification for this is difficult, and must be left until a much later stage; but it can be shown that, provided that we concern ourselves only with motion in a straight line, the results which we shall obtain will be valid.

EXERCISE 3(c)

1. An engine of mass 200 tonnes pushes a coach of mass 40 tonnes with an acceleration of 0.2 m s^{-2}. Draw diagrams showing the forces on (i) the engine, (ii) the coach. Neglecting resistances, find the force transmitted through the coupling and the driving force from the engine. (1 tonne = 1000 kg.)

2. A car of mass 900 kg tows a caravan of mass 700 kg. If the driving force from the engine is 320 N, find the force transmitted through the towbar and the acceleration of the car.

3. An electric train consists of three coaches, their masses (starting from the front) being 40 tonnes, 24 tonnes, 36 tonnes. When the brakes are applied, only the wheels of the front coach are locked, and these produce a resistance of 100 kN. Find the retardation of the train and the force transmitted through each coupling.

4. A tug tows three barges in line, and has an acceleration of 0.02 m s^{-2}. Each barge displaces 80 tonnes. The water offers resistance of 12.5 kN to each barge. If the towing ropes are horizontal and along the line of the barges, find the tension in each coupling.

5. An 80 kg man is descending in a lift of mass 500 kg with an acceleration of 1.5 m s^{-2}. Draw diagrams showing the forces acting on (i) the man, (ii) the lift; find the tension in the lift cable, and the force between the man and the floor.

6. A mass of 200 gm is suspended by a vertical string. To a hook on the underside of the mass is attached a second vertical string, which carries a mass of 300 gm. The masses are raised by a vertical force of 5 N applied to the upper string. Find the acceleration with which they rise, and the tension in the lower string.

7. If in Question 6 the upper string were cut and the masses were allowed to fall, what would be the tension in the other string?

8. A rope is slung over a smooth beam. Two children, of which the heavier weighs 60 kg, hang on to the rope, one at either end; the heavier child is found to descend with an acceleration of 2 m s^{-2}. Find the tension in the rope, and the mass of the lighter child. (Take $g = 10$ m s^{-2}.)

Questions 9–12 refer to the mechanical arrangement in Ex. 8, pp. 49–50. (Take $g = 10$ m s^{-2}.)

9. What hanging load would be necessary to give the truck an acceleration of 6 m s^{-2}?

10. What would be the acceleration if the truck were filled with 150 kg of sand?

11. With what force would the truck have to be pulled in order to *raise* the load with an acceleration of 2 m s^{-2}? What would be the tension in the rope then?

12. What would be the tension and the acceleration of the truck if its motion were hindered by a friction resistance of 25 N?

13. Masses of 3 gm and 4 gm are joined by a thread, which is placed over a light, smoothly-running pulley so that one mass hangs vertically on either side. Find the acceleration with which the larger mass descends, and the tension in the string. (Take $g = 9\cdot8$ m s^{-2}.)

14. Two unequal masses connected by a thread are slung over a smooth peg, and released so that each mass moves in a vertical line. Argue whether the tension in the thread is greater than, equal to, or less than the average weight of the two masses.

15. Two empty buckets, each of mass 2 kg, have their handles connected by a rope which passes over a wheel free to turn smoothly about a horizontal axis. How much water must be poured into one of the buckets in order that they may move with an acceleration of $\frac{1}{5}g$? If twice this quantity of water is now poured into the other, with what acceleration will they move?

†**16.** A mass of 10 kg is on a rough table 2 m from the edge. It is connected by a smooth string running at right angles to the edge of the table to a 2 kg mass which hangs vertically. The system starts from rest, and after 2 s the 10 kg mass reaches the edge of the table. Find the friction force.

†**17.** Masses of 5 kg and 3 kg are connected by a thread which runs over a smooth peg. They are released from rest when the 5 kg mass is 1·25 m above the floor. How long will it be before the other mass is again at rest? (Take $g = 10$ m s^{-2}.)

†**18.** Masses of 8 gm and 3 gm are tied to the ends of a string which passes over a rough peg and hangs in two vertical parts. The roughness of the peg results in the tension on one side being double that on the other. Find the acceleration of the masses. (Take $g = 9\cdot8$ m s^{-2}.)

†**19.** A string passes over a smooth peg with masses 2 kg and 3 kg tied to its ends. The system starts from rest, and after the 3 kg mass has fallen for 5 s it lands on a horizontal platform. What is the acceleration when both are moving? After what further time will the 3 kg mass be picked up again?

†**20.** Two monkeys, each of mass 10 kg, cling together to one end of a very long rope which hangs over a very high smooth beam, and a monkey of mass 15 kg clings to the other end. 7 seconds after they start to move, one of the 10 kg monkeys falls off. When will the other monkeys again be at rest, and how far will they have moved by then?

†**21.** Masses of 20 gm and 30 gm are tied to the ends of a string which passes over a smooth peg. Find their accelerations and the tension in the string if the peg is accelerated upwards at a rate of 20 cm s^{-2}. (Take $g = 9\cdot8$ m s^{-2}.)

CHAPTER 4

FORCES AT AN ANGLE

4.1 *EXAMPLE 1. A cargo ship of displacement* 5000 *tonnes is being towed by two tugs. The cables attaching each tug to the ship are horizontal and make an angle* θ *with the direction of motion of the ship, and each has a tension of* 10^5 *newtons. With what acceleration will the ship move, ignoring the resistance of the water?*

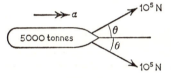

Fig. 1

If the cables were to run parallel to the direction of motion of the ship, the problem could be solved by using the equation $F = ma$ with $F = 2 \times 10^5$ N, $m = 5 \times 10^6$ kg, giving

$$a = \frac{2 \times 10^5 \text{ N}}{5 \times 10^6 \text{ kg}} = 0.04 \text{ m s}^{-2}.$$

With the cables at an angle we should expect the acceleration to be less than this, since only part of the tension in the cable is effective in pulling the ship along. Moreover, we should expect the effectiveness of the cables in accelerating the ship to depend on the angle θ, and to get smaller as θ is increased.

We can get no further with the solution of this problem without introducing a new principle, which we shall state without proof. Applied to this particular example, this is that each force of 10^5 newtons at an angle θ to the direction of motion has the same effect as would a force of $10^5 \cos \theta$ newtons parallel to the direction of motion. Both cables produce the same effect in this direction, so that we may apply the equation of motion $F = ma$ with $F = (2 \times 10^5 \cos \theta)$ N, whence

$$a = \frac{2 \times 10^5 \cos \theta \text{ N}}{5 \times 10^6 \text{ kg}} = 0.04 \cos \theta \text{ m s}^{-2}.$$

In support of this statement we may remark that when $\theta = 0°$, $\cos \theta = 1$, leading to the same answer as that obtained above in this special case; that this formula has the desired property of giving a smaller value of a as θ

53

increases; and that when $\theta = 90°$, $\cos \theta = 0$ and so $a = 0$, which is reasonable, since in this case the tugs are merely pulling against each other and making no contribution to the motion of the ship.

4.2 In order to make the ideas of the foregoing example precise and general, a definition will be introduced:

DEFINITION. *The* RESOLVED PART *of a force F in a direction $\mathcal{2}$ is $F \cos \theta$, where θ is the angle between $\mathcal{2}$ and the direction of F.*

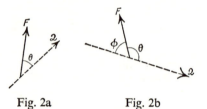

Fig. 2a   Fig. 2b

The resolved part of F is the name used to describe the 'effect' of P in the given direction.

It should be noted that, if θ is an obtuse angle, the resolved part of F is a negative quantity. Writing $\phi = 180° - \theta$ (see Fig. 2b), we observe that the resolved part of F is

$$F \cos \theta = F \cos (180° - \phi) = -F \cos \phi$$

so that the resolved part of F in the direction $\mathcal{2}$ is minus its resolved part in the direction opposite to $\mathcal{2}$.

EXAMPLE 2. *A particle of weight W rests on a slope of angle α. It is prevented from slipping down the plane by a frictional force of F which acts up the plane. Find the resolved parts of W, F and the normal contact force N in the directions: (1) vertically upwards, (2) horizontal to the right, (3) up the plane, (4) along the upward perpendicular to the plane.*

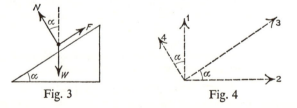

Fig. 3   Fig. 4

It is easily shown by geometry that the perpendicular to the slope makes an angle α with the vertical. The reader should verify for himself that the results are:

Direction	Resolved part of		
	W	F	N
1	$-W$	$F \cos (90° - \alpha) =$ $F \sin \alpha$	$N \cos \alpha$
2	0	$F \cos \alpha$	$-N \cos (90° - \alpha) =$ $-N \sin \alpha$
3	$-W \cos (90° - \alpha) =$ $-W \sin \alpha$	F	0
4	$-W \cos \alpha$	0	N

4.3 We can now state the principle which enables us to solve problems in which the forces act at any angle. In a later volume this will be shown to be a direct consequence of the vector form of the equation of motion and of the vector laws; for the present it must be regarded as a new principle, which may be verified experimentally (see Example 5).

The Resolution Principle. *The sum of the resolved parts of the forces acting on a body in a given direction is equal to the mass of the body multiplied by its acceleration in that direction. In particular, if a body has no acceleration in a particular direction the sum of the resolved parts of the forces in that direction is zero.*

The process of applying this principle in a particular direction $\mathscr{2}$ is called RESOLVING IN THE DIRECTION $\mathscr{2}$. We shall frequently abbreviate this by writing $\mathscr{R}(\mathscr{2})$ in the left margin by the side of the corresponding equation.

EXAMPLE 3. Find the forces N and F of Example 2 in terms of W and α.
Since the particle does not slide down the slope, the second part of the resolution principle holds in all directions. Applied in the four selected directions in turn, this gives:

$\mathscr{R}(1)$ $\qquad -W + F \sin \alpha + N \cos \alpha = 0;$
$\mathscr{R}(2)$ $\qquad F \cos \alpha - N \sin \alpha = 0;$
$\mathscr{R}(3)$ $\qquad -W \sin \alpha + F = 0;$
$\mathscr{R}(4)$ $\qquad -W \cos \alpha + N = 0.$

It will be noticed that not all of the four equations are required to obtain the solution. In fact, equations (3) and (4) yield immediately

$$F = W \sin \alpha, \quad \text{and} \quad N = W \cos \alpha.$$

The reader should satisfy himself that these solutions fit the first two equations also.

We observe that all the available information can be obtained by resolving in two chosen directions.

EXAMPLE 4. A lantern of mass 3 kg hangs from the ceiling by a string which passes through a rough ring at the top of the lantern. The two parts of the string, AB and AC, are at 30° and 40° to the vertical. Find the tensions in the two parts of the string.

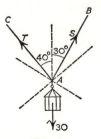

Fig. 5

Taking g as 10 m s^{-2}, the weight of the lantern is 30 N. Let the tensions in AB and AC be S newtons and T newtons. Although the string is continuous, the tensions in the two parts are not equal because of the friction where it passes through the rough ring.

The solution is most simply obtained by resolving in directions at right angles to the unknown forces. We thereby get equations from which one unknown is absent, since a force has zero resolved part in the direction perpendicular to its line of action.

We resolve first at right angles to the string AB. The forces S, T, and the weight make with this direction angles of 90°, 20°, and 120°; their resolved parts are therefore 0, $T \cos 20°$, and $-30 \cos 60°$, so that

$\mathscr{R}(\perp \text{ to } AB)$ $T \cos 20° - 30 \cos 60° = 0.$

Similarly

$\mathscr{R}(\perp \text{ to } AC)$ $S \cos 20° - 30 \cos 50° = 0.$

Therefore $S = \dfrac{30 \cos 50°}{\cos 20°} = 21, \quad T = \dfrac{30 \cos 60°}{\cos 20°} = 16.$

In Chapter 9 we shall discuss another method of solving problems of this kind, by means of the Triangle of Forces.

EXAMPLE 5. In the system shown in Fig. 6 the two pulleys can turn freely about horizontal axes and are in the same vertical plane. The two strings passing over the pulleys have masses of X attached to their ends, and the string which hangs vertically carries a mass of M. The three strings are

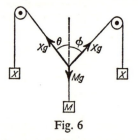

Fig. 6

knotted together. Find an equation connecting X, M, and the angles which the first two strings make with the vertical, when the system is in equilibrium.

The tensions in the strings are equal to the weights of the masses which they carry, which are Mg and Xg (twice). Let the strings which pass over the pulleys make angles θ, ϕ with the vertical. Considering the equilibrium of the tensions in the three strings which meet at the knot, we have

$$\mathscr{R}(\rightarrow) \qquad Xg \cos (90° - \phi) - Xg \cos (90° - \theta) = 0,$$

so that
$$\sin \theta = \sin \phi,$$
$$\theta = \phi.$$

Also
$$\mathscr{R}(\uparrow) \qquad Xg \cos \phi + Xg \cos \theta - Mg = 0;$$

therefore, since $\theta = \phi$,

$$\cos \theta = \frac{M}{2X}.$$

This example suggests a simple way in which the resolution principle could be verified experimentally. Different values of M and X could be selected, and the corresponding value of θ measured and compared with the value calculated from the equation given above.

4.4 The next example shows an application of the resolution principle to a dynamical problem.

EXAMPLE 6. *A man on skis is towed behind a car. He holds on to a rope whose other end is attached to the rear bumper of the car and which is inclined at an angle $\bar{\omega}$ to the horizontal.*[1] *The mass of the man is 80 kg, and the friction and air resistance on the skier amount to 40 N. Find the tension in the rope and the normal contact force between the man and the ground when the car has an acceleration of* 0·3 *m s⁻².*
Let the tension in the rope be T and the normal force N, both measured in newtons. The weight of the man, taking g as 9·8 m s⁻², is $80 \times 9·8$ N $= 784$ N.

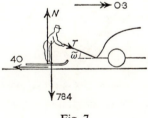

Fig. 7

The forces affecting the horizontal motion of the man are the tension in the rope and the resistance of 40 N.

$$\mathscr{R}(\rightarrow) \qquad T \cos \bar{\omega} - 40 = 80 \times 0·3.$$

[1] See p. 3 for a definition of the angle $\bar{\omega}$.

Since $\cos \bar{\omega} = \frac{4}{5}$,

$$\tfrac{4}{5}T = 40 + 24,$$
$$T = 80.$$

$\mathscr{R}(\downarrow)$ $T\cos(90° - \bar{\omega}) + 784 - N = 0.$

Substituting $T = 80$ and $\cos(90° - \bar{\omega}) = \frac{3}{5}$,

$$\tfrac{3}{5} \times 80 + 784 \approx 830.$$

The tension is 80 N and the normal force 830 N, approximately.

4.5 *EXAMPLE 7. A body is acted on by forces in a horizontal plane: 60 newtons, due S; 5 newtons, due W; 25 newtons, $\bar{\omega}$ W of N. Find the fourth force, which, together with these, will preserve equilibrium.*

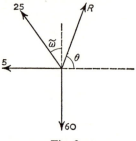

Fig. 8

The given forces have a total resolved part to the southward of

$$60 + 5\cos 90° - 25\cos\bar{\omega} = 60 - 25 \times \tfrac{4}{5} = 40 \text{ N},$$

and one to the westward of

$$5 + 60\cos 90° + 25\cos(90° - \bar{\omega}) = 5 + 25 \times \tfrac{3}{5} = 20 \text{ N}.$$

The required force must therefore have resolved parts in northerly and easterly directions. Let the force be R newtons in a direction θ N of E. Then

$\mathscr{R}(\uparrow)$ $R\cos(90° - \theta) - 40 = 0,$

$\mathscr{R}(\rightarrow)$ $R\cos\theta - 20 = 0,$

so that

$$R\sin\theta = 40, \quad R\cos\theta = 20.$$

These equations can be solved for R and θ in the following way. Since, for any angle θ,

$$\frac{\sin\theta}{\cos\theta} = \tan\theta, \text{ and } \cos^2\theta + \sin^2\theta = 1,$$

we can write

$$\tan\theta = \frac{R\sin\theta}{R\cos\theta} = \frac{40}{20} = 2,$$

and $\qquad R^2 = R^2(\cos^2\theta + \sin^2\theta) = (R\cos\theta)^2 + (R\sin\theta)^2$
$$= 20^2 + 40^2 = 2000,$$
so that $\qquad\qquad\qquad \theta = 63° \quad\text{and}\quad R = 45.$

A force of 45 newtons in a direction 63° N of E is needed to maintain equilibrium.

4.6 Equations of the form
$$R\cos\theta = X, \qquad R\sin\theta = Y$$
occur frequently in mechanics, and they can always be solved by the method described in Example 7. This gives, in general,
$$\tan\theta = \frac{R\sin\theta}{R\cos\theta} = \frac{Y}{X}$$
and $\qquad\qquad R^2 = (R\cos\theta)^2 + (R\sin\theta)^2 = X^2 + Y^2,$
so that $\qquad\qquad\qquad R = \sqrt{(X^2 + Y^2)}.$

Alternatively, the following geometrical method of solution may be

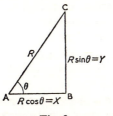

Fig. 9

used. If a right-angled triangle ABC is drawn with hypotenuse AC of length R units and angle A equal to θ (see Fig. 9), then
$$AB = R\cos\theta = X, \quad\text{and}\quad BC = R\sin\theta = Y.$$
It is immediately clear from this figure that
$$R = \sqrt{(X^2 + Y^2)}, \quad\text{and}\quad \tan\theta = Y/X.$$

EXERCISE 4

Questions 1–8 refer to a smooth plane of angle $\bar\omega$ on which is placed a body of mass 6 kg. All forces act in a vertical plane through a line of greatest slope. Take $g = 10$ m s^{-2}.

1. What force up the plane will keep the mass in equilibrium?

2. What horizontal force will keep the mass in equilibrium?

3. What force at 60° to the plane will keep the mass in equilibrium?

4. A horizontal force of 100 N is applied to the mass tending to push it up the plane. What other force acting in the plane will be needed to preserve equilibrium? What will be the normal contact force?

5. The mass is allowed to slide down the plane. Find its acceleration, and the distance it will move in 2 seconds from rest.

6. The mass is projected up the plane with a speed of $4 \cdot 2$ m s^{-1}. How far up the plane will it move before coming to rest?

7. The mass is pushed up the plane by a force of 90 N up a line of greatest slope. Find its acceleration.

8. The mass is pushed up the plane by a horizontal force of 90 N. Find its acceleration.

Questions 9–16 refer to a particle of mass 1 kg suspended by a string from a fixed point and pulled aside from the vertical in various ways. Take $g = 10$ m s^{-2}.

9. The particle is acted on by a horizontal force and the string is at an angle $\tilde{\omega}$ to the vertical. Find the force.

10. The particle is acted on by a force at right angles to the string, which makes an angle $\tilde{\omega}$ to the vertical. Find the force.

11. The string is at 30° to the vertical, and the force on the particle makes 60° with the downward vertical. Find the force, and the tension in the string.

12. The particle is pulled aside with a horizontal force of 10 N. What angle does the string make with the vertical, and what is the tension in the string?

13. Repeat Question 12 with a force of 5 N.

14. The particle is pulled with a force of 5 N at right angles to the string. What angle does the string make with the vertical, and what is the tension in the string?

15. The upper end of the string is fixed to a point in the roof of a railway carriage. If at some time the string makes a steady angle of 5° with the vertical, find the acceleration of the carriage.

16. If in Question 15 the acceleration of the carriage is $2 \cdot 5$ m s^{-2}, find the angle that the string makes with the vertical.

17. A bead of mass 100 gm is threaded on a smooth vertical wire and is raised with an acceleration of 2 m s^{-2} by the tension of a string which always makes an angle of 60° with the wire. Find the tension in the string.

18. A 2000 kg truck on smooth rails is pulled by a force of 800 N at an angle of 60° to the rails. Find its acceleration.

19. A 5 kg body C is suspended by strings AC, BC attached to two points A, B in the same horizontal line. If $AB = BC = CA$, find the tension in each string.

20. Two dogs are taking a small boy for a walk. Fido pulls on his lead with a force of 50 N southwards, and Boxer pulls with a force of 30 N westwards. With what force and in what direction must the boy pull to preserve equilibrium?

21. A 10 gm mass hangs from a fixed point by a string. It is pulled aside by a force of 50 mN inclined upwards at $\bar{\omega}$ to the horizontal. Find the tension in the string and the angle it makes with the vertical.

22. What force is needed to counteract the combination of forces of 60 kN at N 20° E and 80 kN at N 70° W?

23. A load of 100 N is carried by two strings, one inclined at 10° and the other at 20° to the horizontal. Find their tensions.

†**24.** A string hangs from a fixed point A and supports a mass of 5 kg. To a point B of the string is firmly knotted a second string, which passes over a pulley C and carries at its other end a mass of 3 kg. It is found that AB makes an angle of 31° with the downward vertical. Find the angle which BC makes with the vertical, and the tension in the string AB.

CHAPTER 5

ROUGH SURFACES

5.1 When there is a tendency for one surface to slide over another, forces of friction are usually brought into play. These forces act in the common tangent plane of the surfaces, at right angles to the normal contact force, and they are governed by a number of principles, which are deduced from experiment.

The first of these is that friction is essentially a 'passive' force; it acts in such a way as to oppose the motion of sliding, but it never causes such motion.

A book resting on a rough horizontal table is in equilibrium under the action of its weight and the normal contact force from the table (Fig. 1a). If a small horizontal force is applied to the book, it does not

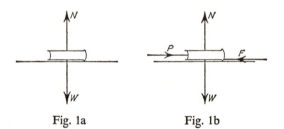

Fig. 1a   Fig. 1b

move; this is because a friction force of equal magnitude has come into play in the opposite direction to preserve equilibrium (Fig. 1b). As soon as the applied force is removed, the friction vanishes as well.

This does not mean that friction cannot sometimes assist motion. Indeed, most forms of locomotion would be impossible without the force of friction – as anyone knows who has tried to walk on smooth ice. When we walk, a muscular force is applied backwards to our feet; if we are on a smooth surface there is nothing to oppose this force, and our feet merely slide backwards over the surface. If the surface is rough, however, a friction force comes into play and prevents this relative motion; this force is directed forwards, and enables us to move.

The first principle of friction can be stated as follows:

(i) *When sliding does not take place, the force of friction is just sufficient to prevent the relative motion of the two surfaces.*

5.2 We return to the illustration of the book on the table. If the horizontal applied force is gradually increased, for a time the book will still not move; all this time the friction force is also increasing, remaining exactly equal to the applied force. There will come a time, however, when the book begins to move; the friction is no longer sufficient to counteract the applied force. It is found that a further increase in the applied force will not cause any further increase in the friction. We deduce that there is a limit to the size of the friction force.

This 'limiting friction' force is not an absolute quantity. It would be larger if the weight of the book were larger, or if the same effect were simulated by exerting an extra force downwards on the top of the book. In fact, it can be shown experimentally that a good approximation in many situations is that the limiting friction force depends on the normal contact force between the two surfaces, and that it is directly proportional to this force.

(ii) *There is a limiting value to the possible friction force that can exist, and this is proportional to the normal contact force between the two surfaces.*

If F is the friction force, and N the normal force, this second principle states that

$$F \leqslant \mu N.$$

The constant μ is called the COEFFICIENT OF FRICTION, and the quantity μN the LIMITING FRICTION.

It might be thought that the area of contact and the shape of the region of contact between the two surfaces would also affect the limiting friction. It is found that, within the limits of experimental accuracy, this is not the case. The limiting friction depends only on the normal force and on the roughness of the two surfaces.

(iii) *The value of μ depends only on the roughness of the two surfaces.*

For wooden surfaces sliding across each other the value of μ lies between about 0·25 and 0·5, and for metal surfaces it is between about 0·15 and 0·3. These values can be considerably reduced by lubrication.

5.3 We have seen that when sliding does not take place the friction may or may not be limiting. When it is limiting, we say that the surfaces are 'on the point of sliding'. When sliding does occur, however, the friction force does its utmost to oppose this motion. This is the gist of the fourth principle:

(iv) *When relative motion is taking place between two surfaces, the friction always has its limiting value, and acts in such a direction as to oppose the relative motion.*

To be quite accurate, for two given surfaces, the ratio of the limiting friction to the normal force when there is no motion is slightly greater than the ratio of the friction to the normal force when there is motion. Two different values should be given for the coefficient of friction, one for use in statical problems and another for dynamical problems in which sliding takes place between the surfaces. Furthermore, there is a slight variation of the dynamical coefficient of friction for very high relative speeds. In elementary work, however, it is customary to neglect these small differences in the value of μ.

EXAMPLE 1. A table of mass 30 kg stands on the floor; the coefficient of friction between the legs and the floor is 0·6. (i) How large a force may be applied horizontally without moving it? (ii) If it is pushed with a force of 200 N, with what acceleration will the table move?

(i) Using the approximation $g = 10$ m s^{-2}, the weight of the table is 300 newtons. If the contact force in newtons is N, then

$$\mathscr{R}(\uparrow) \qquad\qquad N - 300 = 0.$$

The limiting friction is therefore $0·6 \times 300 = 180$ newtons, and the friction F cannot be larger than this. Also

$$\mathscr{R}(\rightarrow) \qquad\qquad P - F = 0,$$

so that the maximum force which can be applied is 180 newtons.

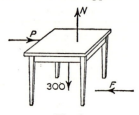

Fig. 2

(ii) Since there is motion, the friction is limiting. The normal force is the same as in the first part of the question, so that the limiting friction is 180 newtons. The force accelerating the table is $(200 - 180)$ newtons = 20 newtons. The equation of motion is therefore

$$20 = 30a$$

which gives $\qquad\qquad a = \tfrac{2}{3}.$

The acceleration of the table is $\tfrac{2}{3}$ m s^{-2}.

5.4 *EXAMPLE 2. A particle of weight W rests on a plane of angle α, and μ = ½. What can be said about α if equilibrium is possible?*
From § 4.3 (p. 55) we know that

$$F = W \sin \alpha, \quad \text{and} \quad N = W \cos \alpha.$$

Since $$F \leqslant \mu N,$$

$$W \sin \alpha \leqslant \tfrac{1}{2} W \cos \alpha,$$

so that $$\tan \alpha \leqslant \tfrac{1}{2},$$

$$\alpha \leqslant 27° \text{ approximately.}$$

Fig. 3

It is useful to note that, more generally, the greatest slope on which a particle can rest unsupported is given by the equation

$$\tan \alpha = \mu.$$

EXAMPLE 3. A particle of mass 0·5 kg rests on a rough plane of angle $\tilde{\omega}$, and μ = ½. Find (i) the smallest force applied parallel to the plane that will prevent it from sliding down; (ii) the largest force that can be applied parallel to the plane if it is not to slide up; (iii) the largest force that can be applied horizontally if it is not to slide up; (iv) its acceleration if it is allowed to slide down the plane.
Since $\tan \tilde{\omega} = \tfrac{3}{4}$, and this is greater than $\tfrac{1}{2}$, it follows from Example 2 that the particle could not rest on the plane in equilibrium without some supporting force.

The weight of the particle is approximately 5 newtons (taking $g = 10 \text{ m s}^{-2}$). We denote the normal force by N, the supporting force by P and the friction by F (all in newtons), adding different suffixes for different parts of the Example.

In parts (i) and (iv) the friction acts up the plane, whilst in (ii) and (iii) it acts down. In each case the friction is limiting, so that we may write $F = \tfrac{1}{2}N$.

(i) See Fig. 4.

$\mathscr{R}(\perp \text{ to plane})$ $N_1 - 5 \cos \tilde{\omega} = 0.$

$\mathscr{R}(\| \text{ to plane})$ $\tfrac{1}{2}N_1 + P_1 - 5 \sin \tilde{\omega} = 0.$

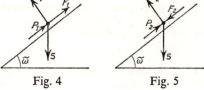

Fig. 4   Fig. 5

Therefore $N_1 = 5 \times \frac{4}{5} = 4,$

and $P_1 = 5 \times \frac{3}{5} - \frac{1}{2} \times 4 = 1.$

   (ii) See Fig. 5.

   $\mathscr{R}(\perp$ to plane) $N_2 - 5 \cos \tilde{\omega} = 0.$

   $\mathscr{R}(\parallel$ to plane) $P_2 - \frac{1}{2}N_2 - 5 \sin \tilde{\omega} = 0.$

Therefore $N = 4$, as in (i), and

$$P_2 = 5 \times \frac{3}{5} + \frac{1}{2} \times 4 = 5.$$

We see from (i) and (ii) that to maintain the particle in equilibrium on the plane by a force parallel to the plane we must apply a force of at least 1 newton and not larger than 5 newtons. If it were pushed with any force between these two extremes, the particle would remain in equilibrium, but friction would not be limiting.

   (iii) See Fig. 6.

   It is best, as in (i) and (ii), to resolve first at right angles to the direction

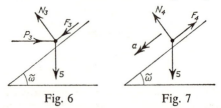

Fig. 6   Fig. 7

of P, thereby cutting out this unknown force from the equation. We therefore resolve vertically and horizontally in this part.

   $\mathscr{R}(\downarrow)$ $5 + \frac{1}{2}N_3 \sin \tilde{\omega} - N_3 \cos \tilde{\omega} = 0,$

from which we find $5 = \frac{4}{5}N_3 - \frac{3}{5} \times \frac{1}{2}N_3 = \frac{1}{2}N_3,$

so that $N_3 = 10.$

We notice that the normal force is larger than in the previous parts of the question, because the horizontal force P has a resolved part perpendicular to the plane which must be counteracted by an increased normal force. This in turn means that the limiting friction force will be larger in this case.

   $\mathscr{R}(\rightarrow)$ $P_3 - N_3 \sin \tilde{\omega} - \frac{1}{2}N_3 \cos \tilde{\omega} = 0,$

whence $P_3 = 10 \times \frac{3}{5} + 5 \times \frac{4}{5} = 10.$

   (iv) See Fig. 7. Let the acceleration in m s^{-2} be a.

   $\mathscr{R}(\perp$ to plane) $N_4 - 5 \cos \tilde{\omega} = 0.$

   $\mathscr{R}(\parallel$ to plane) $5 \sin \tilde{\omega} - \frac{1}{2}N_4 = 0 \cdot 5a.$

Therefore $N_4 = 5 \times \frac{4}{5} = 4$, as in (i) and (ii), and

$$0 \cdot 5a = 5 \times \frac{3}{5} - \frac{1}{2} \times 4 = 1,$$

$$a = 2.$$

5.5 *EXAMPLE 4. A boy pulls a toboggan of mass 10 kg across a horizontal snowfield; $\mu = 0 \cdot 1$. If the rope with which he pulls it makes an angle $\tilde{\omega}$ with the* *horizontal, and the toboggan moves at a steady speed, find the tension in the rope.*

Taking g as 9·8 m s⁻², the weight of the toboggan is 98 newtons. Since it

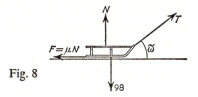

Fig. 8

moves at a steady speed, the forces are in equilibrium and friction is limiting. Let the normal force be N and the tension T, both in newtons.

$\mathscr{R}(\rightarrow)$ $T \cos \tilde{\omega} - \mu N = 0,$

so that $0{\cdot}8T = 0{\cdot}1N,$

$\mathscr{R}(\uparrow)$ $T \sin \tilde{\omega} + N - 98 = 0.$

Therefore $0{\cdot}6T + 8T = 98,$

$$T = \frac{98}{8{\cdot}6} = 11{\cdot}4.$$

5.6 *EXAMPLE 5. If a motor car can attain an acceleration of 3 m s⁻², find the minimum possible coefficient between the tyres and the ground, assuming that the total normal contact force on the driving wheels at this acceleration is $\frac{3}{5}$ of the weight.*

If the front wheels are of negligible mass and can rotate freely, there is no friction force between them and the ground. The forces are therefore as shown

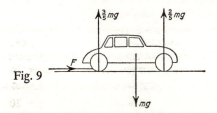

Fig. 9

in Fig. 9, F being the total friction force between the driving wheels and the ground. The equation of motion is

$$F = m \times 3.$$

But the friction condition gives also

$$F \leqslant \tfrac{3}{5}\mu mg.$$

Hence, taking $g = 10$ m s⁻²,

$$\tfrac{3}{5}\mu \times 10m > 3m,$$

$$\mu > \tfrac{1}{2}.$$

EXERCISE 5

1. A horizontal force of 10 N will just move a block of mass 5 kg on a table. Find the coefficient of friction.

2. The coefficient of friction between a suitcase of mass 30 kg and the floor is $\frac{1}{3}$. How large a force, applied horizontally, is needed to move it?

3. A sofa of mass 50 kg is dragged onto a van up a ramp at 25° to the horizontal. If $\mu = \frac{1}{3}$, what force parallel to the ramp is needed to pull it up at a steady speed?

4. In Question 2, how large a force is needed if the suitcase is pulled by means of a rope inclined at an angle $\bar{\omega}$ to the horizontal?

5. In Question 2, how large a force is needed if the suitcase is pushed along the floor by a force inclined at $\bar{\omega}$ to the horizontal?

6. A curling stone of mass 18 kg slides 32 m before coming to rest. If $\mu = 0.1$, what was its initial speed? (Take $g = 10$ m s^{-2}.)

7. An ice-hockey puck of mass 0·2 kg is hit with a speed of 15 m s^{-1} and travels 75 m before coming to rest. Find μ.

8. A dictionary of mass 3 kg is pushed across a table with a constant horizontal force; $\mu = 0.4$. If it is pushed 1 m from rest in $\frac{1}{2}$ s, what is the force? How much further will it move when the force is removed? (Take $g = 10$ m s^{-2}.)

9. A toy barge of mass 3 kg rests on the floor; $\mu = 0.3$. A child pulls it with a force of 20 N inclined at 40° to the horizontal. Find the acceleration.

10. A floor polisher of mass 5 kg is pushed along the floor at a steady speed; $\mu = 0.7$. If the handle (whose mass is negligible) is inclined at 35° to the horizontal, how hard must it be pushed?

11. A ramp 13 m long leads up to a platform 5 m high. A packing-case of mass 65 kg stands on the ramp; $\mu = 0.35$. A rope tied round the case is held parallel to the line of greatest slope of the ramp. What is the smallest tension in the rope that will prevent the case from sliding down? (In Questions 11 to 14 take $g = 10$ m s^{-2}.)

12. In Question 11, how large must the tension be before the case starts to slide up the ramp?

13. In Question 11, what would be the acceleration of the case down the ramp if the rope were cut?

14. In Question 11, how hard must the rope be pulled to give the case an acceleration of 1·2 m s^{-2}?

15. Prove that it is impossible for a ladder to rest on smooth horizontal ground against a rough vertical wall.

16. A book of mass 0·8 kg rests on a desk lid. If the lid is at more than 35° to the horizontal the book will slide down. Find μ. Find also what force acting (i) up the lid, (ii) down the lid, will be needed to move the book on the lid when its inclination is 20°.

17. What horizontal force would be necessary to prevent a brick of mass 3 kg from sliding down a roof inclined at $\bar{\omega}$ to the horizontal if $\mu = 0.4$?

18. A sack of mass 25 kg will just rest on a slope of angle $\tan^{-1}(\frac{3}{5})$ with friction limiting. What horizontal force will push it at a uniform speed up a slope of angle $\tan^{-1}(\frac{2}{5})$?

19. Prove that the acceleration of a toboggan down a slope of angle θ is $g(\sin \theta - \mu \cos \theta)$.

†**20.** A particle is supported in equilibrium on a rough slope by a force acting up the plane along a line of greatest slope. If the greatest possible value of the force is twice the least possible value, find the angle of inclination in terms of μ.

†**21.** A truck will run at constant speed down a track of inclination α. What will be its acceleration down a track of inclination β ($>\alpha$), assuming that the frictional resistance bears the same ratio to the normal force in each case?

†**22.** A particle of mass M is projected up a rough plane of angle θ (where $\mu < \tan \theta$). Prove that when it again attains its original speed u, it will be a distance $u^2\mu \sec \theta / g(\tan^2 \theta - \mu^2)$ down the plane from the point of projection.

†**23.** Two equal rings of weight w are movable along a rough curtain rod. The rings are connected by a string which hangs down and has on it a smooth ring of weight W. If θ is the greatest possible angle between the two parts of the string in equilibrium, prove that

$$\tan \tfrac{1}{2}\theta = \frac{\mu(W + 2w)}{W}.$$

MISCELLANEOUS EXERCISE A

The questions in miscellaneous exercises are arranged in sets of five.

1. A train, which is moving with uniform acceleration, is seen to travel 800 m in one minute and 1200 m in the next minute. Find its speed at the beginning of the first minute and at the end of the second minute. Determine the acceleration of the train.

2. Simultaneous values of velocity and time for a train are given in the table below. Draw the v–t graph and estimate the acceleration in m s^{-2} at the end of the second minute and the distance passed over in attaining a speed of 90 km h^{-1}.

Time in seconds	0	50	100	150	200	250	300
Velocity in km h^{-1}	0	44·3	65·4	78·6	87·0	92·3	96·2

3. A balloon of mass 1000 kg is drifting horizontally and 20 kg of ballast is thrown out. With what acceleration will the balloon begin to ascend? (Take $g = 9 \cdot 8$ m s^{-2}.)

4. Two masses of 3 kg and 5 kg are tied one to each end of a light cord, which is then hung over a smooth pulley. Find the acceleration with which each mass begins to move. If the cord breaks when each mass has moved 3·2 m, find the further time which elapses before the 3 kg mass ceases to rise. (Take $g = 10$ m s^{-2}.)

5. A lorry is travelling at 36 km h^{-1}. What force, expressed as a fraction of the weight of the lorry, is needed to stop it (i) in 10 s, (ii) in a distance of 10 m?

6. A car increases its speed from 18 to 54 km h^{-1} in a distance of 800 m. Assuming the acceleration to be uniform, find the speed of the car in km h^{-1} when half the distance has been travelled. If the mass of the car is 640 kg, what is the accelerating force?

7. A particle A is projected vertically upwards with an initial velocity of 30 m s^{-1}. Draw the v–t graph of this motion. At the instant of projection a second particle B is released from rest. Insert its v–t graph on your diagram and show that the two graphs are parallel. If initially B is 45 m vertically above A, find when and where the two particles meet. (Take $g = 10$ m s^{-2}.)

8. A balloon of mass 350 kg is descending with a constant acceleration of 0·5 m s^{-2}, when 30 kg of ballast is thrown out. Find the resulting acceleration. If the velocity of the balloon downwards was 2 m s^{-1} when the ballast was thrown out, find how far the balloon falls before it starts to rise.

9. Masses of 125 gm and 120 gm are connected by a light string which passes over a smooth pulley. The heavier mass is allowed to descend, and

70

after 3 s the velocity is observed to be 0·54 m s⁻¹. What value do these figures as they stand give for g, the acceleration due to gravity, and what corrections are necessary?

*10. For a body moving in a straight line the acceleration a varies as t; $a = 5$, $v = 30$ and $s = 120$ when $t = 6$ (all in metre-second units). Find (i) v when $t = 0$, (ii) s when $t = 12$.

11. A body starting from rest moves in a straight line, and the following observations are taken:

Time in seconds	0	0·2	0·4	0·6	0·8	1·0	1·2	1·4	1·6
Distance in mm	0	5·5	21	48	85	132	185	237	290

Plot an s–t graph, and find as accurately as you can the velocities of the body at the middle of each interval of time. What conclusions do you draw as to the nature of the motion?

12. A car moving with constant acceleration is observed to take 20 s over 200 m and 15 s over the next 200 m. What is its acceleration? What is its speed at the end of the second 200 m?

The mass of the car is 350 kg; find the accelerating force.

13. A weightless string passes over a smooth horizontal peg and carries a scale-pan of mass 1 kg at one end and a particle of mass 1 kg at the other. If a particle of mass 2 kg is placed in the scale-pan, find, during the subsequent motion, (i) the acceleration of the system, and (ii) the contact force between the particle and the scale-pan.

14. A body of mass 5 kg moving with a velocity of 8 m s⁻¹ is acted on by a force of 20 N in the direction of its motion. What are (i) the acceleration of the body, and (ii) the distance the body covers in the first 4 seconds during which the force acts?

15. A uniform chain is of total length 3 m. A length x of the chain lies on a rough table in a straight line perpendicular to the edge of the table, and the remainder hangs vertically. If the coefficient of friction between the chain and the table is $\frac{2}{3}$ and the chain is in limiting equilibrium, find x.

16. Prove the formula $s = ut + \frac{1}{2}at^2$ for uniformly accelerated motion.

A train travelling at 72 km h⁻¹ is brought to rest by the constant retardation due to its brakes in a distance of 144 m. Prove that in each second the speed is reduced by 5 km h⁻¹.

17. Two strings are attached to a mass of 1 kg; the other ends of the strings are attached to particles of mass 1·5 kg and 2·5 kg respectively, which can move on a smooth horizontal table. If the mass of 1 kg hangs freely over the edge of the table with the strings taut and perpendicular to the edge of the table, find (i) the acceleration of the system, (ii) the tension in each string, during the motion. (Take $g = 10$ m s⁻².)

18. A block of mass 3000 kg is being drawn up a smooth inclined plane of slope 1 in 20 at a steady speed of 5 m s⁻¹ by means of a rope parallel to the plane. Find the tension in the rope.

If the rope breaks, how much further up the plane will the block move before starting to slide back? (Take $g = 10$ m s⁻².)

*19. A point moves in a straight line from rest so that its acceleration in m s^{-2} is $15 - 3t$, where t is the time in seconds from the start. Prove that it next comes to rest again in 10 seconds. Find the distance covered in this time.

20. A block of mass 30 kg can just be moved on a rough horizontal table by a horizontal force of 98 N. What force will be needed to move the block if the direction of the force makes an angle with the horizontal of 30° (i) upwards, (ii) downwards? (Take $g = 9.8$ m s^{-2}.)

21. The distance between two stations on an electric railway is 3450 m. The trains accelerate uniformly, run at a maximum speed of 90 km h^{-1} and then are uniformly retarded. The time taken for retardation from maximum speed is one-half of the time taken to attain this maximum. If a train takes $2\frac{1}{2}$ min to travel from station to station, find the rate of acceleration in m s^{-2}.

22. A car is found to increase its speed from 8 to 80 km h^{-1} in 40 s. Find the acceleration (supposed uniform) in m s^{-2}. Plot a space–time graph, and from it determine the time taken to travel the last 300 m of the observed motion.

23. A small body is placed on a rough plane of angle $\bar{\omega}$ and allowed to slide down. If the coefficient of friction between the body and the plane is $\frac{1}{4}$, find the speed v of the body when it has moved 18 m from rest down the plane. If the body is stopped at this point and given this speed v up a line of greatest slope of the plane, find how far it will travel up the plane before coming momentarily to rest. (Take $g = 10$ m s^{-2}.)

24. A mass of 5 kg lies on a smooth horizontal table, and a string connects it to another mass, hanging over the edge, which is let go. The two masses move through 1 m in 1 second. Find the tension in the string, and the suspended mass.

25. A mass of 25 kg resting on a plane begins to slip when the plane is tilted to an angle of 30° with the horizontal. What force up the plane will be necessary to keep the mass from slipping when the angle of slope is increased to 45°?

26. The ends of a train, 100 m long, pass a point with velocities of 9 and 11 m s^{-1}; show that its acceleration (assumed constant) is 0.2 m s^{-2}, and find the time taken.

Two trains, A and B, moving in opposite directions, pass one another. Their lengths are 100 m and 70 m respectively. At the instant when they begin to pass, A is moving at 9 m s^{-1} with a constant acceleration of 0.2 m s^{-2} and B has a uniform velocity of 7 m s^{-1}. Find the time the trains take to pass.

27. A block of mass 2 kg is placed on a rough plane, inclined to the horizontal at an angle of 30°, and starts to slide down the plane. Indicate clearly by means of a diagram the forces acting on the block. If the coefficient of friction between the block and the plane is $\frac{1}{4}$, calculate the force of friction acting on the block, and also the acceleration of the block down the plane.

28. A monkey climbs a light rope at a uniform speed, and it is found that the tension in the rope is 100 N. Find the tension in the rope when (i) the monkey slides down at constant speed, (ii) the monkey slides down with an acceleration of 3 m s^{-2}. (Take $g = 10$ m s^{-2}.)

29. A body of mass 3 kg is held on a smooth plane of angle 30°. A light, inextensible string is attached to the body and passes over a smooth peg at the top of the plane, and hangs vertically with a mass of 2 kg at the other end. Find the tension in the string and the acceleration of the masses after the system has been released. If initially the system is at rest with the 2 kg mass 1 m from the ground, find how long it will be before this mass reaches the ground. (Take $g = 10$ m s^{-2}.)

30. A stone slab lies on a horizontal board, the coefficient of friction between them being 0·27. To what angle can the board be tilted before the stone slips?

If the board is tilted to this angle, find the force needed to pull the slab up the plane, if the mass of the slab is 100 kg and the force is parallel to the plane surface of the board.

31. An electric train travelled from rest at station A to station B, a distance of 2100 m. For the first 20 seconds it accelerated steadily, reaching a speed of 90 km h^{-1}. It maintained this speed until the brakes were applied and the train brought to rest at B with uniform retardation over the last 125 m. Find this retardation in m s^{-2}, and the total time taken in seconds.

32. A cork is ejected vertically from a bottle. It hits a lamp 4 m above the point of projection in its upward flight after 0·4 s. Find the velocity with which it left the bottle and the greatest height the cork would have reached had it not hit the lamp. (Take $g = 10$ m s^{-2}.)

33. A small body of mass 2 kg rests on a smooth plane inclined to the horizontal at an angle of 25°. The body is held in equilibrium by the pull of a string attached to it and inclined to the horizontal at 45°. Find the tension in the string and the normal reaction of the plane on the body.

34. A light string, passing over a smooth pulley, supports a scale-pan at each end; the mass of each scale-pan is 1 kg. A mass of 1 kg is placed in one scale-pan and a mass of 2 kg in the other, and the system is released from rest with the string taut. Show that, using the approximation $g = 10$ m s^{-2}, the acceleration of either scale-pan is 2 m s^{-2}. Find the tension in the string and the reactions between the masses and the scale-pans.

One second after the motion starts the string breaks. Show that the scale-pan containing the 1 kg mass comes to instantaneous rest 1·2 m above its starting position.

35. A load of mass 10 kg resting on a rough plank is on the point of slipping when the plank is inclined at 30° to the horizontal. What is the least force up the plank needed to prevent this load slipping when the angle of slope is 60°? (Take $g = 10$ m s^{-2}.)

36. A particle moves in a straight line in such a way that its velocity v at time t (in metre-second units) is given for the first 6 seconds by the following table:

t	0	1	2	3	4	5	6
v	0	1·5	2·45	3·1	3·55	3·9	4·2

Plot the v–t graph, and from it estimate (i) the acceleration at time $t = 2$, (ii) the distance travelled in the 6 s.

37. A train takes 4 min $5\frac{1}{2}$ s to go between two stations 3120 m apart, starting from and finishing at rest. The acceleration is uniform for 45 s, and the retardation is uniform for the last 30 s, the speed being constant for the remaining time. Find this speed and the values of the acceleration and retardation.

38. A truck is launched at a speed of 36 km h^{-1} up an incline of 1 in 98. Neglecting frictional forces, find the rate of retardation of the truck, and the distance it travels before it comes to rest. (Take $g = 9\cdot8$ m s^{-2}.)

39. A balloon, which with load has a total mass of 320 kg, is floating in the air at a constant height, when a man with his parachute, of mass (combined) 70 kg, drops out. Calculate the distance through which the balloon will rise during the next 5 seconds.

40. A block of mass 60 kg is just prevented from sliding down a rough plane of angle 45° by a force of x newtons acting up the plane. If the coefficient of friction between the block and the plane is $\frac{1}{3}$, find x.

41. An express train travelling at 90 km h^{-1} and a slow train travelling in the same direction at 36 km h^{-1} are on the same track. The driver of the express sees the tail of the slow train 750 m ahead of him and immediately puts on his brakes. The slow train does not increase its speed. What is the least retardation (in m s^{-2}) that the brakes must provide if a collision is to be prevented?

42. A balloon moves from rest on the ground with vertical acceleration of $\frac{1}{80}g$; sketch the velocity–time graph to show its vertical velocity during the first 40 seconds of its motion. After 40 s a part A of its undercarriage falls off. Extend the v–t graph to show the time when A comes instantaneously to rest. Hence or otherwise calculate the time when A reaches the ground.

43. A mass of 300 gm on a rough horizontal table is connected by a string passing over a smooth pulley at the edge of the table to a mass of 200 gm hanging freely. The masses move with an acceleration of 1·6 m s^{-2}. What is the coefficient of friction between the 300 gm mass and the table?

44. A body of mass 10 kg rests on a rough slope inclined at an angle of 30° to the horizontal. The least force directed up the plane which will move the body is 120 N. Find (i) the coefficient of friction, (ii) the least force directed down the plane which will move the body.

45. A package of mass 10 kg stands on the floor of a train travelling at 12 m s^{-1}. The train is braked suddenly and comes to rest with a retardation of 2·5 m s^{-2}. What is the friction force between the package and the floor (i) if $\mu = 0\cdot3$, (ii) if $\mu = 0\cdot2$? Find how far the package moves across the floor if $\mu = 0\cdot2$. (Take $g = 10$ m s^{-2}.)

46. A train, travelling at 90 km h^{-1} on a level track, is retarded uniformly to 18 km h^{-1} by its brakes in 1 km. Show that the total resistance to motion is 300 N per tonne of train.

If the total resistance to motion were increased to 400 N per tonne, how far would the train travel in coming to rest from 108 km h^{-1}, and in what time?

47. A boat slipway has a slope of 1 in 10 (i.e. it rises 1 m vertically in 10 m along the slipway). If a boat of mass 400 kg can be pulled down the slipway by a force of 200 N, find the force required to pull it up the slipway, assuming the force to be applied parallel to the slipway in each case. Find also the coefficient of friction.

48. The mass of a train (including the mass of the engine) is 600 tonnes, and the mass of the engine alone is 140 tonnes. The train reaches a speed of 54 km h^{-1} in 100 s starting from rest. Find (i) the acceleration (supposed uniform), (ii) the tension in the coupling between the engine and the first carriage, (iii) the frictional force between the driving-wheels of the engine and the rails.

49. Two particles are connected by a light string. One particle, of mass 100 gm, is placed on a smooth plane of angle 30°; the string, after passing over a small, smooth pulley at the top of the plane, supports the other particle, of mass 25 gm, which hangs vertically. The system starts from rest with the string taut. Taking g to be 10 m s^{-2}, find the acceleration of either particle and show that the tension in the string is 0·3 N.

50. A mass of 5 kg can rest in equilibrium on a rough plane inclined at an angle of 30° to the horizontal, but would start to slide down the plane if the inclination were increased beyond 30°. Find the force acting up the plane which is necessary to move the mass up the plane with an acceleration of 2 m s^{-2}.

51. A particle moves so that its velocity v at time t (in metre-second units) is given by $v = \frac{2}{3}t + 15$. Find the acceleration and the distance travelled in the time interval from $t = 3$ to $t = 12$. When $t = 12$ the acceleration changes to a retardation of 2 m s^{-2}. When does the particle come to rest?

52. A packing-case of mass 100 kg is in a moving lift. If the vertical reaction between the floor of the lift and the case is 940 N, calculate the acceleration of the lift.

If the tension in the supporting cable is 2820 N during the motion, calculate the mass of the lift cage.

53. A leather belt is moving horizontally at 6 m s^{-1}. A slab of iron of mass 10 kg is gently laid on the belt, the coefficient of friction between iron and leather being 0·3. Calculate (i) the time taken for the slab to acquire the velocity of the belt, and (ii) the distance through which the belt has then moved relative to the slab. (Take $g = 10$ m s^{-2}.)

54. Masses of 1·2 kg and 1·25 kg are connected by a string passing over a smooth pulley. With what acceleration does the greater mass descend? After descending 4·9 m from rest, this mass is brought to rest again on reaching the ground. What interval elapses before the string again becomes taut? (Take $g = 9·8$ m s^{-2}.)

55. A body of mass 10 kg is projected directly up a rough plane inclined to the horizontal at an angle of 30°. The coefficient of friction is one-third. Find (i) the resolved part of the weight of the body acting down the plane, (ii) the frictional force opposing the body's motion, and (iii) the retardation of the body.

After the body has come to rest it begins to slide down the plane. Find its acceleration during this period of its motion.

56. Two stations A and B are 495 m apart. A train starting from A is uniformly accelerated for 15 s to a speed of 54 km h^{-1}, which is maintained until the train is 90 m from B, when it slows up uniformly and stops at B. Find the values of the acceleration and retardation, and the total time taken.

57. A body moves in a straight line with uniform acceleration and has an initial velocity of 2 m s^{-1}. In the fourth second of its motion it moves through $12\frac{1}{2}$ m. Find the total distance moved during the first 4 seconds of its motion.

58. A mass of 3 kg is held on a smooth plane inclined at an angle of 30° to the horizontal. A string fastened to the mass passes directly down the plane and over a smooth pulley at the bottom; from the other end of the string a mass of 2 kg hangs freely. The system is released and starts moving. Calculate (i) the tension in the string, and (ii) the acceleration of each mass. (Take $g = 10$ m s^{-2}.)

59. A balloon together with its ballast has mass M and is falling with an acceleration a. At the instant when its velocity is v a mass m of ballast is thrown out. The balloon then comes to rest in a distance s. Prove that

$$v = \sqrt{\frac{2s(mg - Ma)}{M - m}}$$

60. A body of mass 10 kg rests in equilibrium on a rough plane of angle 20°. Calculate the friction force, when (i) a force of 25 N acts on the body up the plane, (ii) a force of 5 N acts on the body down the plane, (iii) a force of 15 N acts on the body at 20° to the plane and up the plane, and (iv) a horizontal force of 15 N acts on the body towards the plane.

CHAPTER 6

LARGE BODIES

Numerical calculations in statical problems are simplified by taking the approximate value 10 *m s*$^{-2}$ *for g. This practice has been followed throughout the purely statical chapters of this book.*

Parallel forces

6.1 Up to now it has been supposed that our problems have been about particles – or, to be more precise, about bodies whose size could be neglected. This approximation is not usually adequate, however, and we are then presented with certain new features:

(i) The bodies may be capable of rotation, as well as translation from one position to another.

(ii) Account must be taken of the points of a body at which the various forces act. Every force has associated with it not only a magnitude and a direction but also a line of action. Forces which act along different lines have different effects on the body.

Both these features can be illustrated by a child's see-saw. Fig. 1 shows a plank which can turn about its centre *O*. Anne and Betty, whose masses are equal, stand on the plank at equal distances of 2 m from *O*. The weights of the two children 'balance', and equilibrium is possible.

Fig. 1   Fig. 2

If, however, Betty moves out to a distance of 2·5 m from *O* (Fig. 2), the plank rotates; Betty goes down and Anne goes up. Betty's weight is the same as before, but its line of action has changed and produced a different effect. The turning effect of Betty's weight has increased because this weight is now further from *O*.

6.2 A problem that arises with large bodies is to decide the line along which the force of gravity acts. It can be shown that there is a point in every rigid body, called its CENTRE OF GRAVITY, at which its weight may in many applications be supposed to be concentrated. This matter is discussed further in Chapter 15, and methods are given there for locating this point in bodies of various shapes.

For many simple bodies of regular shape the centre of gravity coincides with the geometrical centre. Bodies of this kind are said to be *uniform*.

6.3 A fresh kind of force will frequently appear in this chapter: the force exerted by a hinge. Basically this is simply a contact force between the pin of the hinge and the sleeve attached to the body; but since this contact may take place along any line on the inside surface of the sleeve, the direction of the force from the hinge will often be unknown. We then indicate it in diagrams by an arrow on the end of a wavy line, as in Fig. 3.

> **EXAMPLE 1.** *Illustrate the forces acting on the door of a loft propped open at an angle to the horizontal.*

See Fig. 3. *T* is the thrust from the prop, *W* the weight of the door (shown acting through the centre of gravity *G*) and *P* the contact force at the hinge.

The direction of *P* is unknown. It must certainly have an effect to the right, to counteract the effect of *T* to the left. It also probably has an effect upwards, since, if the hinge support were removed, that end of the door would move downwards. Its direction is therefore upwards and to the right. (It will be shown in Chapter 10 that it acts along the line joining the hinge to the point at which the lines of action of *T* and *W* meet.)

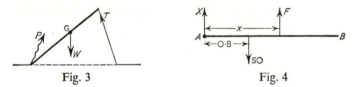

Fig. 3   Fig. 4

6.4 *EXAMPLE 2. A rod AB of mass 5 kg is hinged at A to a wall, and its centre of gravity is 0·8 m from A. It is supported in a horizontal position by a vertical force of F newtons applied at a point of the rod x metres from A. How large is this force?*

In the diagram (Fig. 4) the force of *X* newtons from the hinge has been shown acting vertically. This follows directly from the resolution principle; it cannot have a horizontal resolved part, since there is no other horizontal force to counteract it.

It is a matter of common experience that the value of *F* depends on *x*, and that the further from the hinge the force is applied the smaller will that force need to be. If x is very small, a very large force is needed to hold the rod up; and if x is zero, no force, however large, will serve.

If this experiment were carried out, and the value of F measured by using a spring as the means of support, we should get a series of readings such as the following:

x	0·08	0·1	0·2	0·25	0·4	0·5	0·8	1·0	1·6	2·0
F	500	400	200	160	100	80	50	40	25	20

We notice that, for each pair of values of F and x in this table, the product is 40, so that

$$Fx = 40, \tag{1}$$

or

$$F = \frac{40}{x}.$$

It is of interest to observe that when the rod is supported at its centre of gravity, so that $x = 0·8$, the supporting force is $40 \div 0·8 = 50$ newtons. This is also the weight of the rod (taking g to be 10 m s^{-2}). The presence of the hinge is then superfluous.

The quantity Fx, the product of the magnitude of the force and the distance from the pivot, is a measure of the 'turning effect' of the force. In this example a turning effect of 40 must be provided by the force F to hold the rod up. This can be produced in a variety of ways by giving different values to F and x, provided only that the product of these is equal to 40. The turning effect of a force can be increased either by increasing the size of the force or by increasing its distance from the pivot.

The turning effect Fx is usually called the *moment* of the force about the pivot. Moments may be either clockwise or anticlockwise. In Example 2 the moments about the hinge of the three forces, regarding anticlockwise moments as positive and clockwise moments as negative, are:

Moment of $X = X \times 0 = 0$,

Moment of $F = Fx$,

Moment of weight $= -50 \times 0·8 = -40$.

Equation (1), written in the form

$$Fx - 50 \times 0·8 = 0,$$

now appears as an example of the following principle:

The Principle of Moments: *The sum of the moments about any point of the forces acting on a body in equilibrium, having regard to sign, is zero.*

The process of applying the principle of moments about a particular point A is described as TAKING MOMENTS ABOUT A. We shall frequently abbreviate this by writing $\mathscr{M}(A)$ in the left margin by the side of the corresponding equation.

A pivot about which a body can turn is sometimes called a *fulcrum*.

6.5 *EXAMPLE 3. A rod AB of mass 5 kg and length 2·4 m has its centre of gravity 0·8 m from A. It is hung horizontally from a rafter by two vertical strings, one attached at A and the other at C, which is 0·4 m from B. Find the tensions in the strings.*

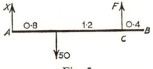

Fig. 5

Although this appears to differ from Example 2, the diagram of forces is, in fact, precisely the same. If the tensions are denoted by X and F (both in newtons), then F is given by

$\mathscr{M}(A)$ $\qquad\qquad F \times 2\cdot 0 - 50 \times 0\cdot 8 = 0,$

so that $\qquad\qquad\qquad\qquad F = 20.$

This is the same as equation (1) of Example 2. X may now be found by applying the principle of moments about C. We have, counting the anticlockwise direction as positive,

$$\text{Moment of } X = -X \times 2\cdot 0,$$
$$\text{Moment of } F = F \times 0 = 0,$$
$$\text{Moment of weight} = 50 \times 1\cdot 2 = 60.$$

Therefore
$\mathscr{M}(C)$ $\qquad\qquad\qquad -2X + 60 = 0,$
$$X = 30.$$

Although it was convenient in this solution to take moments about the two points where the strings are attached, and to regard these as points about which the rod was pivoted, it is also quite possible to take moments about other points. The principle of moments is true about any point whatever. We shall illustrate this by taking moments about B for this example. We have

$$\text{Moment of } X = -X \times 2\cdot 4,$$
$$\text{Moment of } F = -F \times 0\cdot 4,$$
$$\text{Moment of weight} = 50 \times 1\cdot 6 = 80.$$
$\mathscr{M}(B)$ $\qquad\qquad\qquad -2\cdot 4X - 0\cdot 4F + 80 = 0.$

It is easily seen that this equation is satisfied by the solutions $F = 20$, $X = 30$ already found.

The advantage of taking moments about the points through which the unknown forces act is that each equation then only contains one of the two unknowns, which can thus be found immediately.

Another method of completing the solution, once one unknown force has been found by the principle of moments, is to use the equation

$$\mathscr{R}(\uparrow) \qquad\qquad X + F - 50 = 0.$$

This equation is often best kept in reserve as a simple check on calculation.

6.6 EXAMPLE 4. *A non-uniform plank of length 6 m and mass 25 kg is pivoted about its centre. When a 35 kg child sits on one end and a 30 kg child on the other end the plank can rest horizontally. Find the position of the centre of gravity of the plank.*

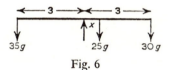

Fig. 6

We take moments about the pivot at the centre of the plank. This avoids introducing into the equations the force which the pivot exerts on the plank, in which we are not interested. The weights in newtons are $25g$, $35g$ and $30g$; it is not necessary in this example to substitute a numerical value for g.

The weight of the 30 kg child has a moment of $30g \times 3 = 90g$ clockwise, and that of the 35 kg child a moment of $35g \times 3 = 105g$ anticlockwise. The weight of the plank must therefore have a clockwise moment to maintain the balance. Let the centre of gravity of the plank be x metres to the right of the pivot. Then, taking clockwise moments to be positive,

$$\mathscr{M} \text{ (pivot)} \qquad 25gx + 90g - 105g = 0,$$
$$x = 0{\cdot}6.$$

6.7 In the last example, and in taking moments about C in Example 3, we have used the principle of moments about a point some way along the body rather than at its end. It is still permissible to calculate the moment of the weight as if it were a single force concentrated at the centre of gravity, even if part of the body is on one side of the fulcrum and part on the other side.

The next example discusses this point further for the special case of a uniform beam. It is, in fact, true for any body.

EXAMPLE 5. To verify, for a uniform beam, that the position of the fulcrum does not alter the effect of gravity.

Consider the moment of a uniform beam of weight W and length l about a point X of the beam at a distance a from the left-hand end. We calculate this in two ways.

(i) Regarding the weight of the whole beam as concentrated at the centre of gravity, i.e. at the centre of the beam (Fig. 7a):

$$\text{Moment} = W(\tfrac{1}{2}l - a).$$

Fig. 7a   Fig. 7b

(ii) Regarding the beam as composed of two uniform beams, one of weight Wa/l on the left of X, the other of weight $W(l - a)/l$ on the right (Fig. 7b):

$$\begin{aligned}
\text{Moment} &= \frac{W(l - a)}{l} \times \frac{(l - a)}{2} - \frac{Wa}{l} \times \frac{a}{2} \\
&= \frac{W}{2l}\{(l - a)^2 - a^2\} \\
&= \frac{Wl(l - 2a)}{2l} \\
&= W(\tfrac{1}{2}l - a),
\end{aligned}$$

which is the same result as before.

EXERCISE 6(*a*)

Take $g = 10\ m\ s^{-2}$ where necessary throughout this exercise.

In Questions 1–4, find the unknown forces. In each case the pivot is marked with a cross.

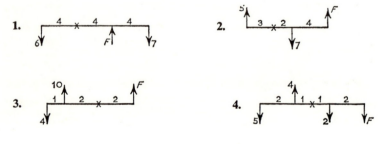

5. A uniform shelf of mass 15 kg and length 4 m is hinged at the left end. It is supported at a point 1 m from the right end. What is the supporting force? If an additional mass of 15 kg is hung from the right end, what does the supporting force become?

6. Two boys push a door with their shoulders with a force of 200 N each, one 0·5 m and the other 0·8 m from the line of hinges. With what force must they be opposed on the other side at 0·4 m from the line of hinges?

7. A see-saw is perfectly balanced when unoccupied. Mary (40 kg) and Jane (36 kg) on one side of the pivot at distances 1·9 m and 1·5 m together balance William (50 kg) on the other side. If Mary takes William's place, and William takes Jane's, where must Jane sit to keep the balance?

8. A car whose weight is 7500 N has its axles 3 m apart. If its centre of gravity is 1·2 m in front of the rear axle, and if each rear wheel bears the same proportion of the weight, what is the normal force at each rear wheel?

9. A see-saw is out of balance, so that Carolyn (30 kg) 3 m from the pivot balances Angela (25 kg) 2 m from the pivot. If Angela takes Carolyn's place, where must Carolyn sit to keep the balance?

10. A pipe of mass 40 gm has its centre of gravity 120 mm from the mouthpiece. It is kept horizontal by forces from the top teeth and lower teeth 8 mm and 15 mm from the mouthpiece. Find these forces.

11. A girder of negligible mass and length 4 m is suspended in a horizontal position by vertical cables attached at points 0·8 m and 2·4 m from one end. From that end is suspended a mass of 6 tonnes, and from the other a mass of 5 tonnes. Find the tensions in the cables.

12. A uniform table top AB of mass 40 kg and length 5 m rests on supports at P and Q at the same level. If $AQ = 3$ m, and the force at Q is 300 N, find the distance AP. If now a load of mass 5 kg is added at A, what is the mass of the additional load at B which will just make the table tilt?

13. A non-uniform plank AB 4 m long rests on supports 1 m from the ends. A load of mass 40 kg at A just makes it tilt, and so does a load of mass 20 kg at B. Where does the weight of the plank act?

14. A non-uniform pine trunk AB 7 m long rests on the ground. C is a point of the trunk 0·7 m from A, and D a point 1·4 m from B. The end A can just be lifted off the ground by a force of 550 N applied vertically at C. B can just be lifted off the ground by a vertical force of 510 N at D. Find the mass of the trunk.

15. A uniform beam 3 m long and of mass 100 kg rests horizontally with its ends on two supports, one of which will not bear a force of more than 6500 N. On what part of the beam can a load of 900 kg safely be placed?

†16. A girder AB of length 10 m and mass 600 kg, whose centre of gravity is 4 m from A, is supported at three points distant 1 m, 5 m and 7 m from A. Find as much as you can about the forces from the supports. What is the largest force that each support may be called on to bear?

†17. A uniform metal tube 5 m long, of mass 25 kg, is being fed horizontally into a machine. It passes under a horizontal guide rail 0·5 m from the left end and over another guide rail 1 m from the left end. If the coefficient of friction is 0·2, what force is necessary to push the tube to the left by the right end?

Forces at an angle

6.8 So far we have only considered parallel forces acting at points in the same straight line. The principle of moments is, however, of much wider application, although we have yet to decide how the moment of a force is to be defined in more general cases.

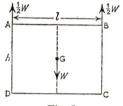

Fig. 8

EXAMPLE 6. A uniform rectangular sheet of metal is hung with two sides vertical by vertical chains attached to its two top corners. Discuss the forces.

Let the weight of the sheet be W, and the lengths of the horizontal and vertical sides be l and h respectively.

The centre of gravity of the sheet is on the vertical line mid-way between the two chains. From considerations of symmetry the tension in each chain is $\frac{1}{2}W$.

Now consider moments about the point A, taking the clockwise sense as positive.

$$\text{Moment of tension at } A = \tfrac{1}{2}W \times 0 = 0,$$

$$\text{Moment of tension at } B = -\tfrac{1}{2}W \times l.$$

If the principle of moments is to hold, the moment about A of the weight of the sheet must be $\frac{1}{2}Wl = W \times (\frac{1}{2}l)$, even though the centre of gravity of the sheet is not at the middle point of AB. Now the length $\frac{1}{2}l$ is the perpendicular distance from A to the line of action of W. It appears therefore that this perpendicular distance is the distance that must be used in calculating the moment of the weight.

DEFINITION. *The* MOMENT *of a force P about a point A is the product of the magnitude of the force and the perpendicular distance from A to its line of action.*

With this more general definition of moment, the principle of moments applies as given in § 6.4.

We see that the effect of a force is completely determined if

(i) its magnitude,
(ii) its direction,
(iii) the line along which it acts,

are given. The particular point of the line at which it is applied is unimportant.

6.9 *EXAMPLE 7. The metal sheet of Example 6 is held in the same position by means of a hinge attached to a fixed point at D and a horizontal force applied at B. Find this force.*

If we take moments about D, the moment of the force from the hinge is zero, since its line of action passes through D. The perpendicular from D to the line of action of P, which is the line BA, has length h; and the perpendicular from D to the line of action of W has length $\frac{1}{2}l$. Taking clockwise moments to be positive,

$$\mathscr{M}(D) \qquad\qquad W(\tfrac{1}{2}l) - Ph = 0,$$

so that

$$P = \frac{Wl}{2h}.$$

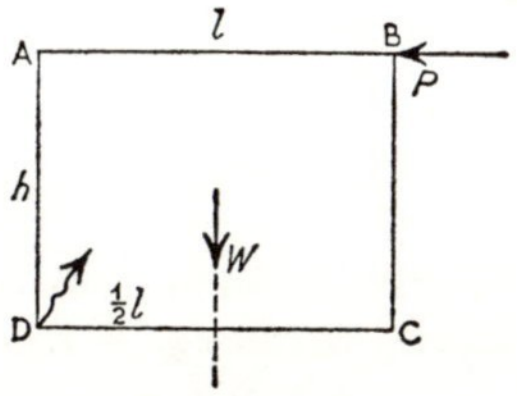

Fig. 9 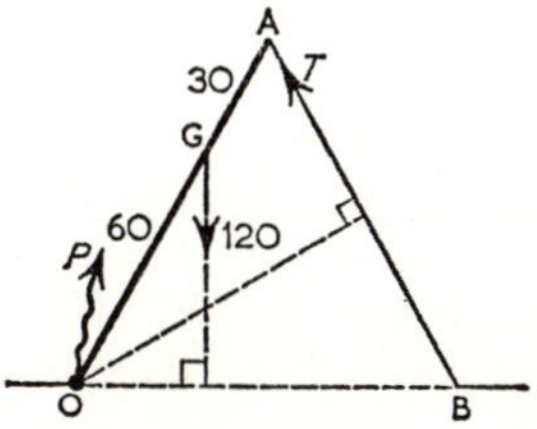   Fig. 10

EXAMPLE 8. Fig. 10 shows a loft door OA of mass 12 kg propped open at 60° to the horizontal by means of a light strut AB. OA = OB = 90 cm, and the centre of gravity of the door is 60 cm from O. Find the thrust in the strut.

The forces on the door were discussed in Example 1 (p. 78). Let P, T be measured in newtons; the weight of the door is 120 N.

The triangle OAB is equilateral. The perpendicular distance from O to the line of action of the weight is $OG \cos 60° = 60 \cos 60°$, so that the weight has a clockwise moment about O of

$$120 \times 60 \cos 60°.$$

The perpendicular from O to AB has length $OA \sin 60° = 90 \sin 60°$, so that the thrust has an anticlockwise moment of

$$T \times 90 \sin 60°.$$

Since the moment of P about O is zero, we have, taking clockwise moments to be positive,

$$\mathcal{M}(O) \qquad 120 \times 60 \cos 60° - T \times 90 \sin 60° = 0,$$

whence
$$T = \frac{120 \times 60 \cos 60°}{90 \sin 60°} = \frac{80}{\sqrt{3}} \approx 46.$$

The thrust in the prop is therefore about 46 N.

It was most convenient to take moments about O because the force acting through O was unknown and was not required.

6.10 *EXAMPLE 9. A ladder 5 m long rests on rough ground against a smooth vertical wall and is inclined at an angle $\tilde{\omega}$ to the vertical. Its mass is 20 kg, and its centre of gravity is 2 m from the lower end. A man of mass 80 kg stands on the ladder 3 m from the lower end. Find the friction force at the ground.*

Let the normal contact forces from the ground and the wall be P and Q, measured in newtons. The weights of the ladder and the man are 200 N and 800 N. Since P and Q are not required, we take moments about X (see Fig. 11). The moments of P and Q are then zero. Therefore

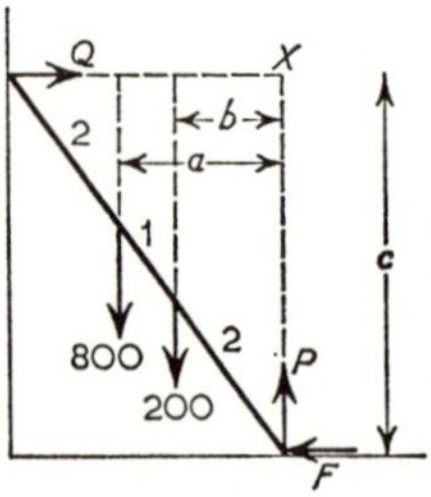

Fig. 11

$$\mathcal{M}(X) \qquad\qquad Fc - 200b - 800a = 0.$$
Now
$$a = 3 \sin \tilde{\omega} = 1·8,$$
$$b = 2 \sin \tilde{\omega} = 1·2,$$
and
$$c = 5 \cos \tilde{\omega} = 4.$$
Therefore
$$4F = 200 \times 1·2 + 800 \times 1·8,$$
$$F = 60 + 360 = 420.$$

The friction force is 420 N.

The remaining forces on the ladder could most simply be found by the resolution principle.
$$\mathcal{R}(\rightarrow) \qquad\qquad Q - F = 0,$$
$$\mathcal{R}(\uparrow) \qquad\qquad P - 800 - 200 = 0,$$

whence $Q = 420$, $P = 1000$. We observe that, for equilibrium to be possible, the coefficient of friction between the ladder and the ground must not be less than F/P, which equals 0·42.

6.11 It is interesting to see what result is obtained in the last example by taking moments about some other point. For example, moments about the centre of gravity of the ladder give

$$Qf + Fd - Pb - 800e = 0. \qquad \text{(See Fig. 12.)}$$

Therefore

$$Q \times 3 \cos \tilde{\omega} + F \times 2 \cos \tilde{\omega}$$
$$- P \times 2 \sin \tilde{\omega} - 800 \times 1 \sin \tilde{\omega} = 0,$$

which reduces to $\quad 6Q + 4F - 3P - 1200 = 0.$

Fig. 12

It will be found that the values of Q, F and P found in § 6.10 satisfy this equation. In fact, we shall show in a later volume that it is not possible to obtain any more information by taking moments about other points. By resolving in two directions and taking moments about one point, all the available information about a particular problem of this kind has been set down.

Conditions for Equilibrium. *A rigid body is in equilibrium if in two different directions the resolved parts of the forces acting on it add up to zero, and the moments about any one point add up to zero.*

6.12 It is sometimes convenient to use a larger number of equations of moments, making a corresponding reduction in the number of resolving equations.

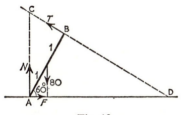

Fig. 13

EXAMPLE 10. A uniform rod AB of length 2 m and mass 8 kg has its lower end on rough ground; it is supported at 60° to the horizontal by a string attached to its upper end and at right angles to the rod. Find the tension in the string and the friction and normal forces at the ground.

Let the tension be T, the friction F and the normal force N, all in newtons. The weight is 80 newtons.

$\mathcal{M}(A)$ $80 \times 1 \cos 60° - T \times 2 = 0$.
$\mathcal{M}(C)$ $80 \times 1 \cos 60° - F \times 2 \sec 30° = 0$.
$\mathcal{M}(D)$ $N \times 2 \sec 60° - 80(2 \sec 60° - 1 \cos 60°) = 0$.

These equations give $T = 20$, $F = 17$, $N = 70$.

EXERCISE 6(b)

Take $g = 10$ m s^{-2} where necessary throughout this exercise.

1. A uniform plank AB of mass 20 kg is pivoted at A and held at an angle of 30° to the vertical by means of a force applied at B perpendicular to AB. Find the force.

2. A light cranked lever ABC is pivoted at B about a horizontal axis. The angle between AB and BC is 120°, $AB = 0.5$ m, $BC = 3$ m. A mass of 30 kg is hung from A. What vertical force applied at C will keep the lever in equilibrium with AB horizontal?

3. A drawbridge 3 m long of mass 800 kg is supported horizontally by two parallel symmetrical chains attached to hooks at the far end of the bridge and at points 4 m above the line of the hinges. Find the tension in each chain.

4. A uniform shelf of mass 10 kg and length 0·9 m is hinged at one end. It is kept horizontal by a light strut attached to a point of the shelf 0·6 m from the hinges and inclined at 60° to the vertical. A man leans on the free end with a force of 150 N. Find the thrust in the strut.

5. The plunger of a pump is pulled vertically upwards, being attached to a point A of a lever ABC, which is pivoted at B. If $AB = 0·2$ m, $BC = 1·2$ m,

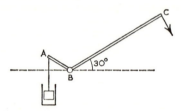

angle $ABC = 120°$, and BC makes 30° with the horizontal, find the force with which the plunger is pulled up by an effort of 200 N applied at C perpendicular to BC.

6. A sun-blind outside a shop is supported in a horizontal position by two struts, one at each end of the blind. The blind, which is uniform, has a mass of 64 kg and the struts make an angle of $\tilde{\omega}$ to the vertical and are attached to the blind at a distance from the hinges equal to $\frac{2}{3}$ of the width of the blind. Find the thrust in each strut.

7. A uniform ladder 12·5 m long, and of mass 48 kg, rests with its top against a smooth vertical wall and its foot on rough ground 3·5 m from the wall. Find the normal and friction forces at the bottom of the ladder.

8. A rod AB of length 2 m and mass 10 kg has its centre of gravity 80 cm from A. It rests horizontally with B against a rough vertical wall. A string is attached to A, and its other end is fastened to a peg in the wall $1\frac{1}{2}$ m above B. Find the normal and friction forces between the wall and the rod; also, if friction is limiting, find μ.

9. The foot of a uniform 30 kg ladder is on rough horizontal ground and its top rests against a smooth vertical wall. The ladder makes 60° with the horizontal and is in limiting equilibrium. Find μ. If a 60 kg man stands three-quarters of the way up the ladder, what horizontal force applied to the foot of the ladder is needed to keep it in equilibrium?

10. Explain why it is safer for a painter to go up a ladder with his mate standing on the bottom rung.

11. A light pedal lever AB is hinged to a firm support at B; it makes an angle $\tilde{\omega}$ with the vertical. A horizontal rod is freely jointed to AB at C, where $CB = \frac{1}{8}AB$. What vertical force applied to the pedal at A will produce a thrust of 120 N in the rod? What is the least force (applied at A in any direction) required to achieve the same result?

12. A light square plate $ABCD$ can turn freely about the corner A. A force of 0·2 N is applied at B in the direction BD, and one of 0·3 N at D in the direction parallel to AC. What is the smallest force that can be applied to the plate which will prevent it from turning? Where and in what direction must it be applied?

†**13.** A rod passes over a peg A and under a peg B, the distances of the centre of gravity from the pegs being a, b $(a < b)$. If θ is the inclination of the rod to the horizontal, prove that μ is not less than $\dfrac{b - a}{b + a} \tan \theta$.

†**14.** A beam of weight W rests against a smooth horizontal rail with its lower end on a smooth horizontal plane. A horizontal force P is applied to the lower end of the beam to hold it in equilibrium at an angle θ to the horizontal. If the weight of the beam acts at a point distant a from its lower end, and b is the height of the rail above the plane, prove that

$$P = \frac{Wa}{b} \sin^2 \theta \cos \theta.$$

†**15.** A heavy uniform rod of length $2a$ and weight W has a weight W fixed to it at one end. The other end rests against a smooth vertical wall, the rod passing over a smooth horizontal rail distant h from the wall. Show that the rod makes an angle $\sin^{-1} \sqrt[3]{\dfrac{2h}{3a}}$ with the vertical.

†**16.** One end of a uniform ladder of weight W rests against a rough wall and the other on a rough horizontal pavement, the coefficients of friction being μ and μ'. Prove that when the ladder is on the point of slipping it is inclined to the vertical at an angle of $\tan^{-1}\left(\dfrac{2\mu'}{1 - \mu\mu'}\right)$.

†**17.** A uniform ladder of length l and weight W rests with its foot on rough ground and its upper end against a smooth wall, its inclination to the vertical being θ. A force P is applied to it horizontally at a distance a from the foot of the ladder so as to push the foot towards the wall. Prove that P must exceed $\dfrac{W(\mu + \frac{1}{2}\tan\theta)}{l - a}$.

†**18.** A circular cylinder of weight W, with its axis horizontal, is supported with its curved surface in contact with a rough vertical wall by a string wrapped partly round it and attached to a point of the wall, the string making an angle θ with the wall. Show that $\mu \geqslant \operatorname{cosec} \theta$, and that the normal force from the wall is $W \tan \frac{1}{2}\theta$.

†**19.** A sphere of weight W resting on a rough plane of inclination $45°$ has a horizontal force P applied to its highest point. Show that equilibrium is impossible if $\mu < \sqrt{2} - 1$, and find the value of P needed to maintain equilibrium if $\mu \geqslant \sqrt{2} - 1$.

Three-dimensional problems

6.13 The problems discussed so far in this chapter have all been two-dimensional in scope, and have thereby obscured one important feature – that moments are always properly taken about a line, rather than about a point. For example, a hinge is correctly located along a line. Taking moments about 'a point A', as we have done in the foregoing examples, is more correctly described as taking moments about 'a line through A' perpendicular to the plane of the diagram.

> *EXAMPLE 11. The feet of the vertical legs of a dining-room chair form a rectangle ABCD; A and B are at the front. The vertical line through the centre of gravity of the chair meets the floor three-fifths of the way between the line AB and the line DC. What proportion of the weight is borne by the leg at A?*

The diagram (Fig. 14) shows the rectangle formed by the feet of the legs on the floor. The weight W acts in a vertical line through K.

From considerations of symmetry the forces at A and B are the same. If they are each equal to P, the equation of moments about the line DC is

$$P \times DA + P \times CB - W \times LK = 0.$$

Since $DA = CB$, and $LK = \frac{2}{5}CB$,

$$P = \tfrac{1}{5}W.$$

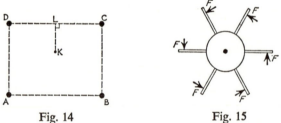

Fig. 14　　　　　　　　　　Fig. 15

Couples

6.14 So far the only kind of action on a body which we have considered is that of a simple force. This is sufficient when the body is a particle, but for large bodies it may also be necessary to consider agencies whose sole effect is to turn the body round. For example, the operation of unscrewing the stopper of a bottle, or of turning a door-knob, only tends to make the body rotate and not to move it bodily. An agency of this sort is called a *couple*, or sometimes a *torque*. Other examples of couples are the forces acting on the rotating part of an electric motor, the braking action on the hub of a motor-car wheel and the forces exerted by men driving a capstan round (Fig. 15).

It will be seen that in all these examples the couple is, in fact, composed of a number of separate forces. For instance, in unscrewing a stopper these forces are friction forces from the fingers all the way round the stopper. But in practice we are only concerned with the total turning effect of the complete set of forces, and it is convenient to regard this as a single entity.

The size of a couple is specified by its turning effect, or moment. Previously the idea of a moment has been used only as a means to an end, but now we must consider it as a physical quantity in its own right. Since moment arises as the product of a force and a distance, the unit in which it is measured is the *newton metre* (N m); we shall often use the letter L^1 to denote moment. Extending still further our algebra of physical quantites, we may if we wish write

$$(1 \text{ N}) \times (1 \text{ m}) = (1 \text{ N m}).$$

(But see § 16.2, where it is shown that the same product can have a quite different interpretation.)

In solving problems in which couples appear, the presence of the couple does not affect the resolving equations, since its effect is purely rotational. The moment of the couple must, however, enter into the equations of moments alongside the moments of the various forces.

It is important to remark that, in specifying a couple, the moment need not be given about a particular point. In fact, the moment of a couple is the same about all points (or, more accurately, about every one of a set of parallel lines).

A fuller discussion on couples is given in Chapter 14. A theoretical treatment is reserved for a later volume.

EXAMPLE 12. A flywheel of radius 0·25 m is driven through a shaft. It runs against the friction of two belts in contact with the flywheel along portions of its circumference diametrically opposite to each other. These belts are tightened so that the tension is 80 N on the taut side and 20 N on the slacker side. Find the torque transmitted through the shaft, supposing the wheel to be running at a steady speed (Fig. 16).

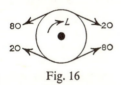

Fig. 16

Let the torque from the shaft be L, measured in newton metres. Since the running speed is steady, the forces are in equilibrium.

$\mathscr{M}$(axis of flywheel)

$$L + 20 \times 0·25 - 80 \times 0·25 + 20 \times 0·25 - 80 \times 0·25 = 0,$$

so that $$L = 30.$$

The torque transmitted to the wheel through the shaft is 30 N m.

---

[1] Some writers prefer to use M or T for moment, or torque. This has been avoided here because of the possibility of confusion with mass or tension, either of which may easily appear in the same problem as moment.

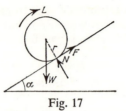

Fig. 17

EXAMPLE 13. A cylinder of weight W and radius r rests with its axis horizontal on a plane of angle α. It is kept in equilibrium by a couple of moment L. Find the value of L, and how large the coefficient of friction must be.

L does not enter into the equations of resolving, but it appears as a term in the equation of moments.

$\mathscr{R}(\parallel$ to plane)	$F - W \sin \alpha = 0.$
$\mathscr{R}(\perp$ to plane)	$N - W \cos \alpha = 0.$
$\mathscr{M}$(axis of cylinder)	$L - Fr = 0.$

Therefore $\qquad\qquad\qquad\qquad L = Wr \sin \alpha,$

and, since $F < \mu N,$ $\qquad \mu > \dfrac{W \sin \alpha}{W \cos \alpha} = \tan \alpha.$

EXERCISE 6(c)

Take g = 10 m s⁻² where necessary throughout this exercise.

1. A table whose top is a regular heptagon *ABCDEFG* has vertical legs at *A, C, F.* Will it stand in equilibrium? Why?

2. A table top of mass 18 kg rests on supports at *A, B* and *C. ABC* is a right-angled triangle with $AB = 2 \cdot 0$ m, $BC = 2 \cdot 1$ m, $AC = 2 \cdot 9$ m. The centre of gravity of the top is $0 \cdot 5$ m from *BC* and $0 \cdot 7$ m from *AB.* Find the forces on the supports.

3. Each of the four brakes on a flywheel is exerting a normal force of 50 N, $0 \cdot 2$ m from the shaft. If the wheel is running at a constant speed and $\mu = 0 \cdot 8$, find the torque which is driving the shaft.

4. A clockwork toy is wound up by applying forces of 10 N with the finger and thumb at points on the key 25 mm apart. Find the torque exerted by the spring.

5. A see-saw is perfectly balanced; the friction at the pivot can produce a couple of moment 15 Nm. A child of mass 20 kg sits 2 m from the pivot. Within what points may a 25 kg child sit in order to balance the other?

6. A uniform inn-sign of mass 5 kg and height 1 m hangs from rusty hinges along its top edge. The friction couple provided by the hinges is such that the sign can rest in any position within 10° of the vertical. What force applied at a point on the bottom edge at right angles to its plane would be needed to hold it at 40° to the vertical, and what force would be necessary to increase this angle still further? (Assume the friction couple remains the same.)

7. A rod of 5 kg is hinged at one end so that it is free to turn in a vertical plane. The centre of gravity of the rod is 0·3 m from the hinge. It is kept in a horizontal position by a torque applied to a handle fixed to the rod near its other end. How large is the torque, and what force is exerted by the hinge?

†**8.** A board rests horizontally on three supports at A, B, C, forming a triangle. Where must the centre of gravity of the board be located if the forces from the supports are to be equal?

†**9.** A ladder rests on rough ground at 45° to the vertical with its foot a distance a from a smooth wall, against which its top is placed. If $\mu = 0.3$, show that equilibrium can be maintained by applying a couple to the ladder, and find the minimum value of the moment of this couple in terms of a and the weight W of the ladder.

CHAPTER 7

VECTORS AND RELATIVE VELOCITY

The Vector Triangle

7.1 Many of the quantities with which we are concerned in mechanics, such as velocity, acceleration and force, require for their description not only a number indicating their magnitude but also an associated direction. We speak of a velocity of 5 km h⁻¹ north-east, or a force of 20 N vertically upwards. Such quantities are called *vector quantities*.

The simplest example of a vector quantity is displacement. If *A* and *B* are two points, the DISPLACEMENT **AB** is specified by (i) the distance between *A* and *B*, and (ii) the bearing of *B* from *A*. The order of the letters is important; **AB** is different from **BA**, for although the distances are the same the bearings are different.

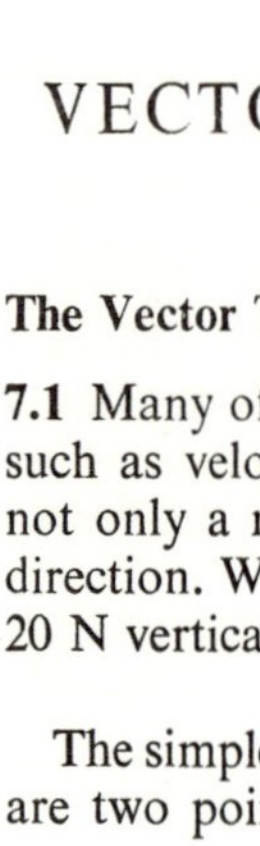

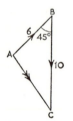

Scale 1mm: 0·4 km

Fig. 1

EXAMPLE 1. A, B and C are three towns such that **AB** *is 6 km NE, and* **BC** *is 10 km S. Find* **AC**.
The towns are represented in Fig. 1, in which the distances are reduced by a suitably chosen scale factor. By measurement we find that *C* is 7·2 km from *A* on a bearing of S36°E, so that **AC** is 7·2 km S36°E. (This result could also be obtained by trigonometry.)

7.2 If we make a displacement from *A* to *B*, followed by one from *B* to *C*, the result is the same as if we had made the single displacement from *A* to *C*. We say that the displacement **AC** is the SUM, or RESULTANT, of the displacements **AB** and **BC**, and we write

$$\mathbf{AB} + \mathbf{BC} = \mathbf{AC}.$$

The symbols + and = are used here in a special sense, and not as in ordinary arithmetic. By = we mean that the two sides of the equation are equal both in magnitude and direction, and by + we mean that the two displacements are combined to give a single resultant displacement.

94

The two separate displacements **AB** and **BC**, which together make up the resultant displacement **AC**, are called COMPONENTS of **AC**.

When lines representing vectors are drawn in a diagram, arrows indicating the sense of the vector should always be placed on them. In Fig. 1 single arrows are given to the two component vectors and a double arrow to the resultant.

7.3 A quantity which is specified completely by its magnitude, and which has no direction associated with it, is called a SCALAR QUANTITY. The most familiar examples from mechanics are mass and time.

The number which specifies the magnitude of any vector quantity is called the SCALAR PART, or the MODULUS, of the vector. The scalar part of any displacement vector is the distance between its extremities.

In this book vectors are always denoted by symbols in bold type, and the scalar part of a vector is denoted by the same symbol in ordinary italic type. In Example 1, **AB** stands for a displacement of 6 km NE, but AB stands simply for a distance of 6 km.[1] In manuscript, vectors can be distinguished by a wavy line drawn under the letters, thus: **AB**, or by writing vector symbols in ink of a different colour.

It should be noticed that, although, in Example 1,

$$\mathbf{AB} + \mathbf{BC} = \mathbf{AC},$$

it is not true that $AB + BC = AC$. For $AB + BC = 6 + 10 = 16$, whereas $AC = 7\cdot2$. The two equations hold simultaneously only if A, B and C are points on a straight line with B between A and C.

Just as we distinguish displacement from distance, so we also distinguish velocity from speed. The word velocity is reserved in mechanics for the vector quantity, its scalar part being called speed. We speak of a speed of 6 m s^{-1}, but a velocity of 6 m s^{-1} SW.

7.4 *EXAMPLE 2. A ship capable of 10 km h^{-1} in still water sets course due S; it is driven off course by a current flowing NE at a rate of 6 km h^{-1}. What is its resultant velocity?*

Consider the motion of the ship for an hour. Effectively the whole of the water surface suffers a displacement of 6 km NE, so that if the ship were drifting it would move in this way. On account of its motion through the water, it also has a displacement of 10 km S. The situation is therefore precisely as in Example 1, and the resultant displacement of the ship in the hour is 7·2 km S36°E (see Fig. 1). If, as seems reasonable, the actual velocity of the ship is constant, it must therefore be a velocity of 7·2 km h^{-1} S36°E.

We now notice that, had the scale in Fig. 1 been taken as 1 mm : 0·4 km h^{-1} instead of 1 mm : 0·4 km, the sides of the triangle ABC could

---

[1] In some books the displacement **AB** is written $\overrightarrow{AB}$ or $\overrightarrow{AB}$.

represent the velocities in this example rather than the displacements. This is an illustration of

The Triangle of Velocities. *If the motion of a body is compounded of two separate velocities, and if a triangle ABC is drawn in which* **AB** *and* **BC** *represent on some scale the separate velocities in magnitude and direction, then* **AC** *represents the resultant velocity in magnitude and direction.*

Care must be taken in applications that the arrows in the triangle have the correct sense (see Fig. 2).

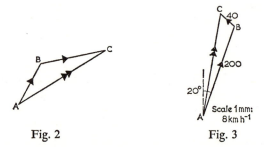

Fig. 2   Fig. 3

EXAMPLE 3. A light aircraft with an airspeed of 200 *km* h^{-1} *sets course N20°E. It is blown off course by a wind of* 40 *km* h^{-1} *from S50°E. Find its velocity as observed from the ground.*

The velocity observed from the ground is the sum of its velocity through the air and the velocity of the wind, represented by **AB** and **BC** in the triangle of velocities (Fig. 3). The sum is represented by **AC**, giving a ground velocity of 217 km h^{-1} N10°E.

7.5 The triangle law of addition is held in common by many kinds of physical quantity, and the word 'vector' is reserved for quantities which obey it. There are examples of quantities specified by a magnitude and a direction which are not compounded in this way, but the student is not likely to be troubled by such exceptions at this stage.

DEFINITION. *A* VECTOR QUANTITY *is a quantity described by a magnitude and a direction which obeys the triangle law of composition.*

EXAMPLE 4. Express a vector of 10 *units N40°E as the sum of two components (i) in directions N and S80°E, (ii) in directions N and E.*

(i) Choosing an appropriate scale, draw a line *AB* to represent the vector (Fig. 4a). Through *A, B* draw lines in directions N and S80°E respectively, meeting at *C*. Then **AC** and **CB** represent the required vectors. By measurement or calculation, and further application of the scale factor, the components are found to be 8·8 units N, and 6·5 units S80°E.

(ii) The method of construction is similar, but the triangle is now right-angled (Fig. 4b). It follows that the two components are now $10\cos 40° = 7\cdot7$ units N, and $10\cos 50° = 6\cdot4$ units E.

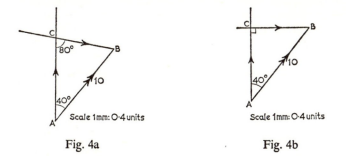

Fig. 4a   Fig. 4b

†**7.6** If a vector **P**, whose scalar part is P, makes an angle θ with a direction $\mathscr{D}$, the quantity $P\cos\theta$ is called the RESOLVED PART of **P** in the direction $\mathscr{D}$. This is a generalization to vectors of any kind of the definition of the resolved part of a force given in § 4.2.

Part (ii) of Example 4 illustrates the following important result:

If a vector is split into two components in perpendicular directions, the components have magnitudes equal to the resolved parts of the vectors in their respective directions.

It must, however, be noticed that this is true only when the components are in perpendicular directions.

This sheds more light on the geometrical method of solving the equations

$$R\cos\theta = X, \quad R\sin\theta = Y$$

discussed in § 4.6. The problem was to find the force whose resolved parts in two given perpendicular directions are X and Y. Since the directions are perpendicular, the components of the force in these directions also have magnitudes X and Y, so that the triangle ABC used in the solution (Fig. 9, p. 59) is really a vector triangle; **AB** and **BC** represent the components, and **AC** the required resultant force.

7.7 It is frequently useful to use single letters to stand for vectors. These are always printed in bold type, the corresponding symbol in italic type being used to denote the scalar part.

Vectors obey rules for addition and subtraction similar to those for ordinary numbers. If $ABCD$ is a parallelogram (Fig. 5), and the displacement **AB** is denoted by **x**, then **DC** is also equal to **x**, since **AB** and **DC** have the same length and the same direction. Similarly, if **BC = y, AD = y** also. Since

$$\mathbf{AB + BC = AC, \quad and \quad AD + DC = AC,}$$

it follows that $$\mathbf{x + y = y + x.}$$

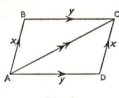

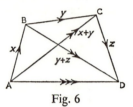

Fig. 5   Fig. 6

Again, it is plain from Fig. 6 that

$$(\mathbf{x + y) + z = x + (y + z),}$$

since both are equal to the vector **AD**. We may therefore without ambiguity refer to the vector $\mathbf{x + y + z}$. The vectors $\mathbf{x}$, $\mathbf{y}$ and $\mathbf{z}$ need not all be in the same plane.

We now define subtraction of vectors. If $\mathbf{x}$ and $\mathbf{y}$ are two vectors, there is just one vector $\mathbf{u}$ such that $\mathbf{x = y + u}$ (see Fig. 7). We call this the vector $\mathbf{x - y}$.

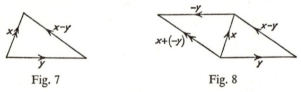

Fig. 7   Fig. 8

By $-\mathbf{y}$ we mean a vector with the same magnitude as $\mathbf{y}$ but in the reverse direction. It will be seen from Fig. 8 that

$$\mathbf{x - y = x + (-y).}$$

In particular, for displacement vectors,

$$\mathbf{BA = -AB,}$$

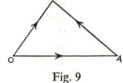

and $\mathbf{AB = OB - OA}$. (See Fig. 9.)

Fig. 9

The second of these rules is frequently used. If O is regarded as an origin, the displacement from A to B is equal to the displacement of B from the origin minus the displacement of A from the origin.

If k is a scalar and $\mathbf{x}$ a vector, we write $k\mathbf{x}$ for the vector in the direction of $\mathbf{x}$ whose magnitude is kx.

7.8 The position of a point P is frequently described by choosing an origin and then specifying the displacement **OP** of the point from the origin. This displacement is called the POSITION VECTOR of the point P referred to the origin O.

If a particle is moving with constant velocity $\mathbf{v}$, its displacement from its original position after a time t is $\mathbf{v}t$. If its original position were specified by means of its displacement $\mathbf{r}_0$ from a given origin, and its position after time t by the displacement $\mathbf{r}_1$ from the same origin, we have

$$\mathbf{r}_1 = \mathbf{r}_0 + \mathbf{v}t.$$

This can be written

$$\mathbf{v} = (\mathbf{r}_1 - \mathbf{r}_0)/t,$$

which expresses in vector form the fact that velocity is the rate of change of the position of a body.

EXERCISE 7(a)

(Many of the questions are best solved by drawing and measurement.)

1. If $\mathbf{AB}$ is 3 km N60°W and $\mathbf{BC}$ is 4 km SE, find $\mathbf{AC}$.

2. If $\mathbf{AB}$ is 2 km N, $\mathbf{BC}$ is 5 km SW, $\mathbf{CD}$ is 3 km S10°E, find $\mathbf{AD}$ and $\mathbf{DA}$.

3. If $\mathbf{OA}$ is 30 km N15°E and $\mathbf{OB}$ is 30 km N65°W, find $\mathbf{AB}$.

4. If $\mathbf{XY}$ is 100 m N60°W and $\mathbf{XZ}$ is 140 m S40°W, find $\mathbf{YZ}$.

5. If $\mathbf{x}$ is 5 units N, and $\mathbf{y}$ is 12 units E, find $\mathbf{x} + \mathbf{y}$, $\mathbf{x} - \mathbf{y}$, $\mathbf{y} - \mathbf{x}$, $\mathbf{x} + 2\mathbf{y}$, $9\mathbf{x} + 5\mathbf{y}$, $4\mathbf{x} - 3\mathbf{y}$.

6. If $\mathbf{u}$ is a velocity of 3 km h^{-1} NW and $\mathbf{v}$ is 5 km h^{-1} W, find $\mathbf{u} + \mathbf{v}$, $\mathbf{u} - \mathbf{v}$, $3\mathbf{u} + 2\mathbf{v}$, $\mathbf{u} - 2\mathbf{v}$.

7. If P is 10 units S, Q is 12 units S20°E, R is 6 units S30°W, find $P + Q + R$, $P + Q - R$, $2P - 3Q + 4R$.

8. Split a vector of 10 units W into two components, one with direction S30°W and the other N40°W.

9. Split a velocity of 50 m s^{-1} N30°E into two components, one in a direction W and the other in a direction N40°E.

10. Split a vector of 16 units SW into two components, one SE and the other due W. Find also the resolved parts of the vector in the two directions.

11. Split a displacement of 20 km N into two components, one N10°E and the other SW. Find also the resolved parts of the vector in the two directions.

12. Split a velocity of 20 knots[1] N40°E into two components, one N and the other E. Find also the resolved parts of the vector in the two directions.

13. A ship is originally 50 nautical miles NE of Trincomalee and it steams due N for 4 h. at 15 knots. What is then its position referred to Trincomalee?

[1] The knot (a speed of 1 nautical mile per hour) is not an SI unit, but has been retained in this chapter since it is still in common use for sea and air navigation.

14. After flying for $\frac{1}{2}$ h on a course N60°E at 800 km h^{-1} an aircraft is 240 km S60°E of Berlin. Where was it originally?

15. A man walks with constant velocity, and in 27 min goes from a point 2 km S of a radio mast to a point 1 km E of it. Find his velocity.

16. Find the vector whose resolved parts in northerly and easterly directions are 12 units and 9 units.

†**17.** Find the displacement whose resolved parts in directions N70°E and N60°W are 2 m and 3 m.

†**18.** *OAB* is a triangle, and *M* is the mid-point of *AB*. Prove that **OM** = $\frac{1}{2}$(**OA** + **OB**).

†**19.** If **x** is 4 units N, **y** is 7 units E, **z** is 4 units vertically upwards, find **x** + **y** + **z** and **x** + **y** − **z**.

†**20**. If **x** is 4 m N, **y** is 5 m S50°E, **z** is 3 m vertically upwards, find **x** − **y** + **z**.

Relative velocity

7.9 Imagine a man standing on the deck of a liner which is steaming at 20 knots[1] due N. An albatross flying at 40 knots on a course N60°E passes directly overhead of the liner.

Three minutes later the liner will be 1 nautical mile farther North, and the albatross will have flown 2 nautical miles on its course of N60°E. The effect of this is to change its position so that it is 2 cos 60° = 1 nautical mile farther North and 2 sin 60° = 1·7 nautical miles farther East. The albatross is therefore due E of the liner and 1·7 nautical miles away (Fig. 10). Similarly after 6 min both the albatross and the liner have moved 2 nautical miles farther North, and the albatross is still due E of the liner, 2·4 nautical miles away.

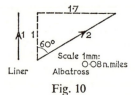

Fig. 10

To the man on the liner the albatross appears to remain due E and to be increasing its displacement from the liner in that direction by 1·7 nautical miles every 3 minutes, i.e. at a rate of 34 knots. We call this velocity of 34 knots due E the RELATIVE VELOCITY of the albatross to the liner.

We now have three velocities: the velocity of the liner of 20 knots due N, the velocity of the albatross of 40 knots N60°E, and the velocity

---

[1] See footnote on p. 99.

of the albatross relative to the liner of 34 knots due E (Fig. 11). We see that these three velocities form the three sides of a vector triangle:

velocity of liner + velocity of albatross relative to liner

= velocity of albatross

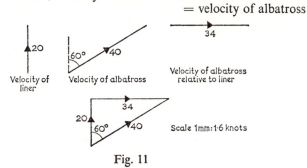

Fig. 11

This is similar to the situation which we encountered in Example 3 (p. 96). The airspeed of 200 km h⁻¹ on a course of N20°E is in fact the velocity of the aircraft relative to the air; on a perfectly calm day this would be the actual velocity of the aircraft. The vector triangle used in solving that example expresses the fact that

velocity of air + velocity of aircraft relative to air

= velocity of aircraft.

7.10. We revert to the example of the liner and the albatross. If it were possible for an observer to detach himself from the earth, he would say that the real velocity of the albatross is not 40 knots N60°E, anyway, since this figure does not take account of the motion of the earth through space or of the rotation about its axis. The velocity we have given is only its velocity relative to the earth. And even this detached observer has no right to claim an absolute judgement, for he has no criterion for finding out whether or not he himself is moving through space; for the measurement of velocity always depends on the presence of some fixed mark.

We conclude, therefore, that there is no such thing as the absolute velocity of any body, but that all velocities must be given relative to some specified origin (more precisely, a specified origin and set of axes, known as a 'frame of reference').

We use the symbol $_A\mathbf{v}_B$ to stand for the velocity of a body A relative to a body B.

In the example at the beginning of § 7.9 the velocities of the albatross and of the liner originally given were velocities relative to the earth. The vector triangle of Fig. 11 therefore expresses the equation:

$$_{\text{albatross}}\mathbf{v}_{\text{liner}} + {}_{\text{liner}}\mathbf{v}_{\text{earth}} = {}_{\text{albatross}}\mathbf{v}_{\text{earth}}.$$

This illustrates a general law:

The Relative Velocity Law. $_A\mathbf{v}_B + {}_B\mathbf{v}_C = {}_A\mathbf{v}_C.$

EXAMPLE 5. The observer in a heavy tank moving at 30 km h⁻¹ due N sights an enemy cruiser tank moving at 40 km h⁻¹ due E. What is the velocity of the cruiser tank relative to the heavy tank?

Both velocities are, of course, relative to the earth. We have the following data:

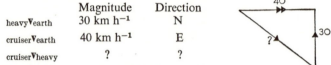

	Magnitude	Direction
heavy**v**earth	30 km h⁻¹	N
cruiser**v**earth	40 km h⁻¹	E
cruiser**v**heavy	?	?

These three velocities are connected by the equation

Fig. 12

$$\text{cruiser}\mathbf{v}_\text{heavy} + \text{heavy}\mathbf{v}_\text{earth} = \text{cruiser}\mathbf{v}_\text{earth}.$$

Fig. 12 shows the triangle of velocities for this equation. The sides representing the two known velocities are drawn first; a double arrow is placed on the side representing the velocity of the cruiser tank, which is the resultant of the other two, and care must be taken that the arrows have their correct senses round the triangle.

A simple calculation shows that the unknown velocity is 50 km h⁻¹ at an angle $\bar{\omega}$ S of E.

This problem may be regarded as one of subtraction of vectors. The equation may be written

velocity of cruiser relative to heavy
$$= \text{velocity of cruiser} - \text{velocity of heavy.}$$

It may also be noticed that, in similar way,

velocity of heavy relative to cruiser
$$= \text{velocity of heavy} - \text{velocity of cruiser}$$
$$= -\text{velocity of cruiser relative to heavy.}$$

It follows that, if the cruiser tank appears to an observer in the heavy tank to be moving relative to him at 50 km h⁻¹ on a course of $\bar{\omega}$ S of E, then to an observer in the cruiser tank the heavy tank appears to be moving at 50 km h⁻¹ in a course $\bar{\omega}$ N of W.

It is very important to observe that Fig. 12 is merely a diagram showing velocities, and bears no relation at all to the actual positions of the two tanks. In fact, the answer to this problem is quite independent of the positions of the tanks.

EXAMPLE 6. A man is cruising in a motor boat which is capable of 10 knots in still water. He is making for a buoy 6 nautical miles away to the NE, and there is a tide running at 3 knots in the direction E. What course should he set, and when should he expect to reach the buoy?

The speed in still water gives the magnitude of his velocity relative to the water, but the direction of this velocity (the direction in which he points the nose of the boat, i.e. the course he sets) is unknown. To reach the buoy his velocity relative to the earth must be in a direction NE, but its magnitude is uncertain. The data are therefore as follows:

	Magnitude	Direction
$_{boat}v_{water}$	10 knots	?
$_{water}v_{earth}$	3 knots	E
$_{boat}v_{earth}$	?	NE

These velocities are connected by the equation

$$_{boat}v_{water} + {}_{water}v_{earth} = {}_{boat}v_{earth}.$$

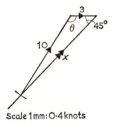

Scale 1mm : 0·4 knots

Fig. 13

Representing this equation by a vector triangle, in accordance with the triangle of velocities law, we have Fig. 13. (The method of construction is indicated in the diagram; the completely known side is drawn first, and then the side whose direction is known.)

By measurement or by trigonometry we find that $\theta = 123°$ and $x = 11·9$. The actual speed of the boat relative to the earth is therefore 11·9 knots, and it covers the 6 nautical miles to the buoy in $6/11·9$ h = 30 min.

EXERCISE 7(b)

1. A man driving North along a straight road at 50 km h^{-1} notices that the wind appears to have a velocity of 50 km h^{-1} from N60°W. What is the actual velocity of the wind?

2. The captain of a liner steaming due W at 16 knots sees that a launch appears to be approaching him from $\tilde{\omega}$ N of W at 20 knots. What is the actual velocity of the launch?

3. A man who can row at 4 knots in still water rows with his boat pointing N20°E in a current of 2 knots due E. How fast and in what direction does the boat move?

4. A man walks along a road at 5 km h^{-1}, and the rain is falling vertically at 8 km h^{-1}. At what angle to the vertical should he hold his umbrella?

5. A bomber flies due N at 1000 km h^{-1} and a fighter aircraft flies to intercept S60°W at 1400 km h^{-1}. With what relative velocity is the fighter approaching the bomber?

6. The speed of Mars in its path round the sun is 24 km s^{-1} and the speed of the earth is 30 km s^{-1}. What is the velocity of Mars relative to the earth (i) when they are collinear with the sun, (ii) when they are moving at right angles to each other? (Assume the planets move in circles.)

7. A ship steams due S at 18 knots and the wind blows from NW at 24 knots. What is the direction of the smoke trail from the funnel? (The particles of smoke lose the speed of the ship when they emerge, and move with the wind.)

8. A man who can row at 2·5 m s^{-1} in still water wishes to cross to the nearest point on the opposite bank of a river 400 m wide. If the stream is running at 1·5 m s^{-1}, how many minutes does it take him to cross?

9. An observer in a car travelling at 50 km h^{-1} in a direction 30°E of N experiences a wind from the north. Relative to the earth, however, the wind is blowing from due W. Find (i) the true speed of the wind, (ii) its apparent velocity when the car is moving at the same speed in the opposite direction.

10. Two ships are sailing at the same speed. The first is sailing SE, while the other appears to be approaching it from the east. Find the direction of motion of the second.

11. A swift which can fly in still air at 100 km h^{-1} is caught in a wind which blows at 90 km h^{-1} from $\tilde{\omega}$ S of W. It wishes to return to its nest, due E of its present position. In what direction, relative to the air, should it fly?

12. Answer Question 11 for a heron, which can fly at 60 km h^{-1}.

13. Discuss the problem confronting a sparrow (which can only fly at 30 km h^{-1}) in Question 11.

14. An aircraft capable of 600 km h^{-1} in still air has to fly to an airport SW of its present position. If there is a wind of 90 km h^{-1} blowing from N20°W, what course should be set? What is the ground speed of the aircraft?

15. A ship is to travel 20 nautical miles due E. If her speed in still water is 5 knots and if there is a current of 3 knots in the direction N30°E, find how long she will take.

16. In a river which flows at 2·5 m s^{-1} a trout swims upstream from A to B and back to A with speed 6·5 m s^{-1} relative to the water; another trout, in the same time and with the same relative speed, swims to the point C on the bank directly opposite to A and back to A. Find the ratio $AB : AC$.

†17. A boat is rowed with uniform speed v relative to a stream which flows at u. The stream has width a and it is necessary to reach the far bank a distance b downstream. Show that there are two directions in which the boat may be steered, provided that v is greater than $ua/\sqrt{(a^2 + b^2)}$ and less than u.

†18. A car is going due E and the driver notices that the wind appears to be coming from a direction N30°E. When he drives due W at the same speed the wind appears to come from N60°W. If he now goes due S at the same speed, find the apparent direction of the wind.

†19. When a ship is steaming due N at 25 knots the direction from which the wind appears to come is N25°E. When the speed is reduced to 10 knots the wind appears to come from N40°E. Find the true direction and speed of the wind.

Relative velocity and relative displacement

†7.11 The equation

$$\mathbf{v} = (\mathbf{r}_1 - \mathbf{r}_0)/t$$

in § 7.8 gave the velocity of a body in terms of its displacements from an origin O at different times. We have now seen that velocity must always be specified relative to some frame of reference. A more complete statement is therefore:

The velocity of a body relative to an origin O is the rate of change of its position relative to O.

For an illustration of this we may turn again to the example of the albatross and the liner discussed in §§ 7.9 and 7.10. The albatross is changing its position relative to the liner by becoming 1·7 nautical miles farther east of the liner every 3 minutes. Its velocity relative to the liner is therefore 34 knots east.

The examples which follow show how this principle can be applied using an origin which is moving relative to the earth.

EXAMPLE 7. A frigate capable of 15 knots sights a pirate 5 nautical miles away to the south which is steering at 18 knots on a course N40°W. In what direction must she steer to intercept the pirate, and how long will it take her to do so?

The actual direction in which the frigate must steer is not yet known. We shall in fact find that there are two possible courses (Fig. 14).

If, however, we consider the motion of the frigate relative to the moving pirate, we see that she wishes to change her position relative to the pirate from that of 5 nautical miles north to that of proximity. An observer on the pirate would see the frigate bearing directly down on him. It follows that the velocity of the frigate relative to the pirate has the direction due S (Fig. 15).

We have therefore:

	Magnitude	Direction
frigate$\mathbf{v}$pirate	?	S
pirate$\mathbf{v}$earth	18 knots	N40°W
frigate$\mathbf{v}$earth	15 knots	?

These velocities are connected by the equation

$$_{\text{frigate}}V_{\text{pirate}} + {}_{\text{pirate}}V_{\text{earth}} = {}_{\text{frigate}}V_{\text{earth}}.$$

The triangle of velocities is drawn in the following way (Fig. 16). Draw the side AB to represent the known velocity of the pirate. Through A draw a line due N of indefinite length; on this is to be represented the velocity of the frigate relative to the pirate. The third side of length 15 can now be drawn through B. There are two possible triangles, shown as ABD and ABC in Fig. 16.

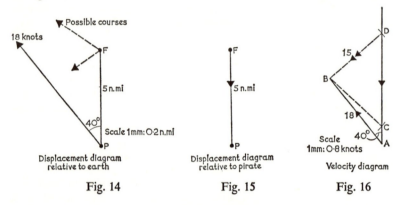

Fig. 14   Fig. 15   Fig. 16

The two possible courses have the directions of the lines DB and CB. It is plain from Fig. 14 that the more southerly course will enable the interception to be made more rapidly. This can also be seen by considering the motion relative to the pirate; since a fixed distance of 5 nautical miles has to be covered relative to the pirate, this can be done more rapidly if the speed of the frigate relative to the pirate, represented in Fig. 16 by the length of either AD or AC, is greater. The side DB therefore represents the course that the frigate should steer.

By measurement or calculation the course is found to be S50°W. The speed of the frigate relative to the pirate is found to be 23·3 knots, so that the distance of 5 nautical miles relative to the pirate is covered in 5/23·3 h = 13 min.

It is easily seen that if the frigate steers in any direction between the two possible courses for interception, she will reach the line along which the pirate is moving before the pirate would arrive at that point.

EXAMPLE 8. At 11 *a.m. an aircraft A is* 300 *km N50°E of another aircraft B. A is flying at* 800 *km h⁻¹ N70°W and B at* 600 *km h⁻¹ N10°W. How close to each other do they approach, and at what time are they closest to each other?*

Fig. 17 shows the positions and velocities of the aircraft relative to the earth. The problem is most easily solved by calculating all positions and velocities relative to B. The data are:

	Magnitude	Direction
$_A\mathbf{v}_{earth}$	800 km h^{-1}	N70°W
$_B\mathbf{v}_{earth}$	600 km h^{-1}	N10°W
$_A\mathbf{v}_B$	?	?

Fig. 18 shows the triangle of velocities based on the equation

$$_A\mathbf{v}_B + {}_B\mathbf{v}_{earth} = {}_A\mathbf{v}_{earth}.$$

By measurement or calculation we find that $_A\mathbf{v}_B$ is 722 km h^{-1} S64°W. (It must again be pointed out that Fig. 18 is a triangle of velocities and that it is not concerned at all with the positions of the aircraft.)

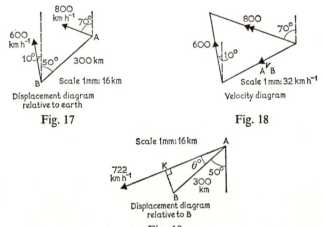

Displacement diagram
relative to earth

Fig. 17

Velocity diagram

Fig. 18

Displacement diagram
relative to B

Fig. 19

Fig. 19 shows the motion of the aircraft A relative to B. It starts 300 km N50°E of B and travels on a course S64°W so that the angle θ is $64° - 50° = 14°$. The two aircraft are closest together when A reaches the point K, the distance apart then being $300 \sin 14° = 73$ km. A has then travelled a distance $300 \cos 14° = 291$ km relative to B at a speed of 722 km h^{-1} relative to B which takes 291/722 h or 24 min.

The aircraft are therefore closest to each other at 11.24 a.m.

Acceleration as a vector

†7.12 So far we have only considered bodies moving with uniform velocity. Acceleration is also a vector quantity; if a body has a constant acceleration $\mathbf{a}$ it changes its velocity in time t by $\mathbf{a}t$. If $\mathbf{u}$, $\mathbf{v}$ denote the velocities of the body before and after this acceleration, we have

$$\mathbf{v} = \mathbf{u} + \mathbf{a}t$$

This can be rearranged in the form

$$\mathbf{a} = (\mathbf{v} - \mathbf{u})/t,$$

which expresses the fact that the acceleration is the rate of change of the velocity.

EXAMPLE 9. An electron in a television tube leaves the cathode with a speed of 10^7 m s^{-1}. It passes through an electric field which for a period of 3×10^{-9} s produces an acceleration of 2×10^{15} m s^{-2} at right angles to the original direction of motion of the electron. Through what angle will it be deflected?

The vector **a**t has magnitude

$$(2 \times 10^{15} \text{ m s}^{-2}) \times (3 \times 10^{-9} \text{ s}) = 6 \times 10^6 \text{ m s}^{-1}.$$

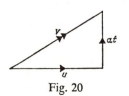

Fig. 20

The vector **u** is 10^7 m s^{-1} at right angles to this, and the final velocity is represented by the hypotenuse of the vector triangle (Fig. 20). The angle of deflection is given by

$$\tan \theta = (6 \times 10^6)/10^7 = 0.6,$$
$$\theta = 31°.$$

It should be observed that this triangle only determines the final velocity of the electron, and not the path which it follows while under the influence of the electric field (which is actually a parabola).

†EXERCISE 7(c)

1. Two straight roads cross at right angles. A man leaves the cross-roads and walks E at 4·5 km h^{-1}, and at the same time another man leaves a point 10 km due S and walks N at 6 km h^{-1}. After how long will they be closest together and how far apart will they be then?

2. Two trains are travelling on lines that cross at right angles, one at 45 km h^{-1} and the other at 108 km h^{-1}. Find their relative speed. Find also the shortest distance that they are apart if the slower train passes the crossing place one minute before the other.

3. A is 3 km due W of B. A walks due N at 5 km h^{-1}; B starts at the same time and walks at 7 km h^{-1}. In what direction must he walk to meet A? How long will he take to do so?

4. A battleship steaming due N at 16 knots is 5 nautical miles SW of a submarine. What course should the submarine take to close as quickly as possible if it can travel at 12 knots? If it travels on this course, how long will it take to get within 1 nautical mile of the battleship?

5. A ship A steams at 20 knots in a direction N15°E, and a second ship B at 12 knots N30°W. What is the velocity of B relative to A? If at the start B is 5 nautical miles E of A and if they steam uniformly on their courses, what is their shortest distance apart?

6. At a particular instant a liner is 1 nautical mile NW of a tanker. The liner is moving at 18 knots due E and the tanker is moving at 15 knots NE. If these speeds are maintained, what will be the shortest distance between the ships, and after what interval of time will they be in this position?

7. A batsman is at a wicket W and a fielder at deep square leg G, where GW is at right angles to the line of the wickets. The batsman hits the ball with velocity 15 m s⁻¹ on the leg side along a line making 30° with WG. If the maximum speed of the fielder is 9 m s⁻¹, find the direction in which he must run to cut off the ball in the shortest possible time.

8. A boat can be rowed in still water at 2 knots. It is rowed across a river, 200 m wide, which is flowing at 1¾ knots. The boat starts from a point A on one side and reaches the opposite bank at a point B 70 m upstream. If the boat moves in a straight line, how long does the crossing take? In what direction should the boat point on the return journey from B to A? (Take 1 nautical mile = 1850 m.)

9. A wing three-quarter runs down the touch-line at 9 m s⁻¹. At the moment he leaves the half-way line the full-back is on the 'twenty-five' line, 20 m from touch. The distance between the two lines is 25 m. What is the least speed with which the full-back must run if he is to intercept the three-quarter?

10. A corvette leaves port travelling at 10 knots on a course N30°E; 4 h later a destroyer leaves the same port at 20 knots, N30°W. If radio contact can be maintained up to a distance apart of 200 nautical miles, find the length of time the ships can remain in communication.

11. A ship P is steaming SW at a constant speed of 8 knots. A second ship Q is sighted 3 nautical miles SE of P steaming due W at a constant speed. After a certain time Q is due S of P and 1 nautical mile distant. Find the time taken from the instant Q was first sighted to the instant when Q is due W of P and the distance the ships are then apart. Find also the velocity of Q relative to P.

†**12.** A turret gunner in a bomber flying N50°E at 320 m s⁻¹ wishes to fire at a fighter flying S60°W at 360 m s⁻¹. If the muzzle velocity of the gun is 1000 m s⁻¹, in what direction should the gun be pointed when the fighter is due E of the bomber?

†**13.** A cyclist, riding at a speed V, overtakes a pedestrian who can move at a speed not greater than v, the two travelling along parallel tracks at a distance x apart. Show that, if the cyclist rings his bell when the distance between himself and the pedestrian is less than xV/v, he may safely maintain his speed and course regardless of the behaviour of the pedestrian.

†**14.** A ship steams from a point A at 20 knots N60°E. When it starts from A, a submarine starts from B, 4 nautical miles due E of A, and by

travelling at v knots tries to get within 1 nautical mile of the ship. Show that if $v = 5$ this is impossible, but that if $v = 6$ it can get within this range; and find what you can about the course which must be steered to do so.

15. At a particular instant a particle is moving with a velocity of 40 m s^{-1} due N. It experiences a constant acceleration due E and 3 s later it is moving in a direction $\bar{\omega}$ E of N. Find the magnitude of the acceleration.

16. A particle moving with a velocity of 0·2 m s^{-1} SW experiences an acceleration of 0·02 m s^{-2} due W for 5 s. Find its direction of motion after this time.

CHAPTER 8

PROJECTILES

Theoretical basis

8.1 The equation

$$F = ma$$

introduced in Chapter 3 has so far been used only for the motion of a particle in a straight line. Force and acceleration are, however, both vector quantities; a complete statement of Newton's second law includes the fact that the acceleration is in the same direction as the force. This is expressed mathematically by the equation

$$\mathbf{F} = m\mathbf{a}.$$

In this chapter we shall consider one of the simplest two-dimensional applications of this equation, to the motion of a projectile moving under the action of the force of gravity alone; for example, a cricket ball thrown through the air, or a bomb dropped from an aircraft. While the ball is in the thrower's hand, or the bomb is still in contact with the aircraft, there are several forces acting on the projectile. But as soon as the projectile is released, the only force on it (if we ignore the effect of air resistance) is its own weight. The total force is therefore m**g**, where **g** is a vector of magnitude g and direction vertically downwards. Hence the equation of motion is

$$m\mathbf{g} = m\mathbf{a},$$

so that $\mathbf{a} = \mathbf{g}.$

Let **u** denote the velocity of the projectile immediately after it is released, and **v** its velocity t seconds later. Then these velocities are connected by the equation

$$\mathbf{v} = \mathbf{u} + \mathbf{g}t \text{ (see § 7.12).}$$

The corresponding vector triangle is shown in Fig. 1.

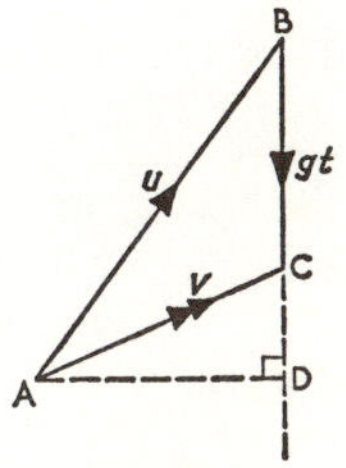

Fig. 1

The consequences of this result are most easily seen if the motion of the projectile is regarded as composed of two parts – the horizontal motion and the vertical motion. The velocity **u** is the sum of horizontal and vertical components represented in Fig. 1 by **AD** and **DB**, and **v** is the sum of components **AD** and **DC**. It follows that the horizontal component of velocity remains constant throughout the motion, being determined once for all by the manner in which the body is thrown. The vertical component of velocity (measured upwards) is decreased in magnitude by an amount gt.

We are thus led to the following principles which govern the motion of a projectile under gravity:

If the horizontal and vertical components of the initial velocity have magnitudes p and q, the horizontal motion of the projectile is the same as that of a body moving in a horizontal straight line with constant velocity p, and its vertical motion is the same as that of a body moving vertically under gravity with initial velocity q.

Horizontal projection

8.2 The conclusions arrived at theoretically in the last section will now be illustrated by an example.

Example 1. A boy throws a stone horizontally from the top of a cliff with a speed of 12 m s⁻¹. Discuss its subsequent motion.

Since the horizontal velocity remains constant, the stone moves 12 m horizontally in every second; that is to say, in each second its distance from the cliff measured in a horizontal direction increases by 12 m.

Its vertical motion is found by using the equation

$$s = ut + \tfrac{1}{2}at^2.$$

Let y be the vertical distance that the stone has fallen. Then since when it is thrown it has no vertical velocity, and since its vertical acceleration downwards is g, we may put $u = 0$ and $a = 10$ (to a sufficiently close approximation). This gives

$$y = 5t^2.$$

Thus it has fallen 5 m after 1 s, 20 m after 2 s, and so on.

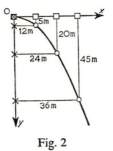

Fig. 2

Fig. 2 shows the curved path of the stone, with the circles indicating its position at successive seconds after the instant of projection from the point O. If another stone were just dropped over the cliff from O at the same instant, its positions at the same times would be indicated by the crosses on the diagram; the vertical motions of the two stones would be identical throughout their fall.

Moreover, if a bird were to fly past the boy just as he threw the stone, flying out to sea at 12 m s⁻¹ horizontally, its position at successive seconds would be at the points marked with a square. The bird would remain directly above the stone for as long as the stone continued to fall through the air.

If x and y denote the horizontal and vertical distances in metres from O of the stone after t seconds, we have the equations

$$x = 12t, \quad y = 5t^2,$$

from which we deduce that

$$y = \tfrac{5}{144}x^2.$$

This is the equation of the path of the stone referred to horizontal and vertical axes (with the y-axis pointing downwards). We observe that the path is a parabola with its vertex at O and its axis vertical.

Notice that in this example the x-coordinate $12t$ can be written as $\mathbf{u}t$, since the initial velocity $\mathbf{u}$ is 12 m s⁻¹ horizontally; and the y-coordinate $5t^2$ is $\tfrac{1}{2}gt^2$, where g represents the gravitational acceleration of 10 m s⁻² vertically. The displacement $\mathbf{r}$ from O could therefore be expressed by the vector equation

$$\mathbf{r} = \mathbf{u}t + \tfrac{1}{2}\mathbf{g}t^2.$$

That is, the total displacement is the vector sum of a displacement $\mathbf{u}t$ from the initial velocity of projection and a displacement $\tfrac{1}{2}\mathbf{g}t^2$ caused by the action of the force of gravity. This is illustrated in Fig. 3.

The similarity of this equation to

$$s = ut + \tfrac{1}{2}at^2,$$

which we have previously met as the equation giving the displacement for motion along a straight line, will be clear. The relation between the two corresponds to that between the equation

$$v = u + at$$

and the vector form

$$\mathbf{v} = \mathbf{u} + \mathbf{a}t$$

derived in § 7.12.

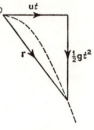

Fig. 3

8.3 *EXAMPLE 2. A stone is thrown horizontally with speed* 15 *m* s⁻¹ *from the top of a vertical cliff of height* 24 *m. How long will it take to fall into the sea, and how far from the foot of the cliff will it fall?*

Vertical motion. Taking g to be 10 m s⁻², we know that $s = 24$, $a = 10$, $u = 0$. Using the equation

$$s = ut + \tfrac{1}{2}at^2,$$

we have $$24 = 5t^2$$

whence $\sqrt{4.8} = 2.2$ approximately.

Horizontal motion. The stone has a horizontal velocity of 15 m s⁻¹ for 2·2 s. In this time it travels a horizontal distance of

$$15 \text{ m s}^{-1} \times 2.2 \text{ s} = 33 \text{ m}.$$

In this example we have considered the vertical motion first, since there are two unknown quantities in the equation of horizontal motion until the time has been calculated.

EXERCISE 8(a)

1. A ball is thrown horizontally out of a window 10 m above the ground with a speed of 6 m s⁻¹. Find how far it has moved horizontally and vertically at intervals of ¼ s after it is thrown until it strikes the ground. Plot a graph of its path through the air.

2. A bullet is fired horizontally across level sand with a speed of 500 m s⁻¹ and strikes the sand 0·2 s later. How far from the firer does it land, and how high above the ground is the muzzle of the rifle?

3. A stone is thrown horizontally at 20 m s⁻¹ from the top of a cliff and is seen to land in the sea 3 s later. How high is the cliff and how far from its foot does the stone hit the sea?

4. An aircraft in level flight at a speed of 140 m s⁻¹ releases a torpedo aimed at a destroyer 1 km away. The torpedo strikes the water 2½ s later. How far from the destroyer does it strike the water? How high is the aircraft flying?

5. A marble rolls along a shelf and over the edge with a speed of 0·14 m s⁻¹. It lands on the floor 0·06 m beyond the point directly beneath the edge of the shelf. Find for how long it was falling, and the height of the shelf above the floor. (Take $g = 9.8$ m s⁻².)

6. A car is driven over a cliff at 50 km h⁻¹, the ground at the top of the cliff being level. The wreckage is found 40 m from the foot of the cliff. How high is the cliff?

7. A boy throws a stone horizontally at 15 m s⁻¹ from the top of a tower 28·8 m high. Find how long the stone takes to reach the ground, and how far from the foot of the tower it lands. (Take $g = 10$ m s⁻².)

8. A stone is catapulted horizontally from the top of a tower 20 m high at 30 m s⁻¹. Find when and where it will strike the level ground on which the tower stands. (Take $g = 10$ m s⁻².)

9. A 'hedge-hopping' raider 49 m above the ground flying at 200 m s⁻¹ drops a bomb on a gun emplacement. How far in advance of the emplacement must the bomb be released? (Take $g = 9.8$ m s⁻².)

10. A stone is thrown horizontally and hits the surface of a lake. It strikes the water at a distance of 6 m from the thrower 0·4 s after being thrown. Find how fast it is thrown, and from what height above the water surface.

11. A coin is knocked with a ruler off a table 0·8 m high and hits the floor 2 m from the table. Find how long it takes to fall, and with what speed it was hit.

12. Water in a fountain is ejected horizontally from the mouth of a gargoyle 2·5 m above the water level in the bowl. The jet enters the bowl a distance 1 m horizontally in front of the point of ejection. With what speed was it ejected? (Take $g = 9.8$ m s⁻².)

13. A cricket ball is thrown horizontally from a height 2 m above the ground, and hits the ground 20 m from the thrower. How fast was it thrown?

†14. A boy throws a ball horizontally from the top of a cliff at 15 m s⁻¹. After how long will he see the ball in a direction 45° below the horizontal?

†15. A tennis ball is served horizontally from a height of 2·25 m. How fast must it be hit to clear the net 1 m high 12 m away from the server? If it is hit at 25 m s⁻¹, how far from the net will it land? (Take $g = 10$ m s⁻²).

†16. A boy hits a squash ball horizontally from a height of 1·25 m. It hits the wall 5 m away and lands at his feet. Assuming that it bounces off the wall with the same speed and at the same angle as that with which it strikes the wall, find how fast the ball was hit. (Take $g = 10$ m s⁻².)

Projection at an angle

8.4 Examples 1 and 2 are concerned with bodies projected horizontally. The same principles apply, however, when the initial velocity is at an angle to the horizontal. Such problems are solved in the same way, either by considering separately the motion in horizontal and vertical directions or using appropriate vector triangles expressing the relationships

$$\mathbf{v} = \mathbf{u} + \mathbf{g}t$$

and $$\mathbf{r} = \mathbf{u}t + \tfrac{1}{2}\mathbf{g}t^2.$$

Since in this chapter the two directions we are considering are at right angles, the horizontal and vertical components of velocity have the same magnitudes as the resolved parts of the velocity in horizontal and vertical directions (see § 7.6). We shall frequently refer to these simply as the horizontal and vertical velocities.

EXAMPLE 3. Discuss the path of a golf ball struck with an initial velocity whose horizontal and vertical components are 30 m s⁻¹ and 12 m s⁻¹.

Vertical motion. In the formula

$$s = ut + \tfrac{1}{2}at^2,$$

with the upward direction as positive, we take $u = 12$, $a = -10$. If y is the height of the ball in metres above the point of projection after t seconds, this gives

$$y = 12t - 5t^2.$$

Horizontal motion. The horizontal velocity has the constant value 30 m s⁻¹. Therefore, if x is the distance in metres moved horizontally by the ball in t seconds,

$$x = 30t.$$

Substitution of different values for t in these equations gives the following table for successive positions of the ball:

t	0	0·5	1	1·5	2	2·5	3 ...
x	0	15	30	45	60	75	90 ...
y	0	4·75	7	6·75	4	−1·25	−9 ...

Fig. 4 shows the path of the projectile plotted from these values. (In this figure the y-axis points upwards.) Of course, if the ground is level, the ball will strike the ground again when $y = 0$, that is after a time between 2 and 2·5 seconds. The values obtained for $t = 2·5$ and $t = 3$ will not then be correct, since new external forces come into play when the ball strikes the ground, causing it to stop or to continue its motion along some other path.

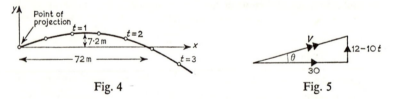

Fig. 4   Fig. 5

The equation of the path may be found by eliminating t from the equations for x and y given above. This gives

$$y = \tfrac{2}{5}x - \tfrac{1}{180}x^2,$$

which is again a parabola; in this case, however, its vertex is not at the point of projection. The graph and the table of values suggest that the vertex is reached by the ball at a time rather closer to $t = 1$ than to $t = 1·5$; say about $t = 1·2$. It will be shown shortly that this is in fact true, and the values of x and y are then 36 and 7·2. This is the highest point of the trajectory.

The velocity of the ball at different points of its path can be found by first finding vertical and horizontal components. The vertical component is found from the formula

$$v = u + at$$

giving in this example the value $12 - 10t$ in m s⁻¹. (We notice in passing that this is zero when $t = 1\cdot2$. This gives the time when the ball reaches its highest position.) The horizontal component is constant and equal to 30 m s⁻¹. The actual speed V and the direction of motion θ to the horizontal are then found by combining these components by the triangle rule (see Fig. 5). This yields:

t	0	0·5	1	1·5	2	2·5	3 ...
Vertical component	12	7	2	−3	−8	−13	−18 ...
Horizonal component	30	30	30	30	30	30	30 ...
V		32·3	30·8	30·1	30·1	31·0	32·7	35·0...
θ		22°	13°	4°	−6°	−15°	−23°	−31°...

8.5   In Examples 4 and 5 the two different methods are used to examine aspects of a given situation: Example 4 uses equations of horizontal and vertical motion, Example 5 uses a vector method. Students are recommended to practise both methods in working the Exercise which follows.

EXAMPLE 4. A stone is slung from a catapult with speed 30 m s⁻¹ at an angle $\bar{\omega}$ to the horizontal across a stretch of level ground. Find (i) *the greatest height it reaches,* (ii) *the distance it goes before striking the ground.*

We shall assume that the stone is projected from ground level. The initial horizontal and vertical velocities are $30 \cos \bar{\omega} = 24$ m s⁻¹ and $30 \sin \bar{\omega} = 18$ m s⁻¹.

(i) *Vertical motion* from point of projection to the top of its path. Let the greatest height reached be h metres. When it is at the highest point its vertical velocity is zero. In the formula

$$v^2 = u^2 + 2as$$

we have, therefore, $u = 18$, $v = 0$, $s = h$ (the positive direction being upwards) and we will again take $a = -10$. This gives

$$0 = 18^2 - 20h,$$

so that $h = 16\cdot2$.

We observe that the greatest height reached depends only on the vertical component of velocity.

(ii) *Vertical motion* for the complete trajectory. We still have $u = 18$, $a = -10$. We denote the time before it lands on the ground by T seconds; this is called the TIME OF FLIGHT. When $t = T$, the height of the stone above the ground is given by $s = 0$. Using the formula

$$s = ut + \tfrac{1}{2}at^2,$$

we have $0 = 18T - 5T^2,$

$$T(18 - 5T) = 0.$$

The solution $T = 0$ corresponds to the instant of projection, when the height of the stone above the ground is certainly zero. The other solution, which we require, is

$$T = 3\cdot6.$$

Horizontal motion. After 3·6 s the stone has travelled a horizontal distance of

$$24 \text{ m s}^{-1} \times 3·6 \text{ s} = 86 \text{ m approximately.}$$

This is called the RANGE of the projectile on the horizontal plane.

EXAMPLE 5. What is the greatest possible range of the stone in Example 4 for different angles of projection, the initial speed still being 30 m s^{-1}?
We use the fact, expressed by the equation

$$\mathbf{r} = \mathbf{u}t + \tfrac{1}{2}\mathbf{g}t^2,$$

that the displacement at any time can be regarded as the sum of a displacement of magnitude $30t$ due to its initial velocity and a displacement of magnitude $\tfrac{1}{2}gt^2$ due to the force of gravity. When the stone lands on the ground, this resultant displacement is horizontal, so that the vector triangle has the form of Fig. 6. From this we deduce at once, taking $g = 10$, that

$$\sin \alpha = \frac{5t^2}{30t} = \tfrac{1}{6}t,$$

where α is the angle of projection, and therefore

$$R = 30t \cos \alpha = 180 \sin \alpha \cos \alpha$$
$$= 90 \sin 2\alpha.$$

We notice in passing that, if α has the value $\bar{\omega}$, $\sin 2\alpha = 0·96$, giving the value of R previously found in Example 4.

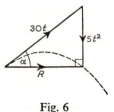

Fig. 6

Now the greatest value which $\sin 2\alpha$ can take is 1, when $\alpha = 45°$. The greatest possible range is therefore 90 m.

It can be shown that the greatest range on a horizontal plane is always obtained by projecting at 45° to the horizontal, provided that there are no air resistance or aerodynamic lift forces on the projectile.

EXERCISE 8(*b*)

1. A cricket ball is struck with a speed of 25 m s^{-1} at an angle $\bar{\omega}$ to the horizontal. Find where it is after successive intervals of $\tfrac{1}{2}$ s until it hits the ground. Find also its speed and direction of motion at these times. Plot a graph of its path.

2. A ball is thrown at 12 m s^{-1} at 60° to the horizontal. Find where it is and in what direction it is moving after one second.

3. An airgun slug is fired at 50 m s^{-1} at an angle $\bar{\omega}$ to the vertical. How long will it be in the air? In what direction will it be moving after 2 s? (Take $g = 10$ m s^{-2}.)

4. A jet of water leaves a hose-pipe with horizontal and vertical velocities of 15 m s^{-1} and 25 m s^{-1}. Find for how long each particle of water is in the air, and how far the jet reaches. (Take $g = 10$ m s^{-2}.)

5. A dive-bomber releases its bomb when descending at 200 m s^{-1} at an angle $\bar{\omega}$ to the horizontal. The bomb strikes the target 1 s later. At what height is the bomb released, and how far does the bomb travel horizontally?

6. A stone is thrown with horizontal and vertical velocities of 15 m s^{-1} and 8 m s^{-1} from a point 12 m from the wall of a house, and strikes an upstairs window. With what speed and at what angle was it thrown? How long will elapse before it hits the window? If it leaves the thrower's hand 1 m from the ground, how high is the window?

7. A ball is thrown at 16 m s^{-1} at 77° to the horizontal. At what height above the point of projection does it hit a wall 9 m away?

8. A batsman gets an edge to an away-swinger, and is caught 1·8 seconds later by third man standing 43·2 m from the bat. If the ball hits the bat 0·2 m above the ground, and leaves it with a speed of 26 m s^{-1}, how high above the ground is it caught? (Take $g = 10$ m s^{-2}.)

9. A stone is catapulted at 20 m s^{-1} at 30° to the horizontal. Taking g to be 10 m s^{-2}, find the time it is in the air, the greatest height reached and the horizontal range.

10. A goal is scored from a place-kick at rugby football. The ball passes over the bar at the top of its path 3·6 m above the ground. Find with what vertical velocity it was kicked and how long elapses before it passes over the bar. If it was kicked 24 m from the goal, find at what angle it was kicked. (Take $g = 9·8$ m s^{-2}.)

11. An athlete putting the shot releases the projectile at a height of 2·25 m above the ground, and it remains in the air for $1\frac{1}{2}$ s. Find the vertical velocity. If he throws it at 32° to the horizontal, how far does he throw it? (Take $g = 10$ m s^{-2}.)

12. Find the range of a shell fired with muzzle velocity of 700 m s^{-1} at 15° to the horizontal.

13. A boy throws a javelin with a speed of 25 m s^{-1} at an angle $\bar{\omega}$ to the horizontal. Ignoring aerodynamic forces and taking $g = 10$ m s^{-2}, find how high it rises, and the length of his throw.

14. A long jumper springs into the air at 7·8 m s^{-1} and rises to a height of 0·45 m. How long is his jump? (Take $g = 10$ m s^{-2}.)

15. A ball hit from a racquet at ground level just clears $1\frac{1}{2}$ s later a vertical wall 3 m away and 6 m high. Find (i) where the ball hits the ground again, (ii) the direction of motion when it was hit, (iii) the direction of motion at the point where the wall is cleared.

16. A rifle bullet hits a target 100 m away. It rises to a maximum height of 18 mm above the horizontal line joining the muzzle to the point of impact. Find the muzzle velocity. (Take $g = 10$ m s^{-2}.)

17. In a room of height 3 m a ball is thrown from a point P at a height 1 m with initial velocity $7\sqrt{2}$ m s^{-1} at 45° to the horizontal. It strikes the ceiling at Q without first striking a wall. Find the length of the straight line PQ. (Take $g = 10$ m s^{-2}.)

18. Two mortars are placed side by side and fire simultaneously with the same speed on the same bearing. One shell is fired at $\bar{\omega}$ to the vertical, the other at $\bar{\omega}$ to the horizontal. Prove that they both land in the same place, but that the first is in the air $1\frac{1}{3}$ times as long as the second. Compare the heights to which they rise.

19. A stone is thrown with a speed of 10 m s^{-1} at 30° above the horizontal from the top of a cliff 100 m high. How far from the foot of the cliff does it land? What is its speed and direction of motion when it lands? (Take $g = 10$ m s^{-2}.)

20. An aircraft is climbing at 180 km h^{-1} at 30° to the horizontal; at a height of 240 m, a package falls from it. When and where will it hit the ground? (Take $g = 9.8$ m s^{-2}.)

21. A stone is projected at 40 m s^{-1} at an angle of elevation of 60°. Find (i) the direction of motion after 2 s, (ii) its speed when it is moving at right angles to its original direction.

†22. In gunnery the greatest height reached by a shell is taken to be $5t^2/4$ metres, where t seconds is the total time of flight in a horizontal plane. Show that this formula is approximately correct.

†23. A shell is fired at a speed V at an angle θ to the horizontal. Find formulae for the height reached, the time it is in the air and the horizontal range.

CHAPTER 9

FORCE AS A VECTOR

Resultant force

9.1 It was stated in Chapter 7 that force is a vector quantity. We now examine some of the consequences of this statement, confining our attention at first to bodies small enough to be regarded as particles.

By the *resultant* of two forces we mean the single force which has the same effect on a body as the two forces acting in combination. When we say that force is a vector quantity we imply that the resultant **R** of two forces **P** and **Q** is found by the triangle law of addition (see Fig. 1).

This is only true, however, of the magnitude and direction of the forces, and not of the lines along which they act. For if the forces **P** and **Q** are acting on a particle, the particle must be at the point where their lines of action intersect, and the resultant must also act through this point. When adding forces it is therefore more convenient to use a parallelogram law than a triangle law; **P** and **Q** are represented by two sides of a parallelogram, and the diagonal represents the result-ant not only in magnitude and direction but also in position (see Fig. 2).

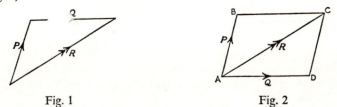

Fig. 1   Fig. 2

The Parallelogram of Forces. *If, in a parallelogram ABCD,* **AB** *and* **AD** *represent on some scale two forces, then* **AC** *represents their resultant in magnitude, direction and line of action.*

The principle that force obeys the vector law of addition is basic in the theory of mechanics. It can be demonstrated experimentally in various ways.

EXAMPLE 1. In a certain position the moon M experiences an attraction from the sun S of 4·35 × 10²⁰ newtons, and one from the earth E of 1·99 × 10²⁰ newtons, and the angle EMS is 65° (see Fig. 3). What is the resultant force on the moon?

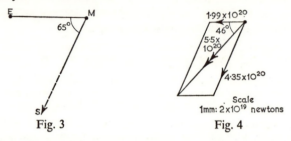

Fig. 3   Fig. 4

Fig. 4 shows the parallelogram of forces, with sides along the lines *ME* and *MS* of lengths proportional to the forces. By drawing or calculation it is found that the diagonal represents on the same scale a force of $5·5 × 10^{20}$ newtons making 46° with *ME*.

9.2 The parallelogram of forces is often used to combine two forces at right angles. Fig. 5 shows the theorem applied to add together two perpendicular forces X and Y. We see that the magnitude of the resultant is $\sqrt{(X^2 + Y^2)}$ and that it makes an angle θ with the direction of X, where $\tan \theta = Y/X$.

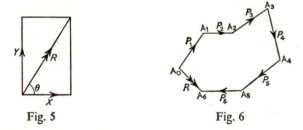

Fig. 5   Fig. 6

9.3 When the resultant of more than two forces has to be found, the triangle rule of addition must be replaced by a polygon rule (as in § 7.7, Fig. 6, p. 98).

The Polygon of Forces. *If forces $\mathbf{P}_1$, $\mathbf{P}_2$, . . ., $\mathbf{P}_n$ act on a particle, and if a polygon $A_0A_1A_2 . . . A_n$ is drawn in which $\mathbf{A}_0\mathbf{A}_1$, $\mathbf{A}_1\mathbf{A}_2$, . . ., $\mathbf{A}_{n-1}\mathbf{A}_n$ represent these forces on some scale in magnitude and direction, then $\mathbf{A}_0\mathbf{A}_n$ represents their resultant in magnitude and direction.*

Fig. 6 shows a polygon of forces with six forces acting.

EXERCISE 9(a)

1. Forces P and Q of 3 and 4 newtons act horizontally at an angle of 60° to each other. Find their resultant.

2. A force of 5 newtons acts due N and a force of 2 newtons acts at an angle $\bar{\omega}$ W of S. Find the resultant of the two forces.

3. Two magnetic forces act on a pole, one of 3·6 newtons due N and the other of 2·8 newtons due W. Find their resultant.

4. Two tugs pull the bows of a ship, one on either side, by means of horizontal cables in which the tensions are 50 and 70 kN. If the cables make angles of 25° and 15° with the line of the ship, find the resultant pull.

5. Two large dogs pull a sledge, one with 100 newtons due N and the other with 80 newtons N35°E. If the forces are horizontal, find their resultant.

6. The cables attached to two tractors hauling a tree-trunk are horizontal and have tensions 1200 N and 2000 N. If the tractors are SW and S60°W of the tree-trunk, find the resultant pull.

7. A catapult is used to sling a stone of mass 60 gm. The prongs are 80 mm apart and the elastic is stretched so that the two parts on either side of the sling have lengths 140 and 160 mm. In this position the two sections have tensions 15 and 20 N. Find the direction of the resultant force on the stone, and determine the acceleration with which it begins to move.

8. Find the resultant of the following forces acting on a particle: 20 units due E, 10 units due N, 8 units N30°W.

9. Forces of 5, 6 and 3 newtons act on a particle in directions E, N30°W, S30°W. Find the magnitude and direction of the resultant.

10. Show that the resultant of four forces, all of magnitude P, acting on a particle in directions due E, N18°E, N54°W, S54°W is of magnitude P in direction N18°W.

Forces in equilibrium

9.4 Consider a particle in equilibrium under the action of three forces **P**, **Q** and **S**. We have seen that, if **P** and **Q** are represented by **AB** and **BC** in a triangle ABC, then their resultant is represented in magnitude and direction by **AC** (Fig. 7a).

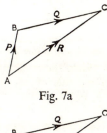

Fig. 7a

Since **P**, **Q** and **S** are in equilibrium, the force **S** must be equal in magnitude and opposite in direction to the resultant of **P** and **Q**. We know that **CA** $= -$**AC**. The force **S** is therefore represented by **CA** (Fig. 7b).

Fig. 7b

The Triangle of Forces. *If three forces act on a particle and are in equilibrium, it is possible to draw a triangle ABC in which the three forces are represented in magnitude and direction by* **AB, BC** *and* **CA.**

EXAMPLE 2. Three strings are knotted together, and masses of 7 kg, 8 kg, 9 kg are attached to their free ends. The strings carrying the two lighter weights are slung over fixed smooth pegs. At what angle to the vertical do these strings rest in equilibrium? (Fig. 8).

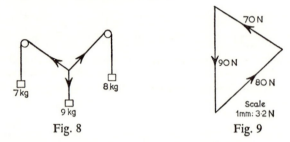

Fig. 8   Fig. 9

Since the pegs are smooth, the tension in each string is the same along its whole length, and is equal to the weight which it carries. Taking $g = 10 \text{ m s}^{-2}$, the weights are 70 N, 80 N and 90 N. We consider the equilibrium of the three forces at the knot.

The triangle of forces can now be drawn (Fig. 9). A vertical line of length 90 units is constructed first, and the triangle is completed with lines of 70 and 80 units. The triangle of forces principle shows that the two strings inclined to the vertical are parallel to these sides of length 70 and 80.

By calculation (using the cosine formula) or by drawing we find that these sides make angles with the vertical of 58° and 48° respectively.

When a triangle of forces is drawn, arrows should always be placed on the sides indicating the directions of the forces. If the figure has been drawn correctly these arrows should all follow each other round the triangle in the same sense.

EXAMPLE 3. A lantern of mass 3 kg hangs from the ceiling by a string which passes through a rough ring at the top of the lantern. The two parts of the string, AB and AC, are at 30° and 40° to the vertical. Find the tensions in the two parts of the string. (See also Chapter 4, Example 4.)
Fig. 10 shows the forces acting on the lantern, and Fig. 11 the triangle of

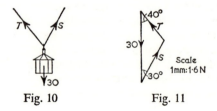

Fig. 10   Fig. 11

forces. The vertical line of 30 units (representing the weight of 30 N) is drawn first, and then the two lines inclined to it at 30° and 40°, parallel to the two parts of the string, complete the triangle.

Using the sine formula,

$$\frac{S}{\sin 40°} = \frac{T}{\sin 30°} = \frac{30}{\sin 110°},$$

whence $\quad S = \dfrac{30 \sin 40°}{\sin 70°} = 21, \quad T = \dfrac{30 \sin 30°}{\sin 70°} = 16.$

EXAMPLE 4. An aircraft of mass 10 tonnes is gliding with the engine cut off at 5° to the horizontal at constant speed. Find the forces of lift and drag.
The weight of the aircraft is 10^4 kg $\times$ 10 m s^{-2}, or 100 kN. The lift force of L kN (the force which supports an aircraft in the air) acts at right angles to the direction of motion, and the drag (or air resistance) of D kN acts parallel to the direction of motion. The forces on the aircraft are shown in Fig. 12.

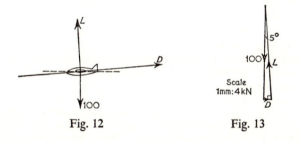

Fig. 12   Fig. 13

Since the speed of the aircraft is constant, the forces on it are in equilibrium. We can therefore draw a triangle of forces (Fig. 13), from which we deduce immediately that

$$D = 100 \sin 5° = 8.7$$
$$\text{and} \quad L = 100 \cos 5° = 99.6.$$

9.5 We now have two methods at our disposal for solving problems in which three forces acting on a particle are in equilibrium. Solution by resolving in suitably chosen directions is usually described as the *analytical method*, and solution by the triangle of forces as the *graphical method*. (The use of the word graphical does not imply that any accurate drawing and measurement will be carried out; in many cases it is most convenient to complete the solution by trigonometry.)

For example, the equations for D and L given at the end of Example 4 are just those which would be obtained by resolving in directions parallel and perpendicular to the direction of motion of the aircraft. The solution of Example 3 by graphical methods given above can be compared with the solution of the same problem by analytical methods in Chapter 4. It would also be possible to solve Example 2 analytically, but in this case the graphical solution is very much simpler.

It can in fact be shown that the resolution principle for statical problems (i.e. when the acceleration is zero) can be deduced from the polygon of forces rule to be given in the next section.

It will be found that some examples are better solved by analytical methods and some by graphical methods. The choice of the method better suited to a particular problem is a matter which becomes easier with experience.

9.6 When the number of forces acting on a particle in equilibrium is greater than three, the triangle of forces must be replaced by a polygon of forces. This can be deduced from the rule given in § 9.3 for finding the resultant of n forces. If the forces $\mathbf{P}_1$, $\mathbf{P}_2$, . . ., $\mathbf{P}_n$ are in equilibrium, their resultant is zero, so that $A_0A_n = 0$. The vectors representing the given component forces then form a closed polygon by themselves without the addition of another side (see Fig. 14).

If forces $\mathbf{P}_1$, $\mathbf{P}_2$, . . ., $\mathbf{P}_n$ acting on a particle are in equilibrium, it is possible to draw a polygon $A_1A_2 \ldots A_n$ in which the forces are represented in magnitude and direction by $\mathbf{A}_n\mathbf{A}_1$, $\mathbf{A}_1\mathbf{A}_2$, . . . , $\mathbf{A}_{n-1}\mathbf{A}_n$.

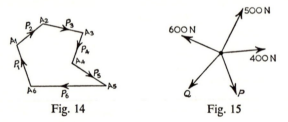

Fig. 14   Fig. 15

EXAMPLE 5. *A particle is in equilibrium under the action of five forces as shown in Fig.* 15. *Find P and Q.*

Fig. 16 shows the polygon of forces. The three completely known sides are drawn first; since the directions of the sides representing P and Q are known, these forces can now be found completely. We find by measurement that $P = 450$ N and $Q = 390$ N.

It should be noticed that this polygon can be drawn in more than one way. For example, by altering the order of the sides we could obtain Fig. 17. This is equally valid as a polygon of forces, and gives the same values for P and Q. It is important to observe, however, that in both Fig. 16 and Fig. 17 the arrows in the polygon follow each other round in a definite sense.

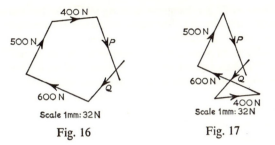

Fig. 16   Fig. 17

The sides of a polygon of forces are not, of course, the actual lines along which the forces act (which all meet at the point occupied by the particle). The principle is concerned solely with the sizes and the directions of the forces.

EXERCISE 9(b)

Take g = 10 m s⁻² where necessary throughout this Exercise.

1–3. Solve by the methods of this chapter Questions 1–3 of Exercise 4.

4. A particle of mass 4 kg is suspended by two strings of lengths 70 and 240 mm respectively, which are attached to two points at the same level and 250 mm apart. Find the tensions in the strings.

5. Forces of magnitude 4, 2 and $\sqrt{12}$ units act on a particle and are in equilibrium. Show that the lines of action of two of them are at right angles.

6–8. Solve by the methods of this chapter Questions 12–14 of Exercise 4.

9. The tensions in two cables that together support a mass of 210 kg are 1260 N and 1680 N. Find the angles that the cables make with the vertical.

10. A packing-case of mass 68 kg is slung by two ropes 15 m and 8 m long from points on two derricks at the same height and 17 m apart. Find the tensions in the ropes.

11. Forces of 6, 4, 8, 2 units act at a point in directions N60°E, N30°W, SW and S30°E. Find what force acting at this point will balance them.

12. The jib of a crane is 12 m long and the vertical post 6 m. The jib projects upwards from the foot of the post at an angle of 30° to the vertical, and its upper end is connected to the top of the post by a tie-bar. Find the thrust in the jib and the tension in the tie-bar when a load of 500 kg is suspended from the end of the jib, neglecting the weights of the jib and bar.

13–21. Solve by the methods of this chapter Questions 9–11 and 19–24 of Exercise 4.

22. In a simple pendulum, a 100 gm bob is fixed to the end of a light rod. Find the least force which must be applied to the bob to maintain equilibrium with the pendulum at 30° to the vertical.

23. A mass of 50 gm hangs on a string. What is the inclination of the string to the vertical when the mass is held aside by a force of 0·3 N in a direction 20° above the horizontal?

24. A mass of 50 gm hangs on a string. The mass is pulled aside by a force of 0·3 N so that the string makes an angle of 30° with the vertical. In what direction is the force applied?

25. A mass of 10 kg is pushed at a constant speed up a smooth plane of angle 48° by a force acting from a direction 30° below the horizontal. Find this force and the normal contact force.

26. A spider of mass 0·1 gm finds himself supported in the air by two strands of his web. If the tensions are 1·8 mN and 1·9 mN, find the angles that the strands make with the vertical.

27. A ship is towed at a constant speed by the horizontal pulls of two cables from tugs. If the tensions in the cables are 50 and 70 kN and the resistance to motion is 110 kN, find the angles made by the cables with the direction of motion.

28. A smooth straight wire is inclined to the horizontal at 30°. Find the magnitude and direction of the least force needed to keep a 200 gm bead threaded on the wire in equilibrium.

29. An electric light of mass 3 kg is suspended above a street by two wires attached at the same height to posts 8 m apart. Find the tensions in the wires if they are of lengths 4 and 5 m.

30. Forces of magnitude P, Q and R act on a particle and are in equilibrium. The angles between Q and R, R and P, P and Q are α, β, γ.

Prove that
$$\frac{P}{\sin \alpha} = \frac{Q}{\sin \beta} = \frac{R}{\sin \gamma}.$$

(This is known as *Lami's Theorem*.)

31. A particle of weight W is supported on a smooth inclined plane of angle θ by a string attached to the body and making an angle ϕ with the plane. Prove that the tension of the string is $W \sin \theta \sec \phi$ and find the normal contact force. Prove that if the force is equal to the tension in the string then $2\theta + \phi = 90°$.

Replacing a force by two components

†**9.7** In § 9.2 it was shown how to combine two forces at right angles into a single resultant. We sometimes reverse this process and replace a single force by two components in perpendicular directions.

EXAMPLE 6. A body of mass 10 kg rests on a smooth roof inclined at 30° to the horizontal. It is kept in equilibrium by means of two strings PA and PB of lengths 3 m and 4 m attached to the body and to two chimney-pots at the same level 5 m apart (see Fig. 18). Find the tensions in the strings.

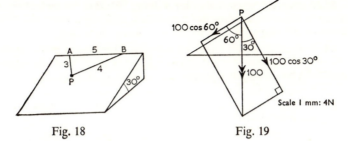

Fig. 18   Fig. 19

The forces on the body are its weight of 100 N, the normal contact force from the roof and the tensions in the strings. It is convenient first to replace the weight by two components parallel and perpendicular to the roof by the parallelogram law. These components have magnitudes $100 \cos 60° = 50$ N, and $100 \cos 30° = 86·6$ N (see Fig. 19).

The number of forces we are considering has now been increased to five. Of these, two act at right angles to the roof and thus have no effect in the plane of the roof. The other three act entirely in the plane of the roof (see Fig. 20), and these must therefore be in equilibrium amongst themselves.

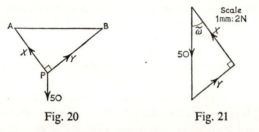

Fig. 20   Fig. 21

It is easily seen from the geometry of the triangle that the angle at P is a right angle, and that PA and PB makes angles of $\tilde{\omega}$ and $90° - \tilde{\omega}$ with the line of greatest slope of the roof. The triangle of forces for the three forces in the plane of the roof therefore has the form shown in Fig. 21. We deduce that $X = 50 \cos \tilde{\omega} = 50 \times \frac{4}{5} = 40$, and $Y = 50 \sin \tilde{\omega} = 50 \times \frac{3}{5} = 30$.

The tensions in PA and PB are therefore 40 N and 30 N.

†**9.8** Before using this method to solve problems by taking moments we must justify the process of replacing a force by two components when these are acting not simply on a particle. What we have to prove is that, if O is any point in a plane, and if two forces P and Q in the plane have a resultant R obtained by the vector law of addition, then the moment of R about O is equal to the sum of the moments of P and Q about O.

It is useful to establish two preliminary results.

(i) If a force **P** acts at a point **A** (Fig. 22), the moment of **P** about O is

$$P \times OA \sin \theta = OA \times P \cos (90° - \theta).$$

Now $P \cos (90° - \theta)$ is the resolved part of **P** in the direction AK at right angles to OA. Therefore *the moment of* **P** *about O is equal to the product of OA and the resolved part of* **P** *in the direction AK.*

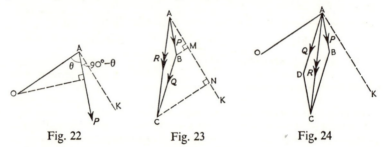

Fig. 22   Fig. 23   Fig. 24

(ii) If **P** *and* **Q** are represented by AB, BC, then their resultant **R** is represented in magnitude and direction by AC (Fig. 23). Let AK be any line through A, and let BM, CN be drawn perpendicular to AK. Then the resolved part of **P** in the direction AK is represented on the chosen scale by $AB \cos BAK = AM$; and the resolved parts of **Q** and **R** are represented similarly by MN and AN. Therefore *the resolved part of* **R** *in the direction AK is equal to the sum of the resolved parts of* **P** *and* **Q**.

We can now prove the main result. If forces **P**, **Q** acting at A have a resultant **R** (Fig. 24), and AK is in the direction at right angles to OA,

Moment of **P** about O + Moment of **Q** about O
$= OA \times$ (resolved part of **P** + resolved part of **Q** in direction AK)
$= OA \times$ resolved part of **R** in direction AK
$=$ Moment of **R** about O.

†9.9 *EXAMPLE 7. A trunk 160 cm long and 40 cm high has a mass of 15 kg uniformly distributed. It is held tilted at an angle of* 10° *to the horizontal by a force P applied to a handle in the middle of one of the end faces. If this force acts at an angle of* 20° *to the vertical, find how large it must be* (Fig. 25).

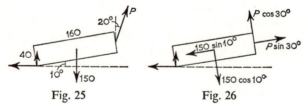

Fig. 25   Fig. 26

Since the normal and friction forces at the floor are not required, we take moments about the edge of the trunk in contact with the floor. The weight of the trunk is 150 N.

The moments of the individual forces are not easy to calculate, because the perpendicular distances from the edge to the lines of action are difficult to find. The solution becomes simpler if we express each force as the sum of components parallel to the edges of the trunk. The diagram of forces is then as in Fig. 26.

$\mathscr{M}$ (edge on floor) $\qquad$ 150 cos 10° × 80 − 150 sin 10° × 20
$$+ \, P \sin 30° \times 20 - P \cos 30° \times 160 = 0.$$

$$\therefore \, P = \frac{12\,000 \cos 10° - 3000 \sin 10°}{160 \cos 30° - 20 \sin 30°} = 88.$$

A force of 88 N is necessary.

EXAMPLE 8. A drawbridge 8 m long is kept in a horizontal position by two chains, attached to points A and B on the bridge 7 m from the hinge and to fixed points C and D at a height of 7·5 m vertically above the hinge. The bridge is uniform and has a mass of 1500 kg; a truck of 900 kg stands on it with its centre of gravity 5 m from the hinge. Find the force from the hinge (Fig. 27).

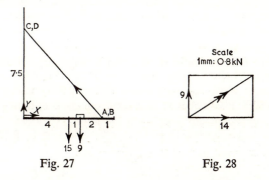

Fig. 27 $\qquad\qquad\qquad$ Fig. 28

The weights of the bridge and the truck are 15 kN, 9 kN. It is convenient to replace the single force from the hinge by horizontal and vertical components of X and Y, also measured in kN. We take moments about the lines AB and CD to avoid introducing the tensions in the chains.

$\mathscr{M}(AB) \qquad\qquad Y \times 7 - 15 \times 3 - 9 \times 2 = 0$.

$\mathscr{M}(CD) \qquad\qquad 15 \times 4 + 9 \times 5 - X \times 7·5 = 0.$

These equations give $X = 14$, $Y = 9$. We now combine these two components by a parallelogram of forces (Fig. 28), and find that the force from the hinge is 16·6 kN at 33° to the horizontal.

†EXERCISE 9(c)

Take g = 10 m s⁻² where necessary throughout this Exercise.

Questions 1–6 refer to a uniform rod *AB* of length 2 m and mass 12 kg which is free to turn in a vertical plane about a hinge at its upper end *A*. It is held aside at an angle θ to the vertical by a force *P* applied at *B*.

1. If *P* is 50 N applied horizontally, what is the force at the hinge?

2. If *P* is horizontal and θ = ω̄, what is the force at the hinge?

3. If *P* is 30 N at right angles to *AB*, what is the force at the hinge?

4. If *P* is at right angles to *AB* and θ = ω̄, what is the force at the hinge?

5. If the rod is supported with θ = ω̄ by *P* acting vertically, find the force at the hinge.

6. If, in Question 5, θ is increased to 60°, what difference does it make to the answer?

7, 8. Find the forces at the hinges in Questions 3 and 4 of Exercise 6(*b*).

9. A laundry basket 0·7 m long and 0·35 m high has a mass of 40 kg uniformly distributed. It is dragged slowly along the floor, tilted at an angle of 20° to the horizontal, by a force applied to a handle at the centre of one end. Find this force if it is inclined at 30° to the vertical.

10. A table of mass 24 kg is 1·2 m square, and its centre of gravity is 0·45 m above the ground. The table is placed on a rough slope of angle ω̄, with one edge parallel to a line of greatest slope. Find the normal contact forces at the legs.

11. A smooth fixed rail at 30° to the horizontal passes through two small rings at *A* and *B*, the upper corners of a uniform rectangular board *ABCD* of mass 10 kg, which hangs in a vertical plane. The board is prevented from sliding down the rail by a collar below the lower ring. If *AB* = 3 m and *AD* = 2 m, find the forces at the rings.

†12. A particle is placed on a rough plane of angle 30° and is acted on by a force *P* acting parallel to the plane and in a direction making 30° with the line of greatest slope. μ = tan 30°. If the value of *P* is gradually increased from zero, find the value of *P* when the particle begins to move, and the direction in which it begins to move.

MISCELLANEOUS EXERCISE B

1. A train starts from rest and moves with uniform acceleration for 6 min. It then moves with constant speed for 20 min and is finally brought to rest by a uniform retardation of magnitude three times that of the initial acceleration. During the fourth minute of the journey the train travels 840 m. Show that the acceleration of the train is $\frac{1}{15}$ m s^{-2}. Find the greatest speed. Find also the distance travelled before the train reaches a speed of 14 m s^{-1}.

Draw a velocity–time diagram for the motion and find the time for the whole journey.

2. A 2 kg mass and a 3 kg mass are tied to the ends of a light string 3 m long which hangs over a small smooth peg 2 m above the ground. The 2 kg mass is pulled down to ground level and then released. Find the acceleration of the system and the speed of the 3 kg mass immediately before it hits the ground.

To what height above the ground will the 2 kg mass rise before coming momentarily to rest? (Take $g = 10$ m s^{-2}.)

3. Masses of 3 kg and 4 kg are suspended from the ends of a uniform rod, itself of mass 1 kg. At what point along the rod could it be suspended to remain in a horizontal position?

4. To a cyclist riding south at 5 m s^{-1} the wind appears to be from SE at 10 m s^{-1}. What is the true velocity of the wind in magnitude (to one place of decimals) and in direction (to the nearest degree)?

5. An aeroplane is flying at a velocity of 720 km h^{-1} at a height of 490 m. At what distance before reaching the target must the bomb be released if the bomb is to hit the target, assumed on the ground? (Take $g = 9.8$ m s^{-2}.)

6. Two railway stations, A and B, are 50 km apart, and are served by electric trains which can decelerate at 5 km h^{-1} per second, and accelerate at 3 km h^{-1} per second. Their maximum speed is 90 km h^{-1}. There are twelve intermediate stations, all more than a kilometre apart.

Find the least time which can be taken to make the journey from A to B (a) by a fast non-stop train, and (b) by a slow train which stops $\frac{1}{2}$ min at every station.

7. A small block of mass 10 kg rests on a smooth plane, inclined at an angle of 30° to the horizontal. Find the magnitude of the horizontal force which would keep the block in equilibrium.

Find also the minimum value of the coefficient of friction if the block rests on a rough plane, inclined at 30° to the horizontal, without any supporting force.

133

8. A uniform bar AB, 1 m long, can be balanced horizontally about a point 100 mm from the end A by hanging a mass of 2 kg at A. Find the mass of the bar.

What additional mass must be added at A, in order to maintain equilibrium, if the point of support is moved 50 mm nearer to A?

9. A vessel is steaming in a direction due E at 10 knots. A naval destroyer is 5 sea miles due S of this vessel and wishes to intercept it. If the destroyer can do 25 knots, in which direction will it steam and how long will it take?

10. A ball is thrown at an angle $\tan^{-1}(\frac{4}{3})$ to the horizontal so that it just clears the top of a wall 57 m distant horizontally. If the ball takes 3·8 s to reach the top of the wall, find (taking $g = 10$ m s^{-2}):

(i) the velocity of projection;
(ii) the time taken to reach the highest point;
(iii) the height of the wall.

*11. A body moves in a straight line, its velocity v at time t (in metre-second units) being given by

$$v = 3t^2 - 18t + 24.$$

(i) For what values of t is the velocity zero?
(ii) What is the acceleration at time t?
(iii) For what range of values of t is the velocity increasing?
(iv) If, when $y = 0$, the body is 10 m from a fixed point in its path measured in the positive direction, find its distance from the fixed point at time $t = 3$.

12. A body of mass 20 kg falls freely under gravity through 80 m. It then meets a constant upward resistance, which stops it in 5 seconds. Find the force of this resistance. (Take $g = 10$ m s^{-2}.)

13. A beam AB, of length 7 m and mass 150 kg, has its centre of gravity at C, 3·6 m from A. It is supported in a horizontal position by two trestles at D and E, where $AD = 2·5$ m and $AE = 5$ m. Find the pressure on each trestle. (Take $g = 10$ m s^{-2}.)

Find the mass of the heaviest man who can sit at either end of the beam without tilting it.

14. Two trains A and B are running steadily, A at 50 km h^{-1} NW and B at a speed x due W. If the velocity of A relative to B is NE in direction, show that it is 50 km h^{-1} in magnitude and find the value of x.

If the speeds of A and B are interchanged, find the velocity of A relative to B in magnitude and direction.

15. A particle is projected with a speed of 60 m s^{-1} at an angle of 30° to the horizontal. Find the greatest height attained above a horizontal plane through the point of projection. Find also the range on this plane. (Take $g = 10$ m s^{-2}.)

Calculate the time taken by the particle in passing from one to the other of the two points at which its height above the plane is 25 m.

16. A mass of 6 kg is at the middle of a smooth plane 15 m long inclined to the horizontal at 30°. It is attached by a string passing over a smooth pulley at the top of the plane to a mass of 4 kg hanging freely. Motion is allowed to take place.

(i) Prove that the masses move with an acceleration of $\frac{1}{10}$ g.

(ii) The string breaks when the 6 kg mass has moved 8 m up the plane. Taking g to be 10 m s^{-2}, find the velocity of the 6 kg mass at this instant, and how much farther it will move up the plane.

17. A weight W rests on a rough inclined plane, the coefficient of friction being μ. A force P, acting along the plane, is the greatest force that will not move the weight upwards when the sine of the angle of inclination of the plane is $\frac{7}{25}$; and the same force P along the plane is the least force that will prevent the weight from slipping downwards when the sine of the angle of inclination is $\frac{3}{5}$. Find μ.

18. A uniform ladder PQ, of mass 24 kg and length 12·5 m, rests with P on a smooth horizontal floor and Q against a smooth vertical wall. The end P is attached by a string of length 3·5 m to the junction of the wall and the floor. Find the tension in the string.

If the tension in the string is not to exceed 245 N, find how far a man of mass 75 kg can ascend the ladder. (Take $g = 10$ m s^{-2}.)

19. A small body is given a velocity of 10 m s^{-1} in a direction due N at time $t = 0$. At the same instant it has impressed on it a constant acceleration of 10 m s^{-2} in a direction 60° E of N. Find its velocity in magnitude and direction after 2 seconds.

20. A boy with a catapult shoots a pellet from one end of a straight tunnel 34·3 m long; the roof of the tunnel is 2·5 m higher than his catapult as he shoots. He finds that he can hit a mark at the other end of the tunnel on a level with his catapult, but that the roof prevents him from hitting anything higher. If he shoots with velocity u at an angle α with the horizontal, find the values of (i) $u \sin \alpha$, (ii) the time to the highest point of flight, (iii) $u \cos \alpha$, (iv) u. (Take $g = 9\cdot8$ m s^{-2}.)

21. A train starts from rest at a station L. For the first 10 s it moves with a uniform acceleration of 1 m s^{-2}. For the next 20 s it moves with a uniform acceleration of 0·5 m s^{-2}. It then moves at a uniform speed before being brought to rest at a station M by a uniform retardation of 2 m s^{-2}. Find the speed and position of the train 18 s after starting. Find also its speed when its distance from L is (a) 32 m, (b) 206 m. If the distance LM is 2 km, show that the time during which the train is moving at constant speed is $77\frac{1}{2}$ s.

22. A string passing over a smooth pulley has a mass of 3 kg fastened to one end. Find what mass must be fastened to the other end so that, if motion is allowed to take place, the 3 kg mass (starting from rest) will descend through 12·6 m in 3 s. (Take $g = 9\cdot8$ m s^{-2}.)

23. A uniform beam AB of mass 100 kg rests in limiting equilibrium with A against a rough vertical wall and B on rough horizontal ground; the coefficient of friction at each end of the beam is $\frac{1}{3}$. Show that the vertical component of the reaction at B is about 900 N, and find the inclination of the beam to the vertical.

24. A vessel travelling due E at 15 knots is 10 sea miles to the NW of a submarine. The submarine submerges at once and travels at 10 knots under water, moving NE. Show that when it crosses the vessel's track it is nearly a sea mile behind and find the nearest distance to which it has approached the vessel.

25. A cricket ball is thrown at an elevation of 45° to the horizontal. At the instant of release the ball is 2 m above the horizontal plane through the wicket at ground level. If the horizontal distance from the thrower to the wicket is 88 m and the ball just reaches the wicket, at ground level, without bouncing, show that the ball was projected at approximately 29 m s^{-1} and calculate the time of its flight.

26. The accelerating force acting on a body, moving in a straight line, is related to the time in such a manner that the force–time curve is a semicircle, the diameter representing time, and lines drawn perpendicular to the diameter to the curve representing force. The scales are such that the total time is 60 s and the maximum force is 100 N. The body has a mass of 200 kg and starts from rest. What will be the velocity after 15, 30, 45 and 60 s?

What is the acceleration 15 and 45 s from the start?

27. A body of mass 5 kg rests on a rough inclined plane, and is attached to a body of mass 3 kg hanging freely by a string passing over a smooth pulley at the top of the plane. The inclination of the plane is slowly increased, and it is observed that the 5 kg mass just begins to move down the plane when the inclination becomes 59° to the horizontal. Find the coefficient of friction, giving your answer to two places of decimals.

28. *ABCD* is a square uniform sheet of thin metal; its mass is 3 kg, and the length of each side is 200 mm. The sheet can revolve freely in a vertical plane about a smooth pivot at X in AB, where $AX = 80$ mm and $BX = 120$ mm. A mass of 9 kg hangs from B, and a mass of M kg hangs from D, keeping the diagonal DB horizontal. Find M.

Find also what value of M would cause the side AB to take up a horizontal position.

29. A ship A is steaming at 14 knots due E, and a ship B is steaming 40° E of N at 8 knots. At noon, B is 5 sea miles N of A. If the limit of visibility is 12 sea miles, for how long after noon is B visible to A?

30. A golfer strikes a golf ball so that its initial horizontal component of velocity is $2v$ and its initial vertical component of velocity is v (in metre-second units). Taking g as 10 m s^{-2}, find, in terms of v, the time of flight and the distance d to the first impact with the ground, which may be assumed to be horizontal. If $d = 160$ m show that $v = 20$ m s^{-1} and calculate the greatest height of the ball.

31. A car A, moving along a straight road with a uniform acceleration of 1 m s^{-2}, passes a point O when its velocity is 2·5 m s^{-1}. Find its velocity and position 8 s after passing O. Find also its velocity when it is 18 m from O.

Another car B travels along the same road in the same direction with a uniform retardation of 1 m s^{-2}. It passes O with a velocity of 12·5 m s^{-1} two seconds after A has passed O. Find the times at which the cars are level and the distance between the two points at which the cars pass one another.

32. A man, whose mass is 80 kg, embarks in a balloon tethered to the ground. The balloon is released, and rises. Immediately his force on the floor of the balloon increases to 800 N, and remains steadily at that figure for 1 min. Find (i) the acceleration, (ii) the height to which the balloon rises in that time, (iii) the upward speed it attains in the same time. (Take $g = 9.8$ m s^{-2}.)

33. A uniform beam AB of length 6 m rests at an angle of 60° with the horizontal, the end A being in contact with a rough horizontal plane. At a point 4 m from A the under-side of the beam is in contact with a fixed smooth cylinder whose axis is perpendicular to the vertical plane containing the beam. If the beam is on the point of slipping, calculate the value of μ, the coefficient of friction between the beam and the plane.

34. A submarine travelling at 10 knots due N sights a cargo boat. Radar observations show that relative to the submarine it is travelling East at 16 knots and will pass 1 nautical mile ahead. A torpedo having a speed of 40 knots through the water is to be aimed at the boat. At what bearing of the boat from the submarine should the torpedo be fired so that it may have the shortest track, what course should it be set to follow and how long will it take to reach the estimated position of the boat?

35. A tile slides down a smooth roof inclined to the horizontal at an angle of 30°. It starts from rest at a point distant 6·4 m from the edge of the roof. Taking $g = 10$ m s^{-2}, show that when the tile reaches the edge its speed is 8 m s^{-1}.

The tile then leaves the roof and strikes the ground at a vertical distance 9 m below the edge of the roof. Show that it strikes the ground 1 s after leaving the roof. Show also that the speed of the tile at the moment of impact with the ground is just over 15 m s^{-1} and find the position of the point of impact.

36. A uniform horizontal girder AB of mass 9 tonnes lies at right angles to two parallel horizontal rails CD and EF. The centre of gravity of the girder is distant x metres from the rail CD as shown in plan in the figure.

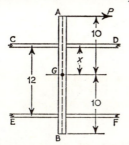

If a horizontal force P is applied at A and just causes both ends of the girder to move, find the distance x and the magnitude of P. The coefficient of friction between the girder and the rails is 0·01.

37. A truck of mass 100 kg attains a maximum speed of 30 km h^{-1} when running down an incline of 1 in 100. If the resistance to motion from all causes is proportional to the square of the velocity and is independent of the load, what is the maximum speed the truck will attain when it carries a load of mass 1000 kg down an incline of 1 in 120, and what will be the acceleration when it has attained one-half of this maximum speed?

38. A rod AB, hinged at A, is 4 m long and of mass 5 kg, with its centre of gravity 3 m from A. A string is attached to B, passes over a smooth pulley 3 m above A, and supports a mass M hanging freely. A mass X hangs from B, and keeps AB in a horizontal position. When $X = 3$ kg, find M; and when $M = 20$ kg, find X.

39. On a certain aircraft carrier, the landing-path on the flight deck makes an angle of 15° with the ship's axis. There is a wind of 25 knots and the ship steams at 30 knots. In what direction relative to the wind should it proceed so that aircraft may land directly into the wind? What is the wind velocity relative to the flight deck?

40. A spy is in the neighbourhood of a gun at sea-level when it is fired out to sea. He counts 15 s between the discharge and the bursting of the shell on its target on the sea, and a further 9 s before the sound of the explosion reaches him. Knowing that sound travels at 350 m s^{-1}, he calculates the velocity (to the nearest 10 m s^{-1}) with which the shell is fired, and hence what the range (to the nearest 100 m) of the gun would be if its elevation were 45°. Find his results.

CHAPTER 10

THREE FORCES ON A LARGE BODY

10.1 *EXAMPLE 1. A flywheel is mounted so that it rotates in a horizontal plane about a vertical axis. It is braked by means of the friction from three shoes, which are placed underneath the wheel near the rim and exert a vertical pressure on the wheel. These shoes are each mounted 0·4 m from the axis and are equally spaced round the flywheel, and each produces a friction force of 10 N. What is the effect of these friction forces on the wheel?*

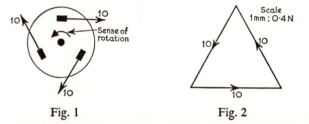

Fig. 1   Fig. 2

Fig. 1 shows the forces from the shoes, which are the only forces with any effect in the horizontal plane. Fig. 2 shows that a triangle of forces can be drawn for these three forces. *But the forces are not in equilibrium*, since they have the effect of slowing down the flywheel. They produce in fact a clockwise turning effect, or what was called in Chapter 6 a couple.

It follows from this example that when a set of forces acts on a large body, the fact that the forces can be represented by the sides of a closed polygon is not sufficient to ensure that they are in equilibrium. We know from Chapter 6 that for equilibrium the sum of the moments must be zero. In Example 1 the total moment of the three forces about the shaft is $10 \times 0·4 + 10 \times 0·4 + 10 \times 0·4 = 12$ N m, so that the forces cannot be in equilibrium.

†**10.2** We have seen in § 9.6 that if a set of forces acting on a particle is in equilibrium a closed polygon of forces can be drawn. For a particle the converse of this is also true: if the polygon can be drawn the forces are in equilibrium.

It can be proved that the principle enunciated in § 9.6 remains true when the forces act on a large body. But in this case the converse is not true. This is illustrated by Example 1.

We may compare this situation with that discussed in Chapters 4 and 6. There we saw that the conditions for equilibrium of a particle were simply that the sum of the resolved parts of the forces in two directions should be zero. For large bodies, however, the conditions also included an equation of moments.

10.3 When a set of forces on a large body is in equilibrium, two conditions must be satisfied: (i) it must be possible to represent the forces by the sides of a closed polygon, and (ii) the moments about some point must add up to zero. However, when the number of forces acting on the body is only three, it is possible to recast this second condition into a much more convenient form.

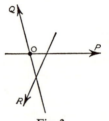

Fig. 3

If the three forces are not all parallel, let the lines of action of two of them, P and Q, meet at O. If we take moments about O for the three forces, the moments of P and Q are zero, since their lines of action pass through O (see Fig. 3). It follows that the moment of the third force R must also be zero, and this can happen only if R also passes through O. Therefore, if the three forces are not all parallel, their lines of action must be concurrent.

The Three-force Conditions. *The conditions for a set of three forces acting on a rigid body to be in equilibrium are* (i) *that a triangle ABC can be drawn in which* **BC, CA, AB** *represent the forces in magnitude and direction, and* (ii) *that the lines of action of the three forces are either concurrent or parallel.*

The value of this principle is that any mechanical problem in which only three forces appear can be solved completely by geometrical methods, rather than by the use of algebraic equations (as was necessary with the methods described in Chapter 6).

It should be observed that when the number of forces is greater than three the second condition does not apply. It is possible for four forces acting on a body to be in equilibrium without their lines of action being either concurrent or parallel; for example, when a ladder stands on rough ground resting against a smooth wall.

10.4 *EXAMPLE 2. A uniform rod AB rests with its lower end B on a smooth plane of angle* 30°. *The rod itself also makes* 30° *with the horizontal. What force P must be applied at the end A to keep it in this position?* (Fig. 4).
There are only three forces: the weight *W*, the normal force *N* from the plane (which acts through *B* at right angles to the plane) and the force *P*.

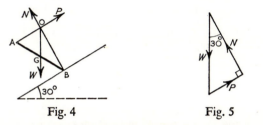

Fig. 4   Fig. 5

We first use the concurrency condition to find the direction of *P*. If the lines of action of *N* and *W* meet at *O*, the line of action of *P* must also pass through *O*; and since *P* is applied at *A*, *P* acts along the line *AO*.

The exact direction of *P* can be found by elementary geometry. Let *G* be the centre of gravity of the rod, which is the mid-point of *AB*. Then *OG*, the line of action of the weight, is vertical, so that the angle *BOG* is 30°. Also, since *BA* makes 30° with the horizontal, the angle *OBG* is also 30°. Therefore angle *OGA* is 60°, and also *OG* = *GB*. But *GB* = *GA*, so that *OG* = *GA*. It follows that the triangle *OGA* is equilateral, and angle *OAG* is 60°. Since the rod also makes 60° with the slope, the direction of *P* is parallel to the slope, at 30° to the horizontal.

We may now draw a triangle of forces for the three forces on the rod (Fig. 5). From this we deduce that

$$P = W \sin 30° = \tfrac{1}{2}W.$$

For equilibrium it is therefore necessary to apply at *A* a force of $\tfrac{1}{2}W$ at 30° to the horizontal.

EXAMPLE 3. Fig. 6 (p. 142) shows a loft door of mass 12 *kg propped open at* 60° *to the horizontal by means of a light strut AB. OA = OB = 90 cm, and the centre of gravity of the door is* 60 *cm from O. Find the thrust in the strut.* (See also Chapter 6, Example 8, p. 85.)
Apart from its weight of approximately 120 N and the thrust of *T* newtons from the strut, the other force acting on the door is that from the hinge at *O*. If *BA* produced and the vertical line through *G* meet at *X*, then the concurrency condition shows that the line of action of this force must pass through *X*, so that the force acts along *OX*.

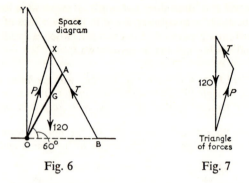

Fig. 6   Fig. 7

Fig. 7 shows the triangle of forces. We observe now that if BA were produced to meet the vertical line through O at Y, then the triangle of forces would be similar to the triangle OXY. Therefore

$$\frac{T}{120} = \frac{XY}{OY}.$$

Now since $OA = OB$ and the angle AOB is $60°$, triangle AOB is equilateral. Therefore XY and OG are equally inclined to the vertical, so that

$$XY = OG = 60 \text{ cm.}$$

Also, from the triangle OAY,

$$OY = 2 \times 90 \cos 30° = 90\sqrt{3} \text{ cm.}$$

Therefore

$$\frac{T}{120} = \frac{60}{90\sqrt{3}},$$

$$T = \frac{80}{\sqrt{3}} = 46.$$

The student should notice how the solution was made simpler by finding a triangle in the figure which was similar to the triangle of forces. This is often a useful device in solving problems of this kind.

The solution may be compared with that of the same example by analytical methods given in § 6.9. The choice of the method best suited to a particular problem can only come from experience.

Although the solutions of both the above examples have been completed by calculation, it is, of course, always possible to complete the solution (once the mechanical principles have been applied) by accurate drawing. In Example 3 the angles of the triangle of forces could have been found by drawing the space-diagram accurately, and T could then be measured from a triangle of forces drawn to scale. The student should never hesitate to adopt this course if he finds his knowledge of trigonometry unequal to the occasion.

10.5 *EXAMPLE 4. A uniform girder AB of length 16 m has chains of length 20 m and 12 m attached to A and B. The other ends of these chains are fastened to a fixed hook O, so that the girder hangs in equilibrium suspended from the hook by the two chains. What angle does the girder make with the vertical?* (Fig. 8).

The forces on the girder are the tensions in the two chains, and its weight, which acts vertically through *G*, the mid-point of *AB*. Since the lines of action of these two tensions meet at *O*, the weight must also act through *O*; that is, *G* must be vertically below *O*.

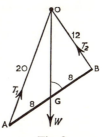

With the dimensions given the angle *OBA* is a right angle. Also $OB = 12$, $GB = 8$, so that $\tan OGB = OB/GB = 1.5$. The required angle is therefore 56°.

It should be noticed that in the solution of this example no triangle of forces was drawn. There are three unknowns in the problem: the

Fig. 8

angle *OGB* and the tensions T_1 and T_2. The tensions could both be found from the triangle of forces, whilst the angle – which is all that we require – is deduced immediately from the concurrency condition. This illustrates the graphical methods described in this chapter at their most powerful.

EXAMPLE 5. A girder AB of length 16 m has the two ends of a light cable of length 24 m attached to its ends. The cable is slung over a smooth hook, and the rod hangs in equilibrium suspended from the hook by the cable. If the centre of gravity of the girder is 10 m from A, what angle does the girder make with the vertical? (Fig. 9).

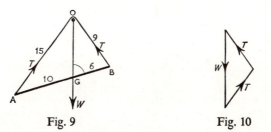

Fig. 9   Fig. 10

This problem appears to be similar to Example 4, but we do not now know the lengths of the two separate portions of the cable *OA* and *OB*. However, since the cable is continuous and passes over a smooth hook, the tension is the same throughout its length. It follows that the triangle of forces (Fig. 10) is isosceles, so that the two portions of the cable make equal angles with the vertical. (This conclusion could also be reached by resolving horizontally.)

This means that OG bisects the angle AOB so that, by the angle bisector theorem,

$$\frac{AO}{OB} = \frac{AG}{GB} = \frac{10}{6};$$

and since $AO + OB = 24$, $AO = 15$ and $OB = 9$.

The solution can now be completed by drawing (the reader would find it an interesting exercise to consider how this would be done) or using the cosine formula of trigonometry as follows:

Denote the angle OGB by θ. Then $OGA = 180° - \theta$, so that

$$81 = OG^2 + 36 - 12 \times OG \cos \theta$$

and

$$225 = OG^2 + 100 + 20 \times OG \cos \theta,$$

since $\cos (180° - \theta) = -\cos \theta$. Subtracting,

$$144 = 64 + 32 \times OG \cos \theta,$$

whence $OG \cos \theta = \frac{80}{32} = 2\frac{1}{2}$.

Also, multiplying the equations by 5 and 3 respectively, and adding,

$$1080 = 8\, OG^2 + 480,$$

so that $OG^2 = 75$.

Therefore $$\cos \theta = \frac{2\frac{1}{2}}{\sqrt{75}} = \frac{1}{2\sqrt{3}} = 0.2887,$$

and the required angle is $73°$.

10.6 In solving problems using the concurrency principle, the figure shown in the Introduction, § 0.4, is often encountered.

EXERCISE 10

Take $g = 10$ m s^{-2} where necessary throughout this Exercise.

1. A metal sphere of radius 100 mm and mass 6 kg rests against a vertical wall, with a string 160 mm long attached to a point of the wall and to a point on the surface of the sphere. Find the tension in the string and the contact force from the wall, assuming that no friction is acting.

2. A heavy uniform rod AB of length 2 m has its end A in contact with a smooth vertical wall; it is held in equilibrium in a position inclined to the vertical by means of a string fastened to a point on the rod 0·5 m from A and to a point on the wall. Find the length of the string.

3. A gate is supported by two hinges in such a way that the force exerted by the upper hinge is horizontal (i.e. all the weight is borne by the lower one). The hinges are 0·9 m apart, and the gate's weight of 300 N acts along a line 1·2 m from the line of the hinges. Find the force exerted by each hinge.

4. A garden roller of 100 kg is standing on a slope of 10°. It is held in equilibrium by a force applied along the handle of the roller (which may be supposed to pass through the centre of the roller), which is inclined at 5° to the slope. Find the size of this force.

5. Two smooth planes of angles 30° and 60° meet in a horizontal line. A plank rests with one end on each plane, at right angles to the common line of the planes. If it rests horizontally, in what ratio does its centre of gravity divide the plank?

6. If, in Question 5, the plank were uniform, at what angle to the horizontal would it be inclined?

7. A uniform rod of length 2 m rests with its lower end on a smooth plane of angle 40°. The rod makes an angle of 10° with the plane, and is held in this position by a string attached to its higher end. What angle does this string make with the vertical?

8–11. Solve by the methods of this chapter Exercise 6(*b*), Questions 1, 3, 5, 6.

12. A uniform metal rod of length 50 cm and mass 400 gm has eyelet holes fixed to it at two points *C* and *D* 24 cm apart. A string of length 48 cm has its ends attached to *C* and *D*, and passes over a smooth hook so that the rod hangs in equilibrium from the string. If the two parts into which the hook divides the string have lengths 30 cm and 18 cm, find (i) the positions of the eyelets in the rod, (ii) the angle to the vertical at which the rod hangs, (iii) the tension in the string.

13. A rod of length 5 m hangs horizontally from a hook by two strings attached to its ends and tied to the hook. The strings have lengths 3 m and 4 m. Where is the centre of gravity of the rod?

14. A uniform rod of length 2 m and mass 5 kg is hung from a fixed point by two strings attached to its ends, and rests at 30° to the horizontal. If the strings are at right angles, find the lengths of the strings and their tensions.

15. A uniform rod rests partly inside and partly outside a hemispherical cavity of radius 1 m with a smooth interior surface and a smooth horizontal rim. One end of the rod rests on the inside surface, and a point of the rod rests against the rim. If the rod makes an angle of 20° with the horizontal, find by accurate drawing its total length.

16. A porch roof is made of a uniform rectangular piece of wood *ABCD* of mass 5 kg, with *AB* = 1 m, *BC* = 0·5 m. The edge *AB* is horizontal and is fixed to the wall by smooth hinges. The corners *C* and *D* are attached by chains 0·8 m long to hooks on the wall 0·5 m above *B* and *A*. Find the tension in each chain and the force exerted by the hinge.

†**17.** A girder *AB* 6 m long of mass 500 kg is being hauled up by two chains passing over pulleys *C* and *D* at the same horizontal level 9 m apart. The chain from *A* to the pulley *C* is 3 m long, and that from *B* to *D* is 1·2 m long. If the 1·2 m chain makes 70° with the horizontal, use an accurate drawing to locate the centre of gravity of the girder, and to find the tensions in the chains.

†**18.** A uniform ladder rests against a smooth wall with its lower end on smooth ground which slopes upwards from the foot of the wall at an angle θ to the horizontal. If the ladder makes an angle ϕ with the vertical, prove that tan ϕ = 2 tan θ.

†**19.** A uniform rod of length $2a$ has one end against a smooth vertical wall and rests on a smooth horizontal rail parallel to the wall and distant h from it. Show that the rod makes an angle $\cos^{-1} \sqrt[3]{\dfrac{h}{a}}$ with the horizontal.

†**20.** OX and OY are smooth fixed wires, OX being vertical and OY inclined at 60° to OX; O is the highest point of both. A uniform rod AB is free to move with its ends attached by light rings to OX, OY. Show that in equilibrium tan $OAB = \frac{2}{3}\sqrt{3}$.

†**21.** ABC is a uniform equilateral triangle lamina of weight W, hinged at A to a fixed point and able to move freely in a vertical plane. It rests with AB vertical and B above A, and with AC resting on a smooth peg at a point X such that $AX = \frac{2}{3}AC$. Prove that the force from the hinge makes an angle $\tan^{-1}(\frac{1}{5}\sqrt{3})$ with the vertical.

†**22.** A uniform rectangular plate of weight W can turn freely in a vertical plane about its highest point P, which is fixed. The side QR rests on a smooth peg at its mid-point, making an angle θ with the horizontal. Prove that the hinge exerts a force $W \sin \theta \sec \phi$, where ϕ is the angle PRQ.

†**23.** The centre of gravity of a plank 3 m long and of mass 25 kg is 1 m from one end. A rope 4·5 m long is attached to the ends of the plank and passes over a smooth nail, from which the plank hangs. Find (i) the lengths of the two parts into which the nail divides the rope, (ii) the cosine of the angle between the two parts, (iii) the tension in the rope, (iv) the angle of inclination of the plank to the horizontal.

†**24.** Three knights A, B and C are sitting at a round table, centre O. B is 120° from A (i.e. the angle $AOB = 120°$) and he pulls the table towards him (along OB) with a force P. Angered, A retaliates by pulling along BA with a force Q. Anxious to keep the peace, C also pulls, and he finds that he can keep the table still. In what direction does he pull? Prove that
$$\cot OBC = \frac{(2P - Q\sqrt{3})}{Q}.$$

CHAPTER 11

THE ANGLE OF FRICTION

11.1 In the discussion on friction in §§ 5.1–3 a number of principles were laid down for determining the magnitude and the direction of action of friction forces. It was shown that the two forces which were specifically due to the contact of two bodies – namely, the friction force and the normal contact force – are closely related to each other.

It is often useful in statical problems to combine the contact forces of these two kinds into a single *total contact force* by means of a parallelogram of forces. By doing this the number of forces in the problem is reduced, and the solution correspondingly simplified. In particular, problems involving three forces have the number reduced to two, and those involving four (and sometimes five) become three-force problems. We know that it is especially easy to state conditions of equilibrium when only two or three forces act on a body.

Let the normal contact force between two rough bodies in contact be N, and the friction force F. The total contact force, which is the resultant of F and N, will be denoted by R, and the angle which the line of this force makes with the common normal to the surfaces by θ. The parallelogram of forces is shown in Fig. 1, and it follows immediately that

$$\frac{F}{N} = \tan \theta.$$

But we know from § 5.2 that

$$\frac{F}{N} \leqslant \mu.$$

We deduce that $\qquad \tan \theta \leqslant \mu.$

Fig. 1

The principle (ii) enunciated in § 5.2 can therefore take the alternative form:

(ii′) *There is a limit to the angle which the total contact force can make with the common normal to two surfaces.*

This limiting angle is the angle whose tangent is equal to the co-efficient of friction. It is usual to denote it by λ, so that

$$\tan \lambda = \mu.$$

It is known as the ANGLE OF FRICTION.

The principle just stated is thus expressed by the simple inequality

$$\theta \leqslant \lambda.$$

It also follows, from (iii) of § 5.2, that

(iii′) *The value of λ depends only on the roughness of the two surfaces.*

11.2 In Example 1 a three-force problem is reduced to a two-force one.

EXAMPLE 1. A particle rests on a rough slope of angle α. What can be said about the angle of friction?

Instead of considering the equilibrium of three forces – the weight, normal force and friction force – we combine the last two of these into a total contact force R. There are now only two forces, the weight and the total contact force, and for equilibrium these must act along the same line. The total contact force is therefore vertical (see Fig. 2).

Now the angle between the normal to the slope and the vertical is α. The friction condition (ii′) then gives

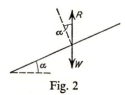

Fig. 2

$$\alpha \leqslant \lambda;$$

that is, the angle of friction must be at least as great as the angle of the slope.

We may observe that, since $\mu = \tan \lambda$,

$$\mu \geqslant \tan \alpha.$$

This is the condition given at the end of § 5.4, Example 2.

11.3 The next two examples illustrate the reduction of four-force problems to three-force ones. The first uses the concurrency principle for its solution, the second the triangle of forces.

EXAMPLE 2. A cotton reel rests on a rough plane of angle $40°$. A thread leaves the reel horizontally at its highest point and is fixed to a point of the plane (ignore the height of the rim). What can be said about the angle of friction? (Fig. 3).

The weight and the tension in the thread act along lines which meet at the highest point of the reel. The total contact force between the reel and the plane must therefore also pass through this point.

The radius through the point of contact is at 40° to the vertical. Let the total contact force make an angle θ with this radius. Then

$$\theta = \tfrac{1}{2} \times 40° = 20°.$$

But the friction condition gives

$$\theta < \lambda.$$

Therefore the angle of friction must be at least 20°. This gives a coefficient of friction of at least tan 20°, or 0·36.

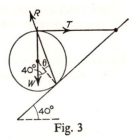

Fig. 3

EXAMPLE 3. A sledge is being dragged up a hill of angle α by a rope. What is the best angle for the rope to make with the slope in order that the least force may be used? (Fig. 4).

We suppose that the sledge is being pulled at constant speed, so that the forces are in equilibrium and friction is limiting.

Fig. 4   Fig. 5

The total contact force makes an angle λ with the normal, that is $\alpha + \lambda$ with the vertical. If the rope makes an angle ϕ with the hill, the triangle of forces is as in Fig. 5. The side W is completely known, the side R is known in direction, but the length of the side representing the tension depends on the angle ϕ. This side is clearly smallest when T is at right angles to R, i.e. when $\phi = \lambda$.

It is therefore best to pull with the rope at an angle to the slope equal to the angle of friction.

The reason why it is better to pull with the rope at an angle to the slope rather than parallel to it is that the normal contact force is then smaller, so that the friction is smaller. This more than compensates for the loss of effective pull directly up the hill.

It should be noticed that for the solution given above to be valid it is essential that $\alpha + \lambda < 90°$. The reader may like to consider what happens when $\alpha + \lambda > 90°$.

11.4 In the final example a problem with five forces, two of which are friction forces, is reduced to one with only three.

EXAMPLE 4. A plank P_1P_2 rests with its ends on two planes of angles α_1 and α_2. The angles of friction are λ_1 and λ_2. (Suppose that in each case $\lambda < \alpha < 45°$.) What can be said about the position of the centre of gravity?
The number of forces on the plank can be reduced to three: its weight and the total contact forces at P_1 and P_2. The friction condition (ii′) limits the possible lines along which the contact forces can act. In fact, if lines a_1 and b_1 are drawn through P_1 making angles of λ_1 on either side of the normal to the plane at P_1, the contact force at P_1 must lie somewhere between a_1 and b_1; similarly at P_2. The lines a_1, a_2, b_1, b_2 enclose a quadrilateral area, and the two total contact forces must meet at some point of it. The weight must therefore also pass through this point, by the concurrency principle, so that the centre of gravity of the plank must lie vertically below some point of the quadrilateral—that is, between X and Y in Fig. 6.

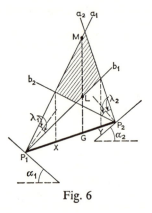

Fig. 6

It is interesting to observe that, if the centre of gravity were at some inter-mediate point G between X and Y, it would be impossible to discover how the friction is shared between the two points of contact. If a vertical line through G cuts the boundary of the quadrilateral in L and M, it would be consistent with all the conditions of equilibrium for the two total contact forces to meet at any point of the line LM. For example, in Fig. 6 it would be possible for the friction at P_1 to act either up or down the plane with any value whatsoever up to the limiting value. This is a problem whose solution is indeterminate.

EXERCISE 11

Take $g = 10$ m s^{-2} where necessary throughout this Exercise.

1. A mass of 20 kg is dragged along the ground by a rope pulled at 10° to the horizontal. If $\lambda = 50°$, with what force must it be pulled?

2. A child drags a toy rabbit of mass 200 gm along the ground by a lead inclined at 65° to the horizontal. If $\lambda = 25°$, what is the tension in the lead?

3. A metal ingot of mass 50 kg rests on the floor. It is pushed with a long stick inclined at 20° to the horizontal. If $\lambda = 15°$, what force is needed to push it?

4. A book of mass 1 kg rests on a desk lid inclined at 15° to the horizontal; $\lambda = 20°$. What force inclined at 20° to the horizontal will push the book up the lid?

5. A brick of mass 3 kg rests on a roof of inclination 50°; $\lambda = 20°$. What force parallel to the plane is necessary (i) to prevent it from sliding down, (ii) to pull it up?

6. A uniform rod AB is pulled along the ground with A on the ground, the angle of friction being 60°, by a string inclined at 60° to the horizontal. What angle does the rod make with the ground?

7. A mass of 1 kg rests on a slope of angle 20°, and $\lambda = 40°$. It is moved up the plane at constant speed by a force P at an angle θ to the slope. Calculate P in terms of θ, and plot a graph of P against θ for all values of θ for which the motion is possible. (Take values of θ for which the mass is pushed into the plane as negative, those for which it is pulled away as positive.)

8. Solve Question 7 for a force P which moves the mass down the plane.

9. Solve Question 7 for a slope of angle 40°, with $\lambda = 20°$.

10. A tree-trunk AB of mass 500 kg and length 12 m has its centre of gravity 4 m from A. It is dragged along by a truck, the end B being lifted off the ground by a crane fixed on the truck. If the trunk makes an angle of 10° with the horizontal, $\lambda = 40°$, and the chain from the crane is fixed to a point on the trunk 1 m from the end B, find the tension in the chain and its inclination to the horizontal.

11. A force of 15 N pulling upwards at 42° to the horizontal is just sufficient to move a mass of 4 kg on rough horizontal ground. What is the angle of friction?

12–20. Solve by the methods of this chapter Questions 2–5, 10, 11, 12, 16, 17 of Exercise 5.

21. A uniform rod is pulled along the ground by a string attached to one end. If the rod makes an angle of 45° to the horizontal and the angle of friction is also 45°, find the angle made by the string with the vertical.

22. A suitcase of mass 50 kg is dragged across a railway platform; $\lambda = 17°$. What is the least force which will move it, and in what direction must it be applied?

23. A 100 kg slab of stone will just rest in limiting equilibrium on a slope of angle 40°. If it is put on a slope of angle 30°, find the magnitude and direction of the smallest force needed to drag it (i) up the slope, (ii) down the slope.

24. A 3 kg brick rests on a level table; $\lambda = 25°$. In what direction should it be pulled to move it with as small a force as possible? If it is pushed along the same line in the opposite direction, what force is needed to move the brick?

25. A uniform ladder 12·5 m long rests with its top against a smooth vertical wall and its foot on rough ground 3·5 m from the wall. Find the least possible angle of friction.

26. A rod AB of length 2 m has its centre of gravity 80 cm from A. It rests horizontally with B against a rough vertical wall. A string is attached to A, and its other end is fastened to a peg in the wall $1\frac{1}{2}$ m above B. Find the least possible value of the angle of friction.

†27. A heavy circular hoop hangs over a rough peg. Show how to find the position of equilibrium when a given mass is suspended tangentially by a string. If the mass of the hoop is 2 kg and $\lambda = 30°$, what is the greatest mass that can be suspended?

†28. A circular cylinder, with its axis horizontal, is supported in contact with a rough vertical wall by a string wrapped partly round it and attached to a point of the wall, the string making an angle θ with the wall. Prove that $\tan \lambda \geqslant \operatorname{cosec} \theta$.

†29. A particle rests on a rough plane of angle α, and $\lambda < \alpha$. P is the smallest force with which it can be prevented from sliding down the plane, and if a force $2P$ in the same direction is applied, the particle will be on the point of sliding up the plane. Prove that $\alpha = 3\lambda$.

†30. One end of a string is attached to a mass M resting on a rough table, the angle of friction being λ. The string passes over a smooth pulley above the table and carries a hanging mass m at the other end. Prove that in limiting equilibrium the part of the string attached to the mass M makes an angle θ with the vertical, where $m \sin (\theta + \lambda) = M \sin \lambda$; provided that, if $M < m$, $\theta > \cos^{-1} (M/m)$. What happens if $\theta \leqslant \cos^{-1} (M/m)$?

CHAPTER 12

INTERACTING BODIES

Equations for separate bodies

12.1 In § 3.10 the following principle was enunciated and given the name of the Interaction Principle:

If a body A exerts a force (of whatever kind) on a body B, then B exerts on A a force of the same magnitude acting along the same line but in the opposite direction.

This principle was applied in Chapter 3 to solve a number of simple problems in particle dynamics. In this chapter we shall apply it to some examples on the equilibrium of systems of bodies, and in the following chapter it will be used to establish the Conservation of Momentum principle in dynamics.

EXAMPLE 1. Two smooth cylinders, each of mass 3 kg and radius 4 cm, rest inside a trough with smooth vertical walls; their axes are parallel and 12 cm apart. A third cylinder of mass 4 kg and radius 6 cm rests on top of these, touching each along a generator (see Fig. 1). Find the forces on the sides and the base of the trough.

It follows easily from the geometry of the figure that the lines *AB*, *AC* make angles of $\tilde{\omega}$ with the vertical.

In order to solve a problem of this sort, we consider the cylinders separately. The forces on the upper cylinder are (Fig. 2):

    1. Its weight (40 newtons).

    2, 3. Normal contact forces from each of the two lower cylinders.

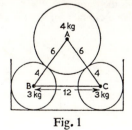

Fig. 1

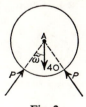

Fig. 2

153

By resolving horizontally we find that the two normal forces are equal in magnitude. We denote them by P newtons. Then

$$\mathscr{R}\,(\uparrow) \qquad\qquad 2P\cos\tilde{\omega} - 40 = 0,$$

so that

$$P = \frac{40}{2 \times \frac{4}{5}} = 25.$$

The forces on the left-hand lower cylinder are (Fig. 3):

1. Its weight (30 newtons).
2. The normal contact force from the upper cylinder. By the inter-action principle this is equal to P, i.e. 25 newtons.
3. The normal contact force Q newtons from the base of the trough.
4. The normal contact force R from the side of the trough.

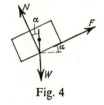

Fig. 3

For this cylinder,

$$\mathscr{R}\,(\rightarrow) \qquad R - P\sin\tilde{\omega} = 0,$$

giving

$$R = 25 \times \tfrac{3}{5} = 15.$$

$$\mathscr{R}(\uparrow) \qquad Q - 30 - P\cos\tilde{\omega} = 0,$$

giving

$$Q = 30 + 25 \times \tfrac{4}{5} = 50.$$

By symmetry the forces on the right-hand lower cylinder are also 15 N from the walls and 50 N from the base.

Finally, we use the interaction principle again to show that, since the sides and base exert on each lower cylinder forces of 15 N and 50 N, each cylinder exerts on a side and on the base forces of 15 N and 50 N.

12.2 It is important to remark that the interaction principle applies to forces of all kinds, including friction and gravitational forces, and not just to normal contact forces and tensions in strings. This is illustrated by the next two examples.

EXAMPLE 2. A car of weight W stands stationary on the slope of a ramp of angle α. The ramp itself has a horizontal base and a weight W', and rests on the ground. Consider the forces on (i) *the car,* (ii) *the ramp,* (iii) *the earth.*

(i) The forces on the car are (Fig. 4):

1. Its weight W, i.e. the gravitational force on it from the earth.
2. The normal contact force N from the ramp.
3. The friction force F, which is also a contact force from the ramp.

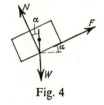

Fig. 4

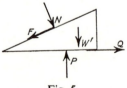

Fig. 5

The equations are:

$\mathscr{R}$ (‖ to ramp) $F - W \sin \alpha = 0,$

$\mathscr{R}$ (⊥ to ramp) $N - W \cos \alpha = 0.$

(ii) The forces on the ramp are (Fig. 5):

1. Its weight W', the gravitational force on it from the earth.

2, 3. Normal and friction contact forces N, F from the car, by the interaction principle.

4, 5. Normal and friction forces P, Q from the ground.

It is very important to notice that the weight of the car is *not* one of the forces acting on the ramp. By definition the weight of the car is the force with which the earth attracts the car; it is a force on the car, not a force on the ramp. The presence of the car is accounted for entirely by the forces F and N.

The equations for the ramp are:

$\mathscr{R}$ (↑) $P - W' - N \cos \alpha - F \sin \alpha = 0,$

$\mathscr{R}$(→) $Q + N \sin \alpha - F \cos \alpha = 0.$

Using the values for F and N obtained in (i), these give

$$P = W' + W \cos^2 \alpha + W \sin^2 \alpha = W + W',$$
$$Q = W \sin \alpha \cos \alpha - W \cos \alpha \sin \alpha = 0.$$

(The fact that there is no friction force from the ground could have been predicted from common-sense considerations. How?)

(iii) The forces on the earth are (Fig. 6):

1. The normal contact force P from the ramp. (Since $Q = 0$, there is no friction force from the ramp.)

2, 3. Gravitational forces from the car and the ramp, equal and opposite (by the interaction principle) to the gravitational attraction from the earth on the car and the ramp.

Fig. 6

The equation for the equilibrium of the earth is

$$P - W - W' = 0,$$

which agrees with the value for P found in (ii).

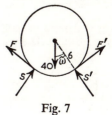
Fig. 7

EXAMPLE 3. If the cylinders in Example 1 were rough and rested on a table without any supporting force from the side, find the necessary coefficients of friction between the cylinders, and between the lower cylinders and the ground.

The forces on the upper cylinder are now (Fig. 7) its weight and the friction and normal forces from the two lower cylinders. Symmetry suggests that the two friction forces and the two normal forces are equal; alternatively, the result can be proved as follows:

$\mathcal{M}$ (axis of cylinder)　　　　　$6F - 6F' = 0.$

$\mathcal{R}\ (\rightarrow)$　　　　$F' \cos \tilde{\omega} - S' \sin \tilde{\omega} - F \cos \tilde{\omega} + S \sin \tilde{\omega} = 0.$

The first equation gives $F = F'$, and we then deduce from the second that $S = S'$.

Using these results,

$\mathcal{R}(\uparrow)$　　　　　$2F \sin \tilde{\omega} + 2S \cos \tilde{\omega} - 40 = 0,$

so that　　　　　$3F + 4S = 100.$

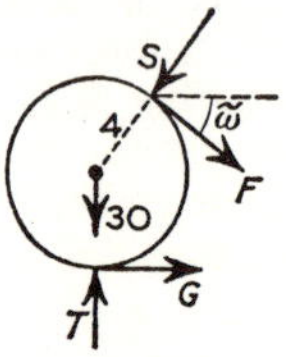

The forces on the left-hand lower cylinder are (Fig. 8) its weight, the normal and friction contact forces from the upper cylinder (equal to S and F, by the interaction principle), and the normal and friction contact forces from the ground. The equations are:

$\mathcal{M}$ (axis of cylinder)　　　　$4F - 4G = 0,$

$\mathcal{R}(\rightarrow)$　　　　$F \cos \tilde{\omega} + G - S \sin \tilde{\omega} = 0,$

Fig. 8　　$\mathcal{R}\ (\uparrow)$　　$30 + F \sin \tilde{\omega} + S \cos \tilde{\omega} - T = 0.$

The first two of these equations give $S = 3F$; combining this with the equation $3F + 4S = 100$ found above gives

$$F = \tfrac{20}{3}, \quad G = \tfrac{20}{3}, \quad S = 20.$$

The last equation then gives $T = 50$.

The coefficient of friction between each lower cylinder and the upper one must therefore be at least $F/S = \tfrac{1}{3}$, and that between each lower cylinder and the ground at least $G/T = \tfrac{2}{15}$.

EXERCISE 12(a)

Take $g = 10\ m\ s^{-2}$ where necessary throughout this Exercise.

1. A weight is suspended by a heavy chain from a hook in the ceiling. Draw separate diagrams to show the forces acting on (i) the hook, (ii) the chain, (iii) the weight.

2. A wedge, whose lower face is rough and whose slant face is smooth, rests on rough horizontal ground. One end of a rod rests on the ground and the other end on the smooth face of the wedge. Draw diagrams to show the forces acting on the wedge and on the rod.

3. Two equal rods AB, BC smoothly hinged at B are placed over a smooth fixed cylinder whose axis is horizontal, and hang symmetrically. Draw a diagram showing the forces acting on each rod and on the cylinder.

4. A light string $ABCD$ is fastened to two points A and D in the same horizontal line. Loads of 12 kg and M kg are hung from B and C. If angle $DAB = 40°$, angle $ABC = 160°$, angle $BCD = 110°$, find M and the tension in BC.

5. A light string $OABC$ hangs from a fixed point O. Equal masses of 2 kg each are attached at A, B and C. Horizontal forces are applied as follows: 30 N to the left at A, 20 N to the right at B and 10 N to the left at C. Find graphically the angles which the different parts of the string make with the vertical, and the tensions.

6. The arms of a pair of nutcrackers are parallel, the nut is 20 mm from the hinge and the force is applied 80 mm from the nut. If the force exerted by the fingers on each arm is 40 N, find the force at the hinge and the forces on the nut.

7. Two uniform planks AB, BC, each of mass 15 kg and length 2 m, are hinged to each other at B. They rest end to end in a horizontal line on just two supports, one of which is at A. Where is the other?

8. A uniform plank AB of mass 50 kg and length 6 m is hinged at B to another uniform plank BC of mass 20 kg and length 4 m. They rest end to end in a horizontal line, AB resting on two supports 1 m from either end and BC on one support 1·5 m from B. Where on the planks is it unsafe for a child of mass 40 kg to stand?

9. A flagstone of length 1 m and mass 120 kg rests on the ground. A metal crowbar of mass 5 kg and length 1·6 m is forced under the flagstone to a distance of 0·2 m and then raised by the far end. What force is needed at first to lift the flagstone? (Assume all forces acting are vertical.)

10. A rough cylindrical metal pipe of mass 15 kg and radius 30 mm is placed on the ground with its axis horizontal and parallel to and 50 mm from a rough vertical wall. A second cylindrical pipe of mass 10 kg and radius 20 mm is placed with its axis parallel to that of the first, resting on the first pipe and against the wall. If equilibrium is preserved, find the smallest possible values for the coefficient of friction between the top pipe and the wall, the two pipes, and the bottom pipe and the ground.

11. Rings of masses 10 gm and 20 gm can slide on a fixed rough horizontal wire; $\mu = 0.6$. They are connected by a thread which hangs below the wire and which has threaded on it a smooth ring of mass 30 gm. If the rings on the wire are as far apart as possible, find the angles between the thread and the wire, and the tension in the thread.

12. A step-ladder is made of two uniform structures APB, AQC, each of mass 10 kg and hinged together at A. P and Q are connected by a horizontal rope, and the ladder stands on a smooth floor at B and C. $AB = AC = 3$ m, $PB = QC = 1$ m and the angle $BAC = 40°$. Prove that the force of interaction at A is horizontal, and find the tension in the rope.

13. A child makes a tunnel for a toy train out of two equal pieces of cardboard, each 0·3 m × 0·2 m, joined together along a pair of longer sides with adhesive paper so that they are free to turn about this side. The tunnel stands on the table with its sides at 60° to the horizontal. Find the minimum possible coefficient of friction.

†14. A cylindrical log of mass 30 kg and radius 0·3 m rests on the ground. A uniform plank of length 2·1 m rests, with one end on the ground, across the cylinder, the line of contact being 1·2 m from the lower end. A child stands on the plank at its centre of gravity, the masses of the child and plank totalling 50 kg. Find by drawing the minimum possible angles of friction between the plank and the ground, the plank and the log, and the log and the ground. (The axis of the log is horizontal.)

†15. Two smooth cylinders of unequal radii and of masses 10 and 20 kg are in contact with their axes horizontal. The first rests on a plane of angle 30°, and the second on another plane, also of angle 30°. Show that in equilibrium the plane containing the axes of the cylinders makes an angle of 60° with the vertical.

†16. Uniform straight rods AB, BC, each of length $4a$ and of weights W, $3W$ are smoothly jointed at B. They rest on a vertical plane in contact with two smooth pegs at D and E. DE is horizontal and of length a, and B is above DE. The rods are kept at 60° to the horizontal by a horizontal force P applied at a point in BC. Find the magnitude of P, where it is applied, and the total force at the hinge B.

†17. A rectangular block of weight W is raised off the ground by light wedges of angle θ forced underneath opposite edges of the block. The angles of friction between the wedges and the block, and between the wedges and the ground, are λ_1 and λ_2. Prove that the horizontal forces applied to the wedges necessary to raise the block are

$$\frac{W \sin (\lambda_1 + \lambda_2 + \theta)}{2 \cos (\lambda_1 + \theta) \cos \lambda_2}.$$

†18. Equal uniform rods BC, CA, AB, each of mass 10 kg, are joined together by means of smooth horizontal pins inserted through holes at their ends. The two holes in each rod are 1 m apart. The framework is hung from a hook by a rope tied to the pin at A, and loads of 20 kg each are hung from the pins at B and C. Show in diagrams the forces acting on each of the three rods and on each of the three pins, and find the magnitudes and directions of these forces.

Internal and external forces

12.3 It will have been noticed that the value found in Example 3 for the normal force between each lower cylinder and the table was the same as that found in Example 1 for the force between each lower cylinder and the base of the trough, namely 50 N. We shall now discuss why this was to be expected, and how the value could be found in another way.

Consider the three cylinders as forming a single body. The only forces acting on this body from outside are its weight of 40 N + 30 N + 30 N = 100 N, the two vertical normal forces, and two equal horizontal forces (from the sides of the trough in Example 1, and the friction from the table in Example 3); these are shown in Fig. 9. Resolving vertically for this body, we see that the normal forces N are 50 N each.

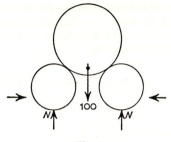

Fig. 9

This illustrates an important distinction between internal and external forces. In solving a problem we must continually bear in mind precisely what body it is that the forces act upon. Forces between component parts of that body are called INTERNAL FORCES; by virtue of the inter-action principle, these always occur in pairs, so that they do not in-fluence the equilibrium of the forces acting on the body as a whole, and they need not be included in the equations. Forces from agencies outside the body are called EXTERNAL FORCES; it is only these that are included in the equations of resolving and moments for that body.

Thus in Example 1 the normal contact forces between the upper cylinder and the two lower ones were external forces when we were considering the equilibrium of the upper cylinder by itself. But when we are regarding the three cylinders as forming a single body, these forces become internal forces and do not appear in the equations. The forces of cohesion between the individual molecules of the upper cylinder are, however, internal forces in either case.

The same point arose in § 3.10, Example 7 (see p. 47). That problem was solved first by considering the motion of the car and the trailer separately, and the force X in the coupling was an external force both on the car and on the trailer, and appeared in the equations of motion of both bodies. It was afterwards shown that the value of the accelera-tion could be calculated by treating the car and trailer as a single unit; the force in the coupling then becomes an internal force and does not appear in the equation of motion.

Equations for a complete system of bodies

†12.4 The examples so far discussed have been solved by writing down equations for the equilibrium of each of the separate bodies of an interacting system. It is often more convenient to solve problems by writing down only some of these equations, replacing the rest by equations for the equilibrium of the complete system; the forces of

interaction between the individual bodies thereby become internal forces and do not appear in the equations. The next example is solved first by the methods used earlier in this chapter, and then by using instead an equation for the complete system.

EXAMPLE 4. Two rods AB, BC of lengths a and b are smoothly hinged together at B. The end A is free to turn about a fixed point, and originally the rods hang vertically from this point. The end C is now pulled aside with a horizontal force of 2 N, and the rods then make angles of 15° and 45° with the vertical. Find the weights of the rods. (Fig. 10).

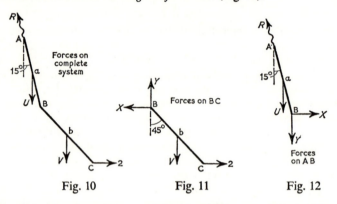

Fig. 10   Fig. 11   Fig. 12

First solution. Let the rods have weights U and V newtons. We consider first the forces on the rod BC, which are shown in Fig. 11; it is useful to replace the force which AB exerts on BC through the hinge by its components in horizontal and vertical directions. Then the equations for BC are:

$$\mathcal{M}(B) \qquad V \times \tfrac{1}{2}b \sin 45° - 2 \times b \cos 45° = 0,$$

$$\mathcal{R}(\uparrow) \qquad\qquad Y - V = 0,$$

$$\mathcal{R}(\rightarrow) \qquad\qquad 2 - X = 0.$$

Since $\sin 45° = \cos 45°$, the first of these equations gives $V = 4$. The others give $Y = 4$, $X = 2$.

Fig. 12 shows the forces on AB. The force from BC exerted through the hinge at B is represented by the two components X, Y in the opposite directions to those in Fig. 11. Since the value of the force R is not required, it is best to take moments about A for this rod.

$$\mathcal{M}(A) \qquad U \times \tfrac{1}{2}a \sin 15° + Y \times a \sin 15° - X \times a \cos 15° = 0.$$

This gives
$$U = \frac{2 \cos 15° - 4 \sin 15°}{\tfrac{1}{2} \sin 15°}$$
$$= 4 \cot 15° - 8 = 6\cdot9.$$

It is interesting to notice that the answers do not depend on the lengths of the rods.

Second solution. We start as in the first solution by finding V from the equation of moments for the rod BC, which gives $V = 4$; but the equations of resolving for this rod are not needed.

When we consider the forces on the pair of rods together (Fig. 10) the forces X and Y become internal forces. Since R is not required, the solution is completed from the equation

$$\mathcal{M}(A) \quad U \times \tfrac{1}{2}a \sin 15° + V(a \sin 15° + \tfrac{1}{2}b \sin 45°)$$
$$- 2(a \cos 15° + b \cos 45°) = 0.$$

Since $V = 4$, the terms involving b disappear, and we find that $U = 6.9$ as before.

The advantage of this method is that the unknown weights have been found from two equations, rather than from four.

Third solution. We use the methods of Chapter 10. Since only three forces act on each of the rods (if the total force at the hinge B is used), the directions of the force at B, and then the force R at A, can be found by applying the concurrency principle to the rods BC, CA in turn (Fig. 13). The weights can then be found by drawing triangles of forces for each of the two rods (Figs. 14 and 15).

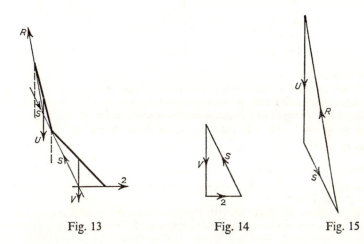

Fig. 13   Fig. 14   Fig. 15

If desired, the two triangles of forces could be combined in one diagram, since they have a common side (although with arrows in opposite directions in the two triangles).

†12.5 The technique used in the second solution of Example 4 can be used again to good effect in the next example.

EXAMPLE 5. A pair of steps consists of two equal legs, smoothly pivoted together at the top. The step half AB has mass 12 kg, and the supporting leg BC a mass 4 kg. A boy of mass 40 kg stands half-way up the steps. Each leg makes an angle of 20° with the vertical, and the legs are kept from slipping apart simply by the friction from the ground. The coefficient of friction between each leg and the ground is the same. Which leg is more likely to slip, and what coefficient of friction is necessary to prevent this occurring?

The weights are approximately 120 N, 40 N and 400 N respectively. Let the normal forces at the feet of the steps and the supporting legs be R and S, and the friction forces E and F, all in newtons. Let the distance between A and C be p.

We first take the forces on the complete system, so that the forces at the hinge B between the two legs are internal forces and need not appear (Fig. 16). The equations are:

$$\mathscr{R}(\uparrow)\quad R + S - 40 - 120 - 400 = 0,$$

$$\mathscr{R}(\rightarrow)\quad E - F = 0,$$

$$\mathscr{M}(A)\quad S \times p - 40 \times \tfrac{3}{4}p - 120 \times \tfrac{1}{2}p - 400 \times \tfrac{1}{2}p = 0.$$

These give $S = 160$, $R = 400$ and $E = F$.

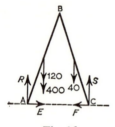

Fig. 16

The two friction forces are therefore equal. But the limiting friction (the maximum possible friction force) is proportional to the normal force, which is greater at A than at C. The steps are therefore more likely to slip at C.

We now isolate the forces on BC (Fig. 17). The force from the rod AB at the hinge is unknown and unwanted, so that the solution is completed by taking moments about B. We observe that the height of B above the ground is $\tfrac{1}{2}p \cot 20°$.

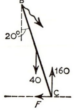

$$\mathscr{M}(B)\quad 40 \times \tfrac{1}{4}p + F \times \tfrac{1}{2}p \cot 20° - 160 \times \tfrac{1}{2}p = 0,$$

whence $\quad F = 140/\cot 20° = 140 \tan 20°.$

It follows that the least possible value of μ is

$$\frac{F}{S} = \frac{140 \tan 20°}{160} = 0.32.$$

Fig. 17

†EXERCISE 12(*b*)

Take g = 10 m s⁻² where necessary throughout this Exercise.

1. Explain why it is impossible to lift oneself up by one's own boot-laces.

2. A heavy rod is hung up by a string attached to each end of the rod and passing over a smooth hook. Draw diagrams to show (i) the external forces acting on the rod, (ii) the external forces acting on the system of the rod and string.

3, 4. Draw diagrams to illustrate the mechanical arrangements given in Questions 2 and 3 of Exercise 12(*a*), showing which forces are external and which are internal in the systems.

5. A uniform plank of length 6·4 m and mass 30 kg projects 1·6 m over the edge of a cliff; another exactly similar plank rests on the first and projects 0·8 m beyond the end of it. How far may a 40 kg boy walk along the top plank?

6. Two uniform rods *AC*, *CB* of equal length, are smoothly jointed at *C*, and have their other ends hinged to the ceiling at *A* and *B*. If *AC* and *CB* have masses of 20 kg and 25 kg, and if the triangle *ABC* is equilateral, find the force at the hinge *C*.

7. A step-ladder consists of two uniform structures each of mass 20 kg and length 4 m, smoothly hinged together at the top and connected at the bottom by a rope. When the rope is taut the ladder makes an angle of 20° with the vertical. A man of mass 60 kg stands on the steps $\frac{2}{3}$ of the way up. Find the horizontal and vertical components of the force at the hinge.

The figure for Questions 8–11 is: *ABCD*, *CDEF* are two rectangular metal plates of masses 40 kg, 20 kg. They are hinged together along *CD*, and *AB* is hinged to a horizontal beam. *AB* = *CD* = *EF* = 3 m, *BC* = *AD* = *DE* = *CF* = 2 m. A force is applied to the edge *EF* in the vertical plane at right angles to that edge.

8. Find the force at *EF* if the plates hang with *EF* vertically below *AB*, each plate being at an angle $\tilde{\omega}$ to the horizontal.

9. Find the force at *EF* if *CDEF* is horizontal and angle *ADE* = 45°.

10. Find the force at *EF* if *CDEF* is horizontal and angle *ADE* = 135°.

11. At what angles do the plates hang if the force at *EF* is 500 N at an angle of $\tilde{\omega}$ to the upward vertical?

12. Two uniform rods *AB*, *BC*, each of length 1 m and mass 5 kg, are smoothly jointed at *B* and have their other ends hinged to points *A* and *C* on a vertical wall. If *A* is 1 m vertically above *C*, find the force at the hinge *B*.

13. Two identical rectangular blocks of mass 90 kg stand side by side on rough ground. A smooth wedge of angle 20° is forced down between the two blocks with a force of 200 N. How large must the coefficient of friction be if the blocks are not to move?

14. The figure illustrates a trestle supporting a table-top. The trestle is rigidly jointed at B, $AB = DB = 0.5$ m, $BC = FB = 1$ m, and the angle $ABD = 60°$. The table-top has a mass of 2 kg and is placed symmetrically

on the trestle. How far from the centre of the table may a piece of cheese of mass 5 kg safely be placed?

If the table-top is attached to the trestle at A and D, and if the mass of the trestle is 3 kg, where may the cheese be placed? Draw a diagram showing the forces acting on the table-top in this case.

†**15.** A pair of steps consists of two uniform ladders, each of length $2l$ and weight W, smoothly hinged at their upper ends. They are joined by a rope tied to each at a distance of $\frac{1}{2}l$ from the lower end and of such a length that the angle between the ladders is 60°. The steps stand on a smooth floor and a man of weight $2W$ climbs up one side. If the tension in the rope is $\frac{1}{2}W\sqrt{3}$, how far up the ladder is the man standing?

†**16.** AB, BC, CA are uniform rods whose lengths and weights are in the ratio $5 : 4 : 3$. They are freely jointed at A, B, C; AB is horizontal, with C below it. The system is suspended in equilibrium by a vertical string of tension $12W$ fastened to AB at a point D. Find (i) the position of D, (ii) the forces on BC in terms of W.

†**Light frameworks**

12.6 An important type of statical problem is that of finding forces in frameworks consisting of several spars, hinged (or 'pin-jointed') to one another at their ends. Three or more spars may be attached to each pin of the framework.

We make two assumptions about such frameworks:

> (i) that the spars (cables, girders, rods, etc.) which compose them are 'light,' i.e. their weights are negligible in comparison with the other forces involved;
>
> (ii) that the spars are smoothly jointed together at their ends, so that there is no friction at the joints.

Each spar making up the framework is then under the action solely of forces from the pins at its two ends. From this it follows that these forces must be equal in magnitude, and that they must act in opposite directions along the length of the spar. If these forces act inwards on the spar, as shown in Fig. 18, the spar is in thrust; if outwards, it is in tension.

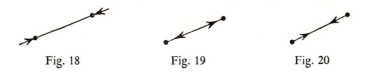

Fig. 18   Fig. 19   Fig. 20

By the principle of interaction, each spar exerts on the pins at its ends forces equal and opposite to those exerted by the pins on the spar. For a spar in thrust, these forces are represented by arrows pointing outward towards the end of the spar (Fig. 19). For a spar in tension, the forces on the pins are as shown in Fig. 20.

These forces do not, of course, cancel each other out. They are forces acting on two different bodies, namely the pins at the two ends. The solution of problems is effected by considering the equilibrium of the forces on the different pins in turn.

It is important to remember that these principles apply only when the spars are light. They could not be applied, for instance, in Example 4, because the weight of each rod is significant in comparison with the forces acting on it. The tension or thrust in a heavy rod in general varies along its length.

EXAMPLE 6. In Fig. 21, AC and BC are two light spars hinged to fixed points on the ground at A and B, pin-jointed at C, and they carry a load of 20 kN at C. Find the forces in AC and BC.

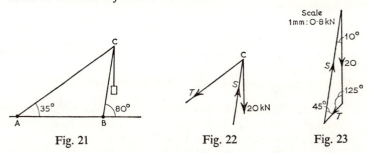

Fig. 21   Fig. 22   Fig. 23

The forces on the pin at *C* are a tension *T* in *AC*, a thrust *S* in *BC* and the load of 2 kN (Fig. 22). Fig. 23 shows a triangle of forces, from which we calculate

$$S = 20 \sin 125°/\sin 45° = 20 \sin 55°/\sin 45° = 23 \text{ kN},$$
$$T = 20 \sin 10°/\sin 45° = 5 \text{ kN}.$$

EXAMPLE 7. Find the stresses in the framework shown in Fig. 24, in which A and B are smoothly jointed to fixed points.

Fig. 25 shows the triangle of forces for the pin *C*, and Fig. 26 that for the pin *D*. From these we calculate

$T = 20$ kN,
$S = 2 \times 20 \cos 30° = 35$ kN,
$P = T \sec 30° = 23$ kN,
$R = T \tan 30° = 12$ kN.

There are tensions of 20 kN and 23 kN in *DC* and *AD*, and thrusts of 35 kN and 12 kN in *BC* and *BD*.

The two triangles of forces have a common side representing the tension *T*. Were the solution being completed by accurate drawing and measurement it would be convenient to superimpose these two triangles on one diagram.

The values of the stresses could also be calculated by resolving in two directions for the forces at *C* and at *D*.

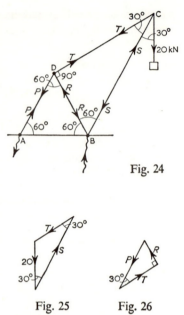

Fig. 24

Fig. 25   Fig. 26

†EXERCISE 12(c)

Find the stresses in the members of the light frameworks illustrated in the diagrams. The rods concurring at each vertex must be supposed smoothly pin-jointed together; large dots indicate points at which the framework is smoothly hinged to a fixed point. Labelled arrows indicate loads applied to the system; other arrows indicate external forces from supports, cables, etc. Forces given are in kN.

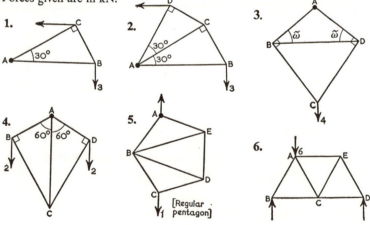

CHAPTER 13

MOMENTUM

Impulse

13.1 *EXAMPLE 1. A motor cycle with rider has a mass of* 200 *kg. If it accelerates from* 10 *m s^{-1} to* 14 *m s^{-1} in* 5 *s, find the driving force (supposed constant).*

We first find the acceleration from the formula

$$v = u + at,$$

which gives

$$14 = 10 + 5a,$$

$$a = 0.8.$$

The constant driving force is then found from the equation of motion

$$F = ma.$$

Therefore

$$F = 200 \times 0.8 = 160.$$

The driving force is 160 N.

13.2 The type of problem illustrated by Example 1 is an important one, and we shall now solve it more generally. If a body of mass m increases its velocity along a straight line from u to v in time t, its acceleration is given by

$$v = u + at$$

$$a = \frac{v - u}{t}.$$

The constant force needed to produce this acceleration is

$$F = m \times \frac{v - u}{t} = \frac{mv - mu}{t}.$$

It is convenient to multiply both sides of this equation by t, obtaining

$$Ft = mv - mu, \tag{1}$$

and to give names to the quantities occurring in this equation.

DEFINITION.   *For any moving body, the quantity*

$$mass \times velocity$$

is called the MOMENTUM *of the body.*

167

DEFINITION. *If a constant force acts on a body over a period of time, the quantity*

$$force \times time$$

is called the IMPULSE *of the force.*

With these definitions equation (1) can be written in the form:

impulse of force = momentum at end − momentum at start,

or   *impulse = increase of momentum.*

*If the force is not constant, this result is still true, provided that the impulse of a variable force is defined as $\int P dt$ instead of Pt. This will be proved in Volume 2.

13.3 The reader will remember that when using the formulae for motion with constant acceleration in Chapter 1 it was necessary to assign positive or negative values to the quantities u, v, a and s according to the direction in which they were measured along the line of motion. The same is true when equation (1) of § 13.2 is used. One sense of motion along the line must be chosen, and momentum and impulse must be taken as positive when they are in that direction and negative when they are in the opposite direction.

When force is measured in newtons and time in seconds, the impulse of a force is measured in newton seconds (N s). Since it is convenient to consider all quantities appearing as terms in an equation to be measured in the same unit, momentum is also measured in N s (rather than in kg m s^{-1}, as is suggested more obviously by the formula mv).

EXAMPLE 2. A truck of mass 200 kg starts from rest on horizontal rails. Find the speed 3 seconds after starting, given that the tractive force exerted by the engine is 100 N.
The impulse of the force is $100 \times 3 = 300$ N s. If the speed in m s^{-1} after 3 s is v, the momentum in N s increases from zero at the start to $200v$. Since the impulse is equal to the increase in momentum,

$$300 = 200v - 0,$$
$$v = 1\tfrac{1}{2}.$$

13.4 It should not be supposed from the use of the word 'impulse' that the force acts only for a very short time. It is quite reasonable to speak of the impulse of a force of 10 N acting for 2 h. Nevertheless, the theory which we are about to develop is often concerned with large forces acting over short periods of time, which we sometimes describe as 'blows' or 'jerks'. For example, when a club strikes a golf ball it may exert on it a force of 5000 N for $\frac{1}{2000}$ s. The impulse given to the ball is then 2·5 N s.

EXAMPLE 3. A rackets ball of mass 35 *gm, travelling horizontally at* 20 *m s⁻¹, strikes the front of the court at right angles and rebounds with a speed of* 16 *m s⁻¹. Find the impulse that has been exerted on the ball.* (Fig. 1).

Take the direction away from the wall as positive. The momentum at the start (i.e. before the impact) is

$$-0{\cdot}035 \times 20 \text{ N s.}$$

The momentum at the end is

$$+0{\cdot}035 \times 16 \text{ N s.}$$

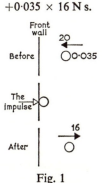

Fig. 1

The impulse, also measured positive in the direction away from the wall, is equal to

momentum at end − momentum at start

$$= 0{\cdot}035 \times 16 + 0{\cdot}035 \times 20$$
$$= 1{\cdot}26 \text{ N s.}$$

We may remark that, by the interaction principle, since the wall exerts on the ball an impulse of 1·26 N s, the ball exerts on the wall an impulse of the same magnitude in the opposite direction.

EXERCISE 13(a)

1. Compare the momentum of the following: a sprinter of mass 70 kg running at 10 m s⁻¹, a bullet of mass 30 gm moving at 550 m s⁻¹, a truck of mass 2000 kg moving at 20 m s⁻¹ and a ship of mass 1000 tonnes moving at 0·3 m s⁻¹.

2. What is the momentum of a 20 gm mass, originally at rest, after a force of 0·012 N has acted on it for 3 s? What speed does it acquire?

3. A car of mass 1000 kg is pushed along a level road, and acquires a speed of 2 m s⁻¹ from rest in 10 s. What is the force pushing it?

4. A stone of mass 20 gm is dropped from the top of a cliff. Find its momentum 4 s later.

5. What force acting for 0·05 s is needed to give a 160 gm cricket ball a speed of 10 m s^{-1}?

6. A 750 kg car is brought to rest in 3 s from a speed of 54 km h^{-1}. Find the impulse and the force produced by the brakes.

7. A hockey ball of mass 0·2 kg receives an impulse of 1·2 N s at a free hit. With what speed does it begin to travel?

8. Six people push a 2000 kg truck, each with a force of 200 N. How long will it be before the truck acquires a speed of 1·5 m s^{-1}?

9. A cup of 90 gm is dropped from a height of 1·25 m. What impulse does it receive on striking the floor if it does not rebound? (Take $g = 10$ m s^{-2}.)

10. A batsman receives a cricket ball of mass 160 gm at a speed of 6 m s^{-1} and returns it straight back to the bowler at 12 m s^{-1}. What impulse does the bat give to the ball?

11. A car of mass 1000 kg has its speed reduced from 81 km h^{-1} to 54 km h^{-1} by brakes producing a force of 1250 N. How long does this take?

12. A brick of mass 3 kg falls into a pond with a speed of 6 m s^{-1}. If its velocity on striking the water is diminished by 60%, find the impulse at the water surface.

13. A destroyer of displacement 1600 tonnes increases its speed from 6 to 8 m s^{-1} in 25 s. If the engines produce a thrust of 300 kN, find the resistance of the water.

14. A toboggan and rider of mass 100 kg runs down a slope of 1 in 5. If the frictional resistance is 75 N, how long does it take to reach a speed of 5 m s^{-1}? (Take $g = 10$ m s^{-2}.)

15. A truck originally at rest is pushed by an engine with a force of 1500 N for 20 s. After this time the engine breaks away and the truck comes to rest 80 s later. If the resistance remains constant throughout the motion, find how large it is.

16. A car of mass 1000 kg is travelling at 20 m s^{-1}. The driver applies the brakes, and 2 s later disengages the clutch. It takes a further 3 s for the car to stop. If the engine provides a force of 2000 N, find the braking force.

17. A coin of mass 5 gm is shoved across a board. It receives an initial impulse of 0·01 N s and stops after sliding 0·5 m. Find the coefficient of friction.

Conservation of momentum

13.5 *EXAMPLE 4. Two trucks of masses 500 kg and 300 kg are connected by a chain which is originally slack. The 500 kg truck moves away from the other with a speed of 4 m s^{-1}, until the chain tightens, after which they go on together at the same speed. What is this speed?*

The 300 kg truck is jerked into motion by the chain, which has a large tension for a short time. This jerk also slows down the 500 kg truck. Since the tension in the chain is the same at either end, and it acts on each truck for the same time, the impulse of the jerk forwards on the 300 kg truck is equal numerically to the impulse of the jerk backwards on the 500 kg truck (see Fig. 2b). It follows that the gain in momentum of the 300 kg truck is equal to the loss in momentum of the 500 kg truck.

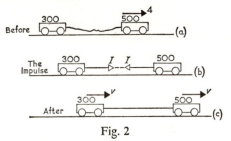

Fig. 2

Thus, if the final common velocity of the trucks in m s^{-1} is v, the gain in momentum of the 300 kg truck is

$$300v - 300 \times 0 = 300v,$$

and the loss in momentum of the 500 kg truck is

$$500 \times 4 - 500 \times v = 2000 - 500v.$$

Therefore
$$300v = 2000 - 500v,$$
$$v = 2.5.$$

13.6 In the solution of Example 4 we used the fact that the gain of momentum of one truck is equal to the loss in momentum of the other. This can be expressed in another way, that the total momentum of the two trucks before the chain became taut is equal to the total momentum of the two trucks afterwards. Initially the total momentum is $300 \times 0 + 500 \times 4 = 2000$, and afterwards it is $300 \times 2.5 + 500 \times 2.5 = 2000$, measured in N s.

A similar situation arises when two bodies collide. Consider two smooth blocks of masses m_1 and m_2 sliding in the same straight line on a smooth horizontal table with speeds u_1 and u_2 (Fig. 3a). Suppose that these collide, and that after the impact the blocks have speeds v_1

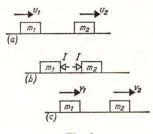

Fig. 3

and v_2 (Fig. 3c). In the short time during which the impact takes place there is a contact force acting towards the left on the left-hand mass, and an equal contact force acting to the right on the right-hand mass (Fig. 3b).

If these forces have an impulse of magnitude I, we have, using equation (1) of § 13.2 for each mass in turn,

$$-I = m_1v_1 - m_1u_1,$$

and

$$I = m_2v_2 - m_2u_2.$$

Adding,

$$0 = m_1v_1 + m_2v_2 - m_1u_1 - m_2u_2,$$

so that

$$m_1u_1 + m_2u_2 = m_1v_1 + m_2v_2.$$

This equation states that

total momentum before impact = total momentum after impact.

It should be noticed that the only force acting on each block in the line of motion is the contact force from the other block. If we consider the two blocks as forming a single system of bodies, these forces become internal forces, so that there is no external force on the system in the line of motion. The same was true for the motion of the two trucks in Example 4. This illustrates:

The Conservation of Momentum Principle. *If there are no external forces acting on a system of bodies in a certain direction, the total momentum of the system in that direction remains unchanged.*

13.7 *EXAMPLE 5. A toboggan of mass (with rider) 80 kg travelling at 8 m s⁻¹ runs into the back of another toboggan of mass 60 kg travelling at 1 m s⁻¹. If they go on together after colliding, find their common speed (Fig. 4).*

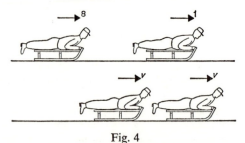

Fig. 4

The total momentum of the two toboggans before impact is

$$80 \times 8 + 60 \times 1 = 700 \text{ N s.}$$

If the speed after the collision is v m/sec, the total momentum afterwards is

$$80v + 60v = 140v \text{ N s.}$$

Therefore, by the conservation of momentum principle,

$$140v = 700$$
$$v = 5.$$

EXAMPLE 6. An anti-tank gun, whose recoiling parts have a mass of 400 kg, fires a shot of 8 kg horizontally with a muzzle velocity of 1000 m s⁻¹. Find the initial speed of recoil, neglecting any initial forces on the recoil system. (Fig. 5).

Since there are no external forces acting horizontally, the total momentum of the barrel and the shot must be the same after the shot is fired as it was before. Initially, however, there was no momentum. Therefore the total momentum after firing must also be zero.

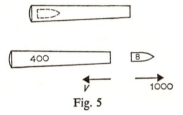

Fig. 5

If the initial speed of recoil in m s⁻¹ is v, the total momentum in N s after firing is

$$8 \times 1000 - 400v,$$

taking the direction of firing as positive. Therefore

$$8000 - 400v = 0,$$
$$v = 20.$$

EXERCISE 13(*b*)

1. A railway truck of mass 1500 kg travelling at 5 m s⁻¹ hits another truck of mass 1000 kg which is stationary. The two trucks couple automatically and go on together. With what speed do they move?

2. A flat truck of mass 225 kg is moving at 4 m s⁻¹. A man of mass 75 kg swings himself onto the truck; with what speed does it continue?

3. A globule of mercury of mass 0·4 gm moving at 8 cm s⁻¹ overtakes another of mass 0·3 gm moving at 1 cm s⁻¹. They join together to form a single globule; with what speed does it move?

4. A bullet is fired with a speed of 550 m s⁻¹ into a block of wood of mass 0·49 kg, and becomes embedded in it. If it gives the block a speed of 11 m s⁻¹, find the mass of the bullet.

5. A stone of mass 90 gm is skidding across the ice with a speed of 4 m s^{-1}. It hits a stationary stone of mass 120 gm and stops dead after the impact. With what speed does the other stone start to move?

6. When a toy truck of mass 240 gm hits another stationary truck of mass 360 gm its speed is reduced from 4 to 1 m s^{-1}. What speed is given to the second truck?

7. In a game of bowls one wood of mass 1 kg hits another stationary wood. Its speed along the line is thus reduced from 2 to 0·5 m s^{-1}, and the other starts to move with a speed of 1·2 m s^{-1}. Find the mass of the second wood.

8. Two spheres of masses 300 gm and 500 gm rest on a smooth table. They are connected by an inextensible string which is initially slack. An impulse of 0·12 N s is applied to the lighter sphere in a direction away from the other one. Find the speed with which this sphere begins to move, and the speed with which the heavy one moves after the string tightens.

9. If in Question 8 the impulse of 0·12 N s were applied in the opposite direction (i.e. towards the other sphere), and if when the spheres collide the lighter sphere is brought to rest, describe the motion, and find the speed with which the two spheres are finally moving.

10. If in Question 8 the impulse were applied to the heavy sphere in the direction away from the light one, find the final speed of the two spheres.

11. The recoiling parts of a gun have a mass of 150 kg. A shot of mass 2 kg is fired horizontally with a speed of 750 m s^{-1}. Find the speed of the recoil.

12. Three men in a boat each fire five 20 gm rounds astern in rapid succession with a speed of 500 m s^{-1}. If the men and the boat together have a mass of 500 kg and the boat was originally stationary, find the speed with which the boat moves forward after the shots have been fired.

13. A gun of mass 4000 kg discharges a shot of mass 30 kg horizontally. The recoil of this gun is opposed by a constant force of 15 kN which brings it to rest in 1·2 s. Find the velocity of the shot.

14. A 20 kg shell is travelling horizontally at 400 m s^{-1} when it explodes into two fragments of masses 8 kg and 12 kg. If the 12 kg fragment has a velocity of 700 m s^{-1} in the original direction of motion, find the velocity of the lighter fragment.

15. A truck of mass 225 kg is moving at 3 m s^{-1}. A man of mass 75 kg runs straight towards it and meets it head-on at a speed of 6 m s^{-1}. If the man jumps onto the truck when he meets it, how fast and in which direction will the truck be moving afterwards?

16. Two punts are connected by a long rope. The first has a total mass (with passenger) of 300 kg and the second a mass of 200 kg. They are punted in opposite directions, and just before the rope tightens the heavier punt has a speed of 3 m s^{-1} and the lighter punt a speed of 2 m s^{-1}. Find the speed of the punts after the rope has tightened, and the impulse transmitted by the rope.

17. Two ball-bearings of masses 20 gm and 30 gm are approaching each other with speeds of 2 cm s⁻¹ and 12 cm s⁻¹. After the collision the 20 gm mass rebounds and moves in the opposite direction with a speed of 13 cm s⁻¹. In which direction does the heavy mass move after the collision, and with what speed?

†**18.** William (39 kg) and Robert (50 kg) stand facing each other on roller skates. William holds a 1 kg parcel, which he throws to Robert. Robert catches it and throws it back to William. If the parcel travels horizontally at 10 m s⁻¹ in each direction, find the speeds with which the boys are moving finally.

†**19.** Two like toy trucks are placed end to end and connected by a string which is initially slack. A small pistol is fixed to one and fired; the bullet lodges in a target fixed to the other. Describe what happens. What is the final result?

†**20.** Two pails each of mass 3 kg are suspended at rest by a string passing over a smooth fixed horizontal bar. A brick of mass 1 kg is dropped into one of them from a height of 2·5 m. Find the initial velocity of the pails. (Take $g = 9·8$ m s⁻².)

†**21.** Masses of 3 gm and 4 gm hang vertically, connected by a thread passing over a smooth peg. The smaller mass rests on the ground, and the larger is supported 70 cm above the ground, the thread being taut. The support is suddenly removed; find the time until the 4 gm mass is first jerked off the ground, and find the impulse in the string and the new velocity just after the jerk. (Assume that the 4 gm mass does not bounce when it hits the ground and take $g = 9·8$ m s⁻².)

†**22.** A train consists of two wagons of m kg each and an engine of mass M kg. The two couplings are light, inelastic chains of length l metres each, and the train is initially at rest on a straight level track with the three vehicles in contact so that the couplings are slack. The engine begins to move, the constant tractive force being F newtons. Find the speed of the train in m s⁻¹ just after the second wagon has started.

†**23.** A string of length l connects two particles of masses m and $7m$. These rest on a smooth, horizontal table with the mass m at the edge, and the mass $7m$ at a distance $\frac{1}{2}l$ from it in a direction at right angles to the edge. Show that when the mass $7m$ is jerked into motion the masses have a common speed $\frac{1}{8}\sqrt{gl}$ and find the total time before the heavy mass reaches the edge.

Continuous change of momentum

†**13.8** So far the impulse–momentum equation has been used to discuss the motion of individual bodies which change their velocities from one value to another. We now show how it can be used when a continuous stream of matter changes its velocity.

EXAMPLE 7. A high-pressure hose delivers water horizontally at a rate of 450 kg per minute with a speed of 20 m s⁻¹ The water strikes a vertical plate and loses all its speed. Find the force on the plate.

If the force on the plate is F newtons, the plate exerts a force of F newtons on the water. Over a period of one minute the impulse of this force is

$$F \times 60 \quad \text{N s.}$$

In this minute 450 kg of water loses its velocity of 20 m s⁻¹. Hence there is a change in the momentum of the water of amount

$$450 \times 20 \quad \text{N s.}$$

Therefore
$$F \times 60 = 450 \times 20,$$
$$F = 150.$$

EXAMPLE 8. A conveyor belt, moving horizontally at 0·9 m s⁻¹, delivers gravel at a rate of 48 tonnes per hour. Find the horizontal force needed to keep the belt moving.

In 1 hour, 48 000 kg of gravel increases speed by 0·9 m s⁻¹, gaining momentum

$$48\,000 \times 0·9 \quad \text{N s.}$$

If the force on the belt (and therefore of the belt on the gravel) is F newtons, the impulse in 1 hour is

$$F \times 60 \times 60 \quad \text{N s.}$$

Therefore
$$3600\,F = 48\,000 \times 0·9,$$
$$F = 12.$$

Momentum as a vector

†**13.9** It was stated in §§ 8.1. and 7.12 that the equations

$$\mathbf{F} = m\mathbf{a}$$

and
$$\mathbf{v} = \mathbf{u} + \mathbf{a}t$$

are in reality vector equations. From these we can deduce, precisely as in § 13.2, that

$$\mathbf{F}t = m\mathbf{v} - m\mathbf{u}.$$

Since force and velocity are vector quantities, the quantities

$$\text{impulse} = \text{force} \times \text{time}$$

and
$$\text{momentum} = \text{mass} \times \text{velocity}$$

are also properly defined as vector quantities. We see from the equation above that if an applied impulse causes a body to change its direction of motion the impulse vector appears as the difference between two momentum vectors in a vector triangle.

EXAMPLE 9. A tennis ball of mass 50 gm moving horizontally with a velocity of 9 m s⁻¹ is returned by a player with a velocity of 12 m s⁻¹ in a direction making 20° with the original direction of flight. Find the impulse exerted by the racquet on the ball. (Fig. 6).

The mass of the ball is 0·05 kg, so the momentum before the ball is hit is $0.05 \times 9 = 0.45$ N s horizontally, and afterwards it is $0.05 \times 12 = 0.6$ N s at 20° to this. The vector triangle is shown in Fig. 7, and the difference of the two momentum vectors gives the impulse vector **I**. This is found by drawing or calculation to be 1·03 N s at 11° to the original direction of flight.

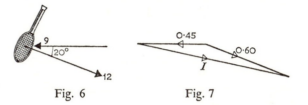

Fig. 6   Fig. 7

†EXERCISE 13(*c*)

1. A machine-gun fires 300 bullets per minute of mass 25 gm with a speed of 600 m s⁻¹. What average force is needed to hold the gun still?

2. A water-pistol discharges 0·05 l horizontally in 5 s with a speed of 6 m s⁻¹. What horizontal force is needed to hold it still?

3. A snow-plough travelling at 9 km h⁻¹ picks up 60 kg of snow every second. Find the force needed to do this.

4. A railway engine travelling at 20 m s⁻¹ picks up 5000 l of water from a trough over a distance of 500 m without reducing speed. What additional force of resistance does the train experience during this time?

5. Water is flowing down a model canal, of cross-section 0·2 m², at 0·3 m s⁻¹. At a certain point its velocity is increased to 1·2 m s⁻¹ by means of a small paddle-wheel, the centre of whose blades is 0·5 m from the axis of rotation of the wheel. Find the couple needed to turn the wheel.

6. Water emanates horizontally from a hose-pipe of çross-sectional area 750 mm² at a speed of 10 m s⁻¹, and strikes a wall a short distance in front of the nozzle without rebounding. Find the force on the wall.

7. What would have been the force on the wall in Question 6 if the water had rebounded at 2 m s⁻¹?

8. In a cloudburst 75 mm of rain falls vertically in an hour at 8 m s⁻¹. An umbrella protects an area of 1·2 m², and the rain does not rebound from the umbrella. What is the average force of the rain on the umbrella?

9. Water falls through a hole in the gutter 11¼ m above the ground at a rate of 40 l per minute. Find the force on the ground. (Take $g = 10$ m s⁻².)

†10. A jet of water issues vertically from a nozzle of cross-sectional area 5 mm² at 2·8 m s⁻¹. A table-tennis ball of mass 2 gm is supported in equilibrium in a smooth vertical tube above the jet by the impact of the water on its under side. Assuming that the water does not rebound, find the height of the ball above the nozzle. (Take $g = 9·8$ m s⁻².)

†11. A vertical sight-screen of mass 300 kg is 3 m high and 4 m long. It is mounted on a horizontal frame. How far in front of and behind the screen must this extend if the screen is not to fall over in a wind of 10 m s⁻¹? (Assume that the mass of 1 m³ of air is 1 kg.)

12. A batsman receives a ball of mass 0·2 kg moving at 15 m s⁻¹, and hits it towards square leg, at 90° to the line of the wickets, at 20 m s⁻¹. Find the magnitude and direction of the impulse given to the ball. (Assume the ball travels horizontally before and after being hit.)

13. Repeat Question 12 if the ball is hit towards extra cover, at $\tan^{-1} (\frac{12}{5})$ to the line of the wickets, at 26 m s⁻¹.

14. Repeat Question 12 if the ball is hit towards third man, at 120° to the line of the wickets, at 15 m s⁻¹.

15. A three-quarter of mass 80 kg is running at 5 m s⁻¹. An opponent pushes him with a constant force so that $1\frac{1}{2}$ s later he is moving at the same speed in a direction making 26° with his original direction of motion. How large is this force?

16. A boat of mass 300 kg moving at a constant velocity of 3 m s⁻¹ NE enters a current which exerts a force on it of 90 newtons SE. Find its velocity 10 s later.

17. An electron of mass 9×10^{-31} kg is moving at 8×10^{6} m s⁻¹ when it enters an electric field which produces a force of $1·8 \times 10^{-15}$ N at right angles to its initial direction of motion for a period of 3×10^{-9} s. Find its final velocity. (Neglect the small variation in mass of the electron with its speed.)

MISCELLANEOUS EXERCISE C

In purely statical questions use the approximation $g = 10$ m s^{-2}. In dynamical questions indication is given where necessary if one particular value is preferred.

1. A light inextensible string of length 0·5 m is fastened at its ends A and B to two pegs 0·42 m apart in the same horizontal line. A mass of 4 kg is attached to the string at C, 0·1 m along the string from A and an equal mass is attached at D, 0·1 m along the string from B. Find (i) the vertical depth of C below AB, and (ii) the tensions in each of the three parts of the string.

2. A block of mass 40 kg is pulled very slowly along a horizontal plane, the coefficient of friction being 0·2. Find the magnitude of the pull if its line of action is (i) horizontal; (ii) at 45°; (iii) such that the pull is a minimum.

3. Find the initial recoil velocity of a gun of mass 1000 kg when a 10 kg shell is fired horizontally with a velocity of 500 m s^{-1} relative to the ground.

If the gun recoils 0·5 m before coming to rest, find the average force exerted by the recoil mechanism.

4. Two forces, 9 N and 10 N, act at a point and are inclined to each other at an angle whose tangent is $\frac{4}{3}$. Find the magnitude of their resultant.

Two new forces P and Q are introduced at the point so that the four forces are in equilibrium; Q acts in a direction opposite to that of the force of 9 N, and P is perpendicular to Q. Find their magnitudes.

5. A body is projected vertically upwards with an initial velocity of 25 m s^{-1}. Find the height to which the body rises.

Another body is projected vertically upwards 2 seconds after the first with an initial velocity of 20 m s^{-1}; find when the two bodies are at the same height, and find also the velocity of each body at this instant. (Take $g = 10$ m s^{-2}.)

6. A uniform plank AB, of mass 28 kg and length 9 m, lies on a horizontal roof in a direction at right angles to the edge of the roof. The end B projects 2 m over the edge. A man of mass 70 kg walks out along the plank. Find how far along the plank he can walk without causing the plank to tip up.

Find also the mass which must be placed on the end A so that the man can reach B without upsetting the plank.

7. A uniform rod BC, of length 60 mm and of mass 2 kg, can turn freely about B. It is supported in equilibrium by a string AC, 80 mm long, attached to a point A in a vertical line through B, the distance AB being 100 mm. Calculate the tension in the string.

Verify your answer by measurement from an accurate force triangle.

8. (i) Find, by drawing or otherwise, the resultant of two forces of 15 N and 17 N inclined at an angle of 50°. State the magnitude of the resultant correct to the nearest integer and state the angle between the resultant and the force of 15 N.

(ii) Calculate the angle between two forces of magnitudes 5 N and 8 N if the resultant of the two forces has a magnitude of 7 N.

9. A cricket ball, mass 160 gm, reaches a batsman with velocity 7 m s^{-1} and is driven straight back with velocity 18 m s^{-1}. Find the impulse of the blow of the bat on the ball.

Find also the average force between the bat and ball if they are in contact for $\frac{1}{10}$ s.

10. A uniform ladder is leaning against a vertical wall on horizontal ground. The coefficients of friction at the wall and at the ground are equal, and the ladder is on the point of slipping. Show that the total reaction at the wall must be at right angles to the total reaction at the ground.

Draw a figure with the ladder inclined at 60° to the ground; by means of a circle with the ladder as diameter, mark on the figure the point where the two reactions intersect.

11. Two masses of 40 gm and 60 gm respectively are connected by a string which passes over two smooth pulleys so that the masses hang vertically. At a point on the string between the pulleys, a second string is attached, and from it hangs a mass of 70 gm. The original string is now depressed. Find the angle between the parts of the first string.

12. A pole whose centre of gravity is 1 m from one end rests with that end on a rough horizontal ground. It is kept at an angle of 45° with the ground by means of a rope fastened 1·5 m from this end and passing over a pulley so that the rope is perpendicular to the pole. The mass of the pole is 12 kg. Find the total reaction of the ground.

If the pole is on the point of slipping, find the value of the coefficient of friction between the pole and the ground.

13. Forces of magnitude 1, 2, 3 and 4 N act at a point in the directions N, W, SW and SE respectively. Find graphically the magnitude and direction of their resultant.

14. A uniform trap-door, hinged about one edge and of mass 15 kg, is held at an angle of 25° with the horizontal by a rope fastened to the mid-point of the edge opposite to the hinge, the rope being also inclined at 25° to the horizontal.

Find the tension of the rope and the angle which the reaction at the hinge makes with the vertical.

15. An aircraft sets out to fly from one point to a second point 200 km due North. In what direction should the pilot set his course if he intends to fly at an air speed of 400 km h^{-1} and there is a wind of 100 km h^{-1} blowing from the NE? If, when he has flown for 20 min on this course, the wind dies down to 60 km h^{-1} and he does not change course, how far from his calculated position will he be at the time when he expects to arrive over his destination?

16. Two strings, 0·4 m and 0·3 m long, are tied to a mass of 12 kg and have their other ends fastened to two nails, 0·5 m apart in a horizontal line. Find the tension in the longer string.

The nails are now replaced by smooth pulleys, over which the strings are passed with masses of 9 kg and 12 kg tied respectively to their free ends and hanging freely. In the new position of equilibrium find the angles which the sloping portions of the strings make with the vertical.

17. Five light bars are smoothly jointed together to form a parallelogram *ABCD* and the diagonal *AC*. *AD* and *BC* are horizontal, with *BC* below *AD*. The angle *ABC* = 45°, and the angle *BAC* = 90°. The system rests on supports at *B* and *C* and takes loads of 150 N at *A* and 50 N at *D*. Find the stresses in the bars, stating which are in compression and which in tension.

18. From a distance of 40 m on level ground from the bottom of a vertical pole 10 m in height, a particle is projected towards the pole, and strikes the top of it after 2 s. Find its speed of projection.

If the particle just skims the top of the pole, find how far from the bottom of the pole it will hit the ground on the other side. (Take $g = 10$ m s^{-2}.)

19. A smooth uniform sphere of radius 90 mm and mass 4 kg rests against a smooth vertical wall. The sphere is supported by a string of length 60 mm. One end of the string is attached to a point on the surface of the sphere; the other end of the string is attached to a point of the wall. Find the tension in the string and show that the thrust exerted by the sphere on the wall is about 30 N.

If the string is doubled in length and the sphere is suspended as before, show that the reaction at the wall is now very nearly $\frac{12}{19}$ of its previous value.

20. Two smooth spheres, each of radius 50 mm and weight *W*, rest one on the other inside a smooth cylindrical tin of internal radius 80 mm. Find the reactions between the spheres and between the spheres and the vertical wall of the tin. (See figure.)

21. A uniform rod *AB* is held up by two strings *AC* and *BC* fastened to a peg at *C*. *AC* makes an angle 65° and *BC* makes an angle 25° with the horizontal. Find the ratio of the tensions in the strings.

If these are *P* and *Q*, show that the weight of the rod is $\sqrt{(P^2 + Q^2)}$.

22. A man is standing three-quarters the way up a ladder of negligible weight which is resting in limiting equilibrium at an angle of 30° with the vertical against a smooth vertical wall. The lower end rests on a rough, horizontal pavement. Find the angle of friction for the ladder and the pavement.

23. The blow of a cricket bat on a ball is equivalent to a force of 320 N lasting for 0·02 s. Find with what velocity a ball of mass 160 gm will be propelled by the bat if the velocity of the ball just before hitting the bat is 15 m s^{-1}. (It may be assumed that the velocities of the ball both before and after impact are in a direction perpendicular to the face of the bat.)

24. A particle moves in a straight line, with an initial velocity and a uniform acceleration. Find how far it travels in 12 seconds, given that it travels 48 m in the first 6 seconds and 32 m in the last 2 seconds. Find also the final velocity.

25. A toy clockwork motor car, of mass $\frac{1}{2}$ kg is placed on a trolley of mass 5 kg. The trolley can run on wheels over a horizontal surface, and the axles of the trolley's wheels and of the car's wheels are parallel. With the car at rest relative to the trolley, both are given a velocity of 1 m s^{-1}. A brake of the clockwork is then released and the car moves relative to the trolley in the same direction as the trolley's motion. If the clockwork produces a thrust of 1 N at the tread of the car's wheels, and if friction in the car and in the trolley can be neglected, how fast will the car and the trolley be moving when the car has travelled $\frac{1}{2}$ m relative to the trolley?

26. A mass of 12 kg is tied at C to a string ABC and hangs by the string from a nail at A. A horizontal force of 140 N acts at the point B of the string, and a horizontal force of 50 N in the opposite direction acts on the weight at C. The system is in equilibrium. Find (i) the tension in the lower part of the string, (ii) the inclination of the upper part to the horizontal.

27. A uniform rod AB of mass 10 kg rests in a vertical plane with the end A in contact with a smooth vertical wall. The end B is below A and AB is inclined at 60° to the vertical. The rod is held in equilibrium by a light string attached to B and to a point C in the wall vertically above A. Show in a diagram the forces acting on the rod and calculate (i) the inclination of the string to the vertical, and (ii) the tension in the string. Prove also that the distance CA is half the length of the rod.

28. A smooth wedge of angle 60° rests on a horizontal plane. A body of mass 4 kg slides down the inclined face of the wedge. Find the horizontal force needed to prevent the wedge moving.

29. Two blocks rest on the line of greatest slope of a rough plane inclined 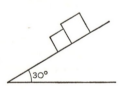 at 30° to the horizontal. The upper block has mass 20 kg and the lower one 10 kg. The coefficient of friction between the upper block and the plane is 0·15 and between the lower block and the plane is 0·30.

Calculate the force between the blocks when they slide down the plane and find the time taken to travel 2 m from rest. (See figure.)

30. The framework ABC consists of three uniform rods, each of mass 3 kg and of the same length. The framework is free to turn about A in a vertical plane, and is supported in equilibrium with AB vertical by a string CD with the angle ACD equal to 45°. Find the tension in the string.

31. A uniform bar *AB* is of mass 4 kg and is 1 m long. It is supported in a horizontal position by a string which is attached to the bar at points 0·25 m from the ends and passes over a pulley; the 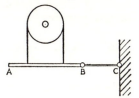 pulley is supported with its axis horizontal. The end *B* of the bar is pivoted to a light rod *BC*, which is 0·5 m long. The end *C* is pivoted to a rigid support. The pivot at *C* is frictionless, but that at *B* requires a torque of 3 N m to allow *AB* to turn relative to *BC*.

A clockwise torque is applied to the axle of the pulley which is just sufficient to produce turning of *BC*. What will be the tensions in the two vertical parts of the string? (See figure. It may be assumed that the string does not slip over the pulley.)

32. A pair of wheels of radius 0·4 m are mounted on an axle of radius 0·2 m. A thin rope is attached to the axle and wound round it, and the free end of the rope leaves the axle tangentially midway between the wheels. The rope is used to draw the wheels and axle slowly up a plane inclined at 30°.

Find the least angle of friction between the wheels and the plane that will make this possible, and the direction in which the rope should be pulled when the angle of friction has this least value.

33. A particle of mass 5 kg is connected to a particle of mass 3 kg by a light string passing over a smooth pulley. The system is released from rest with the string taut. Find the acceleration of either particle and the tension in the string.

After 2 s the ascending particle picks up a stationary particle of mass 4 kg. Find the velocities of the particles immediately afterwards and show that they come to instantaneous rest 4 s after the start of the motion.

34. A uniform 30 kg ladder has its top against a wall *a* metres above the ground, and its foot *b* metres out from the wall. At both ends of the ladder $\mu = \frac{1}{2}$. Find all you can about the friction and normal forces exerted by the wall on the ladder when: (i) $a = 9$, $b = 2$; (ii) $a = 5·5$, $b = 4$; (iii) $a = 5$, $b = 6$.

35. An aeroplane has a speed of *u* in still air, and carries petrol for a flight of duration *d*. If the wind is *v* from the N, find the farthest possible flight (out and home) in a direction θ E of N; and prove that the farthest possible flight in any direction is $\frac{1}{2}d\sqrt{(u^2 - v^2)}$.

36. A mass of 5 kg is supported by two strings of lengths 4 m and 3 m. The ends of the strings are attached to two supports at the same level and 5 m apart. A third string is attached to the mass and is pulled horizontally, with a force of 20 N, in a direction perpendicular to the vertical plane through the points of support. What will be the tensions in the supporting strings?

37. The framework in the figure is made of equal light rods, smoothly jointed, and lightly held in a vertical plane. At A and B the framework rests on smooth piers. It is loaded as shown. Calculate the reaction at A, and find the stresses in the rods AD, AE and DE.

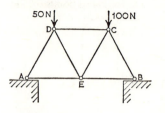

38. A bullet shot from a revolver (not necessarily horizontally) hits a lamp 25 m away, 49 mm vertically below the point at which the barrel is pointing. Find the time of flight and the muzzle velocity. What is the corresponding drop at 50 m range? (Take $g = 9.8$ m s^{-2}.)

39. A ball of mass 30 gm is balanced upon a jet of water which issues vertically from a nozzle of 2·5 mm diameter. Find the speed with which the water leaves the nozzle when the height of the ball above it is 1 m. Assume that all the water meets the ball and is brought to rest by it, and take the density of water to be 1000 kg m^{-3}.

40. Two planes, each initially at 45° to the horizontal, form a 90° V-channel with the line AA', in which the planes meet, horizontal. A thin, uniform rod is placed horizontally with one end in contact with each plane, and lying perpendicular to AA'. The angle of friction between the rod and each plane is λ.

Through what angle can the whole system be rotated about the line AA' before the rod slips relative to the channel?

CHAPTER 14

METHODS OF COMBINING FORCES

Graphical methods

14.1 In Chapter 9 we described a method of combining two forces acting on a particle into a single resultant force, using the theorem of the parallelogram of forces. It is possible to show that this theorem is equally true when the forces act on a large rigid body, although the effect which the forces have on such a body is more complicated than for a particle, since the body can rotate as well as move laterally.

If more than two forces act on the body, two of them may be combined first, and then a third combined with the resultant of the first two, and so on, until usually a single resultant force has been found. It can be proved (though geometrically it is not very easy) that the same result is obtained whatever the order in which the forces are taken. (The polygon of forces, described in § 9.3, is not sufficient to find the resultant of the forces on a large body, since it does not determine the line of action.)

EXAMPLE 1. A square table on smooth castors is moved by three people pushing at the corners A, B and C in the manner shown in Fig. 1. Find how and where a single person must push in order to produce the same effect.

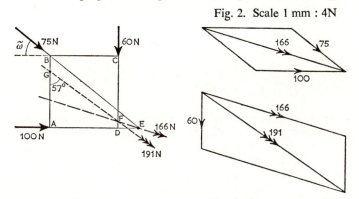

Fig. 2. Scale 1 mm : 4N

Fig. 1

Fig. 3. Scale 1 mm : 4 N

185

The forces of 75 N and 100 N are combined by a parallelogram of forces (Fig. 2) into a single force of 166 N, represented in Fig. 1 by a double-headed arrow. This force must act through E, the point where the lines of action of the forces of 75 N and 100 N meet.

This force of 166 N and the third component force of 60 N are now combined by another parallelogram (Fig. 3) to give a resultant of 191 N, represented in the diagrams with a triple-headed arrow. The lines of action of the 166 N and the 60 N meet at F, so that the complete resultant must pass through F. Denote by G the point where its line of action cuts AB. Then a single person would have to push the table at the point G with a force of 191 N along the line GF.

If desired, the two parallelograms of forces (Figs. 2 and 3) could be superimposed on Fig. 1. They have been kept distinct here for the sake of clarity.

†**14.2** If the parallelogram of forces in a particular example is $OACB$ (Fig. 4), and if the scale factor on which it is drawn is 1 mm : p newtons (with obvious modifications for other units of force and length), then

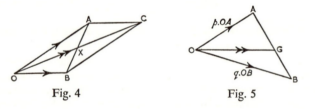

Fig. 4   Fig. 5

the theorem states that the resultant of forces $p\mathbf{OA}$ and $p\mathbf{OB}$ is $p\mathbf{OC}$. If the diagonals of the parallelogram meet at X, so that $\mathbf{OC} = 2\mathbf{OX}$, the theorem can be re-cast in the form:

The resultant of forces $p\mathbf{OA}$ and $p\mathbf{OB}$ is $2p\mathbf{OX}$, where X is the mid-point of AB.

From the theorem in this form we can make a generalization which is sometimes useful:

The resultant of forces $p\mathbf{OA}$ and $q\mathbf{OB}$ is $(p + q)\mathbf{OG}$, where G is the point of AB such that $AG : GB = q : p$.

This is most simply proved by considering the vectors first in magnitude and direction, and then in position. If we are only concerned with magnitude and direction, we may write

$$\mathbf{OA} = \mathbf{OG} + \mathbf{GA}, \quad \text{and} \quad \mathbf{OB} = \mathbf{OG} + \mathbf{GB}$$

by the vector law of addition (see Fig. 5). Therefore

$$p\mathbf{OA} + q\mathbf{OB} = p(\mathbf{OG} + \mathbf{GA}) + q(\mathbf{OG} + \mathbf{GB})$$
$$= (p + q)\mathbf{OG} + (p\mathbf{GA} + q\mathbf{GB}).$$

But we are given that $p\mathbf{AG} = q\mathbf{GB}$;
therefore, since $\mathbf{GA} = -\mathbf{AG}$,

$$p\mathbf{GA} + q\mathbf{GB} = 0,$$

Hence $$p\mathbf{OA} + q\mathbf{OB} = (p + q)\mathbf{OG}.$$

This proves the theorem as far as the magnitude and direction of the resultant are concerned. But since both the given components act through O, the resultant must also act through O, so that $(p + q)\mathbf{OG}$ represents the resultant in line of action also. This completes the proof.

The reader should notice carefully the order in which the letters p and q occur in the statement of the theorem. If p is large compared with q, the ratio $AG : GB$ becomes small, so that G is close to A, as would be expected.

The vectors in this theorem need not be force vectors, although it is for this kind of vector that we shall be applying it. In particular, if the vectors are simple position vectors (i.e. displacement vectors measured from a fixed origin), and if we rearrange the equation in the form

$$\mathbf{OG} = \frac{p\mathbf{OA} + q\mathbf{OB}}{p + q},$$

we have the familiar Joachimsthal formula of analytical geometry for the coordinates of a point dividing the line AB in the ratio $q : p$.

EXAMPLE 2. ABC is a rigid body in the shape of a triangle. Forces act on this body represented by $3\mathbf{AB}$, $2\mathbf{AC}$ *and* $6\mathbf{CB}$. *Find their resultant.*
We first use the theorem just proved to combine the two forces $3\mathbf{AB}$ and $2\mathbf{AC}$ into a single force $5\mathbf{AX}$, where $BX : XC = 2 : 3$ (Fig. 6).

We cannot immediately use the same method to combine $5\mathbf{AX}$ with $6\mathbf{CB}$, since the vectors $\mathbf{AX}$ and $\mathbf{CB}$ do not terminate at the same point. However, since $\mathbf{CB} = \tfrac{5}{3}\mathbf{CX}$, we may write $6\mathbf{CB}$ as $10\mathbf{CX}$. The theorem can now be

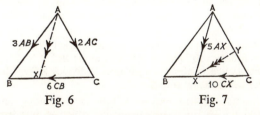

Fig. 6   Fig. 7

used a second time (Fig 7) to combine $5\mathbf{AX}$ and $10\mathbf{CX}$ into a single force $15\mathbf{YX}$, where $AY : YC = 10 : 5 = 2 : 1$. (We here use the theorem with the forces both pointing in towards the common point, rather than both away from it. This may be regarded as combining $-5\mathbf{XA}$ and $-10\mathbf{XC}$ into $-15\mathbf{XY}$ which gives the result quoted.)

The resultant is therefore represented by $15\mathbf{YX}$, where X divides BC in the ratio 2 : 3 and Y divides AC in the ratio 2 :1.

EXERCISE 14(a)

Questions 1–3 refer to a heavy beam AB of length 3 m which rests on the ground. It is pulled by horizontal chains AX, BY attached to the beam at A and B. In each question find, by drawing, the resultant and where it must be applied.

1. The force at A is 200 N at right angles to AB, and the force at B is 250 N; angle $ABY = 53°$.

2. The force at A is 200 N at right angles to AB, and the force at B is 200 N; angle $ABY = 60°$.

3. The forces are 500 N and 250 N. Angle $BAX = 70°$, angle $ABY = 70°$.

4. A square table $ABCD$ of side 1 m is moved by three people. One pushes at A with a force of 25 N along AD, one pushes at B with a force of 75 N along BA and one at C with a force of 50 N parallel to BD. Find how and where a single person must push in order to produce the same effect.

5. In Question 4 the mid-points of the sides AB, BC are X and Y. The three people push as follows: one at C with a force of 50 N in the direction CD, one at X with a force of 50 N in the direction XY and one at Y with a force of 60 N in the direction YD. Find how and where a single person must push in order to produce the same effect.

6. ABC is a triangle; $AB = 50$ mm, and the angles A and B are 60° and 45°. Forces of 3 N and 8 N act along AC and CB. Find by drawing where the line of action of the resultant meets AB.

†7. Forces represented by **2BC, CA, BA** act along the sides of a triangle ABC. Show that their resultant is represented by **6DE**, where D bisects BC and E is the point of trisection of CA nearer C.

†8. Forces represented by **3BA, 4BC, 6CA** act along the sides of a triangle ABC. Find their resultant.

†9. Forces represented by **AB, 3CB, 3AC** act along the sides of a triangle ABC. Show that the line of action of their resultant is parallel to AB and find where it meets AC.

†10. The sides BC, CA and AB of a triangle have lengths 90, 60 and 80 mm. Forces act as follows: 10 N along AB, 9 N along AC, 9 N along BC. Show that their resultant acts along XY, where X divides AB in the ratio $2:3$ and Y divides CB in the ratio $5:6$.

†11. In Question 10 the forces act as follows: 3 N along CB, 4 N along CA and 4 N along AB. Find where the line of action of their resultant meets AB and AC.

†12. Show that the resultant 2**AB** and **CA** is **AD**, where D is the point in the point in CB produced such that $CD = 2BD$.

†13. Show that the resultant of forces λ**AB**, μ**CA** acting along two of the sides of a triangle ABC is $(\lambda - \mu)$**AD**, where D divides BC externally in the ratio $\mu : \lambda$.

†14. Find where the resultant of forces 5AC, 2BA meets the line *BC*.

†15. Find the resultant of forces 2*P*, 3*P*, 4*P* acting along the sides *BC*, *CA*, *AB* of an equilateral triangle.

†16. Prove that the resultant of forces represented by **PA**, **PB** and **PC** is represented completely by **3PG**, where *G* is the centroid of the triangle *ABC*. Is this result true when the point *P* is not in the plane of the triangle *ABC*?

†17. Find the resultant of forces represented by **PA**, **2PB**, **3PC**.

†18. *ABCD* is a plane quadrilateral; *H* and *K* are the mid-points of *AC* and *BD*. Show that the resultant of forces represented completely by **AB**, **CB**, **CD**, **AD** is a force completely represented by **4HK**.

Analytical methods

14.3 The graphical methods of combining forces described so far are appropriate to a wide range of problems, but they become cumbersome when the number of forces to be combined is large, and they present certain difficulties when the component forces are parallel. The examples which follow illustrate an alternative method of solving the problem of combining forces, comparable with the methods for writing down equations for equilibrium which were introduced in Chapters 4 and 6.

The choice of the best technique to adopt with particular problems becomes easier with experience.

Example 3 shows the method applied to find the resultant of forces on a particle, and the succeeding examples concern the forces on a large rigid body.

EXAMPLE 3. Find the resultant of the forces acting on a particle A shown in Fig. 8.
Let the resultant be *R* newtons at an angle θ to the line *AX* (Fig. 9). We

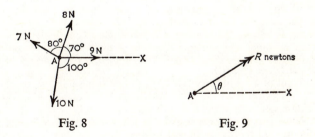

Fig. 8   Fig. 9

use the fact that, since the resultant has the same effect as the separate forces acting in combination, its resolved part in any direction must be equal to the sum of the resolved parts of the component forces.

In the direction AX the given forces have a total resolved part

$$(9 + 8 \cos 70° + 7 \cos 150° + 10 \cos 100°) \text{ N}$$
$$= (9 + 8 \cos 70° - 7 \cos 30° - 10 \cos 80°) \text{ N}$$
$$= 3·938 \text{ N}.$$

The resolved part of the force R in this direction is $R \cos \theta$. Therefore

$$\mathscr{R}(\| \text{ to } AX) \qquad\qquad 3·938 = R \cos \theta.$$

In the direction at right angles to AX up the page the given forces have a total resolved part

$$(8 \cos 20° + 7 \cos 60° - 10 \cos 10°) \text{ N}$$
$$= 1·170 \text{ N}.$$

The resolved part of R in this direction is $R \sin \theta$. Therefore

$$\mathscr{R}(\perp \text{ to AX}) \qquad\qquad 1·170 = R \sin \theta.$$

The solution of these equations is given by

$$\tan \theta = \frac{R \sin \theta}{R \cos \theta} = \frac{1·170}{3·938},$$

$$\theta = 16° \, 33' = 17° \text{ approximately};$$

and $\qquad R^2 = (R \cos \theta)^2 + (R \sin \theta)^2 = (3·938)^2 + (1·170)^2,$

$$R = 4·11.$$

The resultant is $4·11$ N at $17°$ to AX.

It must be noticed that the equations of resolving have on the left side the sum of the resolved parts of the separate forces in some direction, and on the right the resolved part of the resultant in the same direction. This should be contrasted with the equations in Chapter 4, in which the right side is either zero (when the forces are in equilibrium) or *ma* (in dynamical problems).

The solution to the above example is alternative to one using a polygon of forces (see § 9.3). It may be compared to a similar solution to a problem on the equilibrium of forces given in § 4.5, Example 7 (see p. 58).

14.4 *EXAMPLE 4. Find the resultant of the set of forces on the table in Example 1 (see Fig. 10).*

The resultant of a set of forces on a rigid body is the single force which has the same effect on it as the given forces action in combination. We have not yet discussed what effect a set of forces has on a large body such as this table. Nevertheless, it seems reasonable to assume that it depends on the resolved parts of the forces in certain directions and their moments about certain points. We shall solve this problem by assuming that the resultant has the same resolved parts in certain chosen directions, and the same moments about certain points, as the given set of forces.

Inspection of the forces in Fig. 10 suggests that the resultant is in a direction roughly 'south-easterly'. Let it be R newtons making an angle ϕ with the direction of BC, acting at a point X on the side BA such that $BX = x$ (see Fig. 11). We denote the length of the sides of the table by a.

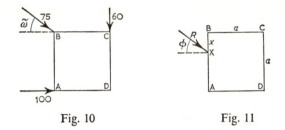

Fig. 10   Fig. 11

We first equate the total resolved part of the given forces to the resolved part of the resultant in the directions BC and BA.

$\mathscr{R}(\parallel \text{ to } BC)$ $100 + 75 \cos \tilde{\omega} = R \cos \phi.$

$\mathscr{R}(\parallel \text{ to } BA)$ $60 + 75 \sin \tilde{\omega} = R \sin \phi.$

These equations give $R \cos \phi = 160, \ R \sin \phi = 105,$

whence $R = \sqrt{(160^2 + 105^2)} \approx 191;$

and $\tan \phi = \frac{105}{160} = 0{\cdot}6562,$

so that $\phi = 33°.$

We shall choose to take moments about the point X, where the line of action of the resultant cuts AB. (It is often a useful device to take moments about some point on the line of action of the resultant.) The perpendicular from X onto the line of action of the force of 75 N is of length $x \cos \tilde{\omega}$; the sum of the moments of the given forces about X in a clockwise sense is therefore

$$60a + 75x \cos \tilde{\omega} - 100(a - x)$$
$$= 160x - 40a.$$

Since the moment of the resultant about X is zero, we have

$\mathscr{M}(X)$ $160x - 40a = 0,$

$$x = \tfrac{1}{4}a.$$

The resultant is therefore a force of 191 N acting at a point one-quarter of the way along the side BA making an angle of 33° with the direction of BC. This is the same answer as that obtained in Example 1 by another method.

14.5 The next example is a generalization of the problem of finding the resultant of a set of forces. Instead of finding a single force with the same effect as the given forces, we find two sets of forces which produce the same effect as each other on a rigid body.

EXAMPLE 5. The table in Example 1 is to be pushed by two people, one pushing at the corner B in an unspecified direction, the other at the mid-point of AB pushing at right angles to AB. How must they push in order to produce the same effect as when the three people pushed it with the forces given in Example 1?

Let the unknown forces be P newtons at B in a direction making an angle θ with BC, and Q newtons at the mid-point of AB. We write down three

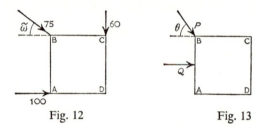

Fig. 12   Fig. 13

equations which express the fact that the two sets of forces (Figs. 12 and 13) have the same resolved parts in two directions and the same moments about point B.

$\mathscr{R}(\| \text{ to } BC)$ $100 + 75 \cos \tilde{\omega} = Q + P \cos \theta.$

$\mathscr{R}(\| \text{ to } BA)$ $60 + 75 \sin \tilde{\omega} = P \sin \theta.$

$\mathscr{M}(B)$ $100a - 60a = Q \times \tfrac{1}{2}a.$

The last equation gives immediately $Q = 80$, whence the other equations reduce to

$$P \cos \theta = 80, \quad \text{and} \quad P \sin \theta = 105.$$

Therefore $P = \sqrt{(80^2 + 105^2)} \approx 132,$

and $\tan \theta = \tfrac{105}{80} = 1 \cdot 3125,$

so that $\theta = 53°.$

This completes the solution.

It is important to notice that in forming the equations the moments and resolved parts of the two sets of forces must be taken in the same sense. For example, in the equations above the moments about B are both calculated with the anticlockwise sense as positive.

Two sets of forces, such as those in this last example, which have the same effect on a rigid body are said to be EQUIVALENT. (The word EQUIPOLLENT is sometimes used.)

14.6 Although in Example 5 the unknowns P, Q and θ were found by resolving in only two directions, and taking moments about one point, it would be found that the two sets of forces also have the same resolved parts in any other direction, and the same moments about any other point.

For example, in the direction BD the first set of forces has a total resolved part (in newtons)

$$100 \cos 45° + 60 \cos 45° + 75 \cos (45° − \tilde{\omega}) = 187.$$

The second set has a total resolved part

$$Q \cos 45° + P \cos (\theta − 45°),$$

which also has the value 187 when the values of P, Q and θ found above are substituted.

Again, the sum of the moments (clockwise) of the first set about the point A is

$$60a + 75a \cos \tilde{\omega} = 120a,$$

whilst the moment of the second set is

$$Q \times \tfrac{1}{2}a + P \times a \cos \theta,$$

which also equals $120a$.

It can be proved that (for two-dimensional problems) the results obtained by resolving in two directions and taking moments about one point always give true equations for other directions and other points. We may compare this with the similar situation discussed in § 6.11 with regard to conditions of equilibrium.

14.7 The next example shows how to find the resultant of a set of parallel forces.

EXAMPLE 6. *Find the resultant of forces of magnitude A along the line $x = a$, B along $x = b$, and C along $x = c$.* (Fig. 14).

Since all three forces are parallel to the y-axis, it is evident that the force whose resolved part in any direction is the same as that of these three forces

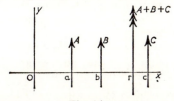

Fig. 14

must also be parallel to the y-axis, and of magnitude $A + B + C$. Let the resultant be $A + B + C$ along the line $x = r$.

Since the resultant of the forces must have the same moment about the origin as the three given forces taken together,

$$\mathcal{M}(O) \qquad Aa + Bb + Cc = (A + B + C)r,$$

whence

$$r = \frac{Aa + Bb + Cc}{A + B + C}.$$

EXERCISE 14(*b*)

In Questions 1–3 find the resultant of the given forces, which in each case act on a particle.

1. 11 newtons due S, 4 newtons due E, 5 newtons at $\bar{\omega}$ N of E.

2. 4 newtons due N, 5 newtons N50°W, 6 newtons S70°E.

3. 3 newtons due N, 3 newtons due E, 5 newtons N80°E, 1 newton S60°W.

In Questions 4–7 the forces act along the sides of a square table *ABCD*. Find in each case the magnitude of the resultant, the angle that it makes with *AB*, and the point *X* at which its line of action meets *AB*, or *AB* produced.

4. 2 along *AB*, 3 along *BC*, 2 along *DC*, 1 along *AD*.

5. 1 along *AB*, 3 along *BC*, 2 along *CD*, 5 along *DA*.

6. 2 along *AB*, 3 along *BC*, 2 along *DC*, 1 along *DA*.

7. 2 along *AB*, 3 along *CB*, 2 along *CD*, 5 along *AD*.

8, 9. Solve Questions 4 and 5 of Exercise 14(*a*) using analytical methods.

10. Forces of magnitude 3, 1 and 2 act along the sides *BC*, *CA*, *AB* of an equilateral triangle. Find the resultant, and where it meets *BC*.

11. *ABC* is a triangle in which *BC* = 50 mm, *CA* = 40 mm, *AB* = 30 mm. Forces of 9, 10 and 11 N act along *AB*, *BC* and *AC*. Find the resultant and where it meets *AB*.

12. Forces 2*P*, 3*P*, *P*, 5*P* act along the sides *AB*, *BC*, *CD*, *DA* of a rhombus whose angle *A* is 60°. Find the magnitude and line of action of the resultant.

13. *ABCDEF* is a regular hexagon. Forces 1, 4, 2, 3, 2, 3 N act along *AB*, *BC*, *CD*, *DE*, *EF*, *FA*. What is the resultant, and where does it meet *AB*?

14. A boy is pushing a heavy square table *ABCD* of side 2 m across the room with a force of 150 N applied at the mid-point of the side *AB* at right angles to that side. Becoming tired, he invites his sister to help. She pushes at *A* towards *C*, and he now applies a force at a point on *AB* 0·5 m from *B*. How hard must each push in order to produce the same effect as before?

15. If in Question 14 the boy's sister pushes with a force of 100 N along *AC*, where and how hard must the boy push?

†16. *ABCD* is a rectangle in which *AB* = 4 m and *BC* = 3 m. A system of forces acts as follows: 10 N at *A* in the direction *AC*, 7 N at *B* in the direction *BC*, and 3 N at the mid-point of *AD* parallel to *AB*. *X* and *Y* are points in *AB* distant 1 m from *A* and from *B* respectively. *P* and *Q* are two forces which together have the same effect as the original system.

If *P* is applied at *X* perpendicular to *AB* and *Q* is applied at *Y*, find the magnitudes of *P* and *Q* and the direction of *Q*.

†17. In Question 16, *Q* is 5 N and is applied at *Y* in a direction parallel to *BD*. Find the magnitude and direction of *P* and the point in *AB* at which *P* must be applied.

†**18.** Find the three forces which, acting along the sides of the triangle *BCD*, will have the same effect as the original system of forces in Question 16.

19. Three elephants push horizontally with forces 1·5, 2 and 2·5 kN at points *A*, *B*, *C* of a tree-trunk resting on the ground. All the forces are at right angles to the tree-trunk, and *AB* = 8 m, *BC* = 12 m. Find the resultant force.

20. If in Question 19 the elephant in the middle pulls instead of pushing, find the resultant force.

21. Three tugs are pulling a liner away from a wharf. The three cables are parallel, each making 30° with the line of the ship. The cables are attached at the bow and at points 20 m and 50 m from the bow. If the tensions are respectively 80, 70 and 50 kN, find where the resultant pull acts.

22. Parallel forces of magnitude *P* and *Q* act at *A* and *B*. Prove that the resultant meets *AB* in the point *C* such that *AC* : *CB* = *Q* : *P*.

Couples

14.8 It is interesting to consider what happens in Example 6 if *A* + *B* + *C* = 0. In order for this to happen, it is, of course, necessary for one or two of the numbers *A*, *B*, *C* to be negative; this simply means that the forces act 'downwards' rather than 'upwards'. The formula for *r* now becomes meaningless, and it appears that the forces have no resultant.

We shall consider a particular example of this in detail.

EXAMPLE 7. Investigate the combination of forces of −5 *along x* = 2, +3 *along x* = 4, *and* +2 *along x* = 7. (Fig. 15).
The sum of the resolved parts of these forces in any direction is clearly zero,

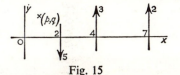

Fig. 15

so that there is no resultant in the ordinary sense. But neither are the forces in equilibrium, for there appears to be a tendency for these forces to turn a body anticlockwise. In fact, the sum of the moments about *O* is 2 × 7 + 3 × 4 − 5 × 2 = 16 anticlockwise.

This is not the first example which we have encountered of a set of forces which has no resultant but which has some turning effect. Another was discussed in § 10.1, Example 1 (p. 139). In § 6.14 (p. 90) the name 'couple' was given to such a set of forces.

It should not be thought that all sets of forces whose resolved parts add up to zero form couples. Had the forces in Example 6 been $+3$ along $x = 2$, -5 along $x = 4$, and $+2$ along $x = 7$, the sum of the moments about O would have been $2 \times 7 - 5 \times 4 + 3 \times 2 = 0$, and the set of forces would have been in equilibrium.

DEFINITION. *A* COUPLE *is a set of forces such that the sum of the resolved parts in every direction is zero, but the sum of the moments about some point is not zero.*

The simplest instance of a couple is a pair of forces of the same magnitude acting along parallel lines in opposite directions (Fig. 16). The sum of the resolved parts is zero in any direction, whilst the moment about a point on the line of action of one of the forces is Ph, which is not zero.

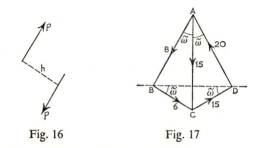

Fig. 16   Fig. 17

EXAMPLE 8. ABCD is a quadrilateral in the form of a kite, symmetrical about the diagonal AC, with AB = AD = 16 m, CB = CD = 12 m, AC = 20 m (Fig. 17). The following forces act on this body: 8 N along AB, 6 N along BC, 15 N along CD, 20 N along DA, and 15 N along AC. Prove that they form a couple.
The sum of the resolved parts along AC is

$$8 \cos \tilde{\omega} + 6 \sin \tilde{\omega} - 15 \sin \tilde{\omega} - 20 \cos \tilde{\omega} + 15 = 0,$$

and that perpendicular to AC is

$$8 \sin \tilde{\omega} - 6 \cos \tilde{\omega} + 20 \sin \tilde{\omega} = 0.$$

Since the sum of the resolved parts in two directions is zero, we know that the same is true in all other directions (see § 14.6).
The moment about A is

$$6 \times 16 + 15 \times 16 = 336 \text{ N m}.$$

The forces therefore form a couple.

14.9 An important feature of couples is:

If a set of forces is a couple, its total moment is the same about all points.

In Example 7, if moments were taken about the general point (p, q) instead of the origin (see Fig. 15), the total moment would be

$$2(7 - p) + 3(4 - p) - 5(2 - p),$$

which equals 16 and is independent of the values of p and q. In Example 8, if moments were taken about C, the total moment would be

$$8 \times 12 + 20 \times 12 = 336 \text{ N m},$$

the same value as we obtained by taking moments about A.

Proofs of this property, and of the converse theorem stated in §14.10, are deferred until a later volume. We can now define uniquely:

DEFINITION. *The* MOMENT *of a couple is the total moment of the set of forces about any point.*

14.10 The property of couples enunciated in the previous section has an important converse:

If the sum of the moments of a set of forces about three different points (not in the same straight line) is the same, and not zero, the set of forces is a couple.

It is easy to see that we must take moments about at least three points and get the same result each time before we can be sure that the set of forces is a couple. For if we have just a single force and take moments about two points equidistant from its line of action we shall get the same answer; but if we then take moments about any other point not collinear with the first two, we shall obtain a different result.

If the total moment about three non-collinear points is zero, the forces are in equilibrium (see § 6.12).

The next example illustrates the use of this converse theorem.

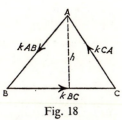
Fig. 18

EXAMPLE 9. ABC is a triangle. Prove that the system of forces $k\mathbf{BC}$, $k\mathbf{CA}$, $k\mathbf{AB}$ is a couple. (Fig. 18).

If h is the length of the perpendicular from A onto BC, the moment of the system about A is

$$hk\ BC + 0 + 0 = 2k\Delta,$$

where Δ is the area of the triangle. Similarly, the moment of the system about B and C is also $2k\Delta$. Therefore, by the theorem just enunciated, the system is a couple of moment $2k\Delta$.

EXERCISE 14(c)

1. Forces 7, −4, −3 act along the lines $x = 0$, $x = 5$, $x = 7$. Prove that they form a couple and find its moment.

2. ABC is an isosceles triangle with $AC = AB = 1$ m, $BC = 1.2$ m. M is the mid-point of BC. Forces (measured in newtons) act as follows: 15 along AB, 12 along BC, 5 along CA and 8 along MA. Prove that they form a couple and find its moment.

3. Forces of 2, X, Y, $3X − Y$ act along the sides AB, CB, CD, AD of a square, the length of whose side is b. Prove that they are not in equilibrium and that there is just one pair of values of X, Y for which the system is a couple. Find the moment of this couple.

4. Forces of 2, 4, $X − Y$, $X + Y$ newtons act along the sides AB, BC, CD, DA of a square of side 2 m. If they form a couple, find X, Y and the moment of the couple.

5. If the coefficient of friction between my finger and thumb and the head of a screw 10 mm in diameter is 0.6, with what force must I pinch the screw head in order that I may turn it with a couple of 3 N m?

6. $ABCD$ is a quadrilateral in which $AB = 30$ mm, $BC = 120$ mm, $CD = 130$ mm, $DA = 40$ mm, $BD = 50$ mm. Forces act as follows: 6 N along AB, 36 N along BC, 39 N along CD, 8 N along DA, 5 N along DB. Prove that they form a couple and find its moment.

7. O is the point at the centre of the regular hexagon $ABCDEF$. Forces act as follows: 1, 3, 5, 7, 9, 11 along AB, BC, CD, DE, EF, FA and 2, 2, 2, 2, 2, X along OB, OC, OD, OE, OF, AO. If the system is a couple, find X.

†8. $ABCD$ is a square of side 2 m, and forces act as follows: 8 N along AB, 2 N along BC, 5 N along CD and 2 N along AD. Prove that this system is equivalent to a force through A together with a couple. Find the magnitude and direction of the force and the moment of the couple.

†9. $ABCDEF$ is a regular hexagon of side 2 m and forces of 1, 2, 3, 4, 5, 6 N act along AB, BC, CD, DE, FE, AF. Prove that they are equivalent to a force of $4\sqrt{13}$ N acting at the centre of the hexagon together with a couple whose moment is to be stated. If, instead, the forces are reduced to a single force, find where its line of action meets AB.

†10. Forces acting on a rigid body are represented in magnitude, direction and position by the sides of a closed polygon taken in order. Show that the system of forces is a couple.

†11. Prove that if forces P, Q, R acting along the sides BC, CA, AB of a triangle form a couple, then $P : Q : R = BC : CA : AB$. Is a similar theorem true for forces acting along the sides of a polygon?

CHAPTER 15

CENTRE OF GRAVITY

One-dimensional problems

15.1 In Chapter 6 the idea of the centre of gravity of a body was introduced, as the point of the body at which its weight could be supposed to act. So far we have dealt mainly with uniform bodies, whose centres of gravity coincide with their geometrical centres. We now discuss how to find the centres of gravity of solids of more complicated shapes, for which there is no obvious centre of symmetry, or of bodies whose distribution of mass is not uniform.

It will be convenient to use the abbreviation C.G. for 'centre of gravity'. Where there is no ambiguity this point will always be denoted by the letter G.

The theory depends on the fact that if a body is made up of a number of parts the weight of the whole body is the resultant of the weights of the separate parts.

EXAMPLE 1. A straight rod AB whose mass is negligible has three masses fixed to it: 4 kg at A, 1 kg at a distance 240 mm from A and 5 kg at 400 mm from A. Where is the centre of gravity of the three masses?
By symmetry we expect the C.G. to be at some point of the rod. The total weight is the resultant of the weights of the three separate masses, and is

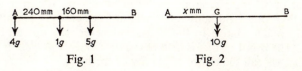

Fig. 1   Fig. 2

therefore (see § 14.7) equal to $(4g + 1g + 5g)$ newtons = 10 g newtons. If the rod is placed horizontally, we have two equivalent systems of forces as shown in Figs. 1 and 2.

If the C.G. is x mm from A, we can equate the moments of the two sets of forces about A, and obtain

$\mathscr{M}(A)$ $4g \times 0 + 1g \times 240 + 5g \times 400 = 10gx$,

so that $x = 224$. The C.G. is at the point of the rod 224 mm from A.

EXAMPLE 2. A cylindrical tin, with a base but no lid, is made from a thin sheet of metal. The base radius is 30 mm and the height 160 mm. Where is its C.G.?

The tin can be broken up into two parts: a circular base of area $\pi \times 30^2 = 900\pi$ mm² with its C.G. at the centre of the base, and a hollow cylinder of area $2\pi \times 30 \times 160 = 9600\pi$ mm² with its C.G. half-way up the cylinder on the axis of symmetry. If the mass of the metal per mm² of area is s kg, these parts have weights of $900\pi sg$ and $9600\pi sg$ respectively, both in newtons, and the total weight of the tin is $10500\pi sg$ newtons.

The C.G. of the tin clearly lies on the axis of symmetry. Let it be at a height

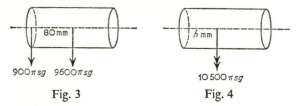

900πsg   9600πsg   10 500 π sg

Fig. 3   Fig. 4

h mm above the base. If the tin is placed with its axis horizontal, we have two equivalent sets of forces as shown in Figs. 3 and 4.

The equation

$\mathcal{M}$(centre of base) $900\pi sg \times 0 + 9600\pi sg \times 80 = 10\,500\pi sgh$

gives immediately $h = 73.$

The C.G. of the tin is on the axis of the cylinder 73 mm above the base.

15.2 It will be seen that the C.G. of the tin in Example 2 is at a point inside the tin at which there is no metal. There is no inconsistency in this; it is indeed rare for the C.G. of a hollow body to be at a point of its surface. It is important to realize that the notion of the C.G. of a body is nothing more than a convenient mathematical fiction. The earth actually attracts each individual particle of which the body is composed, and what we call the weight of the body is simply the resultant of all these separate forces of attraction. It can in fact be proved that for a rigid body this resultant force always passes through a certain point relative to the body, whichever way up the body is placed. (The proof of this is deferred until a later volume.) It is this point that we call the centre of gravity of the body.

15.3 For a set of masses arranged along a straight line (or for a body which can be broken down into this form, such as the cylindrical tin in Example 2), a simple formula can be given for the position of the C.G. Let an origin O be chosen on the line, and let there be n masses: m_1 at a distance x_1 from O, m_2 at x_2 and so on. (Strictly, $x_1, x_2, \ldots$ are displacements, or coordinates, rather than distances. Points on different sides of O are distinguished by different signs for the values of x.) The resultant of their weights, which are m_1g, m_2g, etc, is Mg, where

$$M = m_1 + m_2 + \ldots + m_n.$$

It is customary to denote the coordinate of the C.G. by the symbol $\bar{x}$. Then, supposing the line to be set horizontally,

$$\mathscr{M}(O) \qquad m_1gx_1 + m_2gx_2 + \ldots m_ngx_n = Mg\bar{x}.$$

The reader who is familiar with summation notation will know that this formula can be written, after dividing through by the factor g,

$$\bar{x} = \frac{1}{M}\sum_{r=1}^{n} m_r x_r,$$

where

$$M = \sum_{r=1}^{n} m_r.$$

When applying this formula it is convenient to adopt a tabular arrangement, placing in one row the masses of the separate components and the mass of the whole body, and in the next row the coordinates of the corresponding C.G. For Example 1, this table would have the form:

	SEPARATE MASSES			WHOLE BODY
Mass	4	1	5	10
Distance from A	0	240	400	x

and for Example 2:

Mass	$900\pi s$	$9600\pi s$	$10\,500\ \pi s$
Distance from centre of base	0	80	h

The appropriate equations:

$$4 \times 0 + 1 \times 240 + 5 \times 400 = 10x,$$

and

$$900\pi s \times 0 + 9600\pi s \times 80 = 10\,500\ \pi sh$$

can then be written down at once.

EXERCISE 15(a)

1. Find the C.G. of 2 kg at $x = 2$, 5 kg at $x = 5$ and 3 kg at $x = 6$.

2. Find the C.G. of 6 gm at $x = 0$, 30 gm at $x = 1$, 12 gm at $x = 9$ and 2 gm at $x = 12$.

3. Find the C.G. of 14 gm at $x = -3$, 2 gm at $x = 3$ and 6 gm at $x = 6$.

4. The C.G. of 6 kg at $x = 5$ and one other mass of 2 kg is at $\bar{x} = 6$. Where is the other mass?

5. The C.G. of 4 kg at $x = -2$, 3 kg at $x = 1$ and one other mass of 5 kg is at $\bar{x} = -1$. Where is the 5 kg mass?

6. The C.G. of 3 gm at $x = 0$ and another at $x = 6$ is at $\bar{x} = 4$. How large is the other mass?

7. The C.G of 8 kg at $x = -3$, 4 kg at $x = 1$ and another mass at $x = 13$ is at $\bar{x} = 5$. How large is the other mass?

In Questions 8–17 find the centres of gravity of the bodies.

8. A sledge-hammer has a uniform cylindrical shaft 1 m long of mass $\frac{1}{2}$ kg, which passes through the metal head of mass 5 kg whose C.G. is 60 mm from the end of the shaft.

9. A mallet has a uniform shaft 0·4 m long of mass 125 gm which passes through the head of mass 1 kg whose C.G. is 0·05 m from the end of the shaft.

10. A uniform flagstaff 5 m high of mass 10 kg embedded in a hole in a uniform metal base 0·1 m high of mass 20 kg.

11. A tennis racquet of mass 400 gm and total length 0·7 m. The handle has a mass of 240 gm, and its C.G. is 0·15 m from the end; the C.G. of the oval frame is 0·5 m from the end of the handle.

12. A fly-fishing rod made in three sections, each 1 m long. The butt section has a mass of 150 gm and a C.G. 0·4 m from the end of the butt; the middle section has a mass 60 gm and a C.G. 0·45 m from its lower end; the top section has a mass 25 gm and a C.G. 0·4 m from its lower end.

13. An open wooden box made of wood 10 mm thick with external dimensions 220 mm × 180 mm × 100 mm high standing on the floor.

14. The tin in Example 2 when half-full of water whose weight is one-quarter of that of the metal.

15. A uniform cube of side 20 mm surmounted symmetrically by another cube of the same material of side 10 mm.

16. The body in Question 15 standing on a third cube of the same material and of side 30 mm.

17. A conical tower of four uniform children's bricks each a circular disc 1 cm thick, the radii of the discs being 4 cm, 3 cm, 2 cm, 1 cm.

18. A squash racquet has a total mass of 225 gm. The C.G.s of the handle and of the circular frame are 0·2 m and 0·6 m from the end of the handle. Find the masses of the two parts of the racquet if the C.G. of the whole is 0·36 m from the end of the handle.

19. What happens to the C.G. of a ladies' umbrella when it is opened?

20. Draw a picture of an ice-hockey stick and mark its C.G. approximately.

21. Draw a picture of a walking-stick and mark its C.G. approximately.

22. Approximately $\frac{1}{14}$ of your mass is concentrated in your head, $\frac{4}{7}$ in your trunk and $\frac{5}{14}$ in your legs. Find roughly the position of your C.G. when you are standing upright.

†23. Water is poured into a vessel of any shape. Draw a rough graph showing how the height of the C.G. of the vessel and the contained water varies as the water gradually fills up the vessel. Show that, when the C.G. is lowest, it is at the level of the water.

†24. If the tower of Question 17 had n bricks of thickness 1 cm and radii 1 cm, 2 cm, 3 cm, ... n cm, what fraction of the total height would the height of the C.G. be? What is the limit of this fraction as $n \longrightarrow \infty$?

25. A cricket bat whose handle is 0·3 m long and whose blade is 0·55 m long has its C.G. 0·5 m from the top of the handle. If the handle is uniform and is of mass 0·12 kg, and the blade has mass 1 kg, where is the C.G. of the blade?

Two- and three-dimensional problems

15.4 When the masses are not all on a straight line more than one equation of moments is necessary.

EXAMPLE 3. Find the C.G. of a frame made of uniform wire in the shape of a right-angled triangle with sides 10 m, 24 m, 26 m with a strut joining the mid-point of the hypotenuse to the right angle.

Let the wire have mass p kg per metre length. The wires AB, AC, BC, AD have masses $10p$, $24p$, $26p$, $13p$ kg, the C.G. of each of these being at its

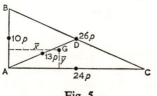

Fig. 5

mid-point. The mass of the whole frame is $73p$ kg; we shall suppose this to be associated with a point G which is $\bar{x}$ metres from the side AB and $\bar{y}$ metres from AC (see Fig. 5).

We suppose the wire to be placed in a horizontal plane. It is now necessary to take moments about a line rather than about a point (see § 6.13). We regard AB and AC in turn as 'hinges', and equate the moments of the weights of the separate parts to the moment of the weight of the whole frame. The masses and their corresponding distances are given in the table:

	SEPARATE MASSES				WHOLE BODY
Mass	$10p$	$24p$	$26p$	$13p$	$73p$
Distance from AB	0	12	12	6	$\bar{x}$
Distance from AC	5	0	5	$2\frac{1}{2}$	$\bar{y}$

Fig. 6a shows the separate weights as they appear when viewed in the direction AB. The equation of moments is

$\mathcal{M}(AB)$ $10pg \times 0 + 24pg \times 12 + 26pg \times 12 + 13pg \times 6 = 73pg\bar{x}$,

which gives $\qquad\qquad\qquad \bar{x} = 9\cdot3.$

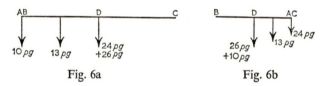

Fig. 6a   Fig. 6b

Similarly, Fig. 6b shows the forces viewed in the direction AC.

$\mathcal{M}(AC)$ $10pg \times 5 + 24pg \times 0 + 26pg \times 5 + 13pg \times 2\frac{1}{2} = 73pg\bar{y}$

giving $\qquad\qquad\qquad \bar{y} = 2\cdot9.$

The C.G. of the frame is 9·3 m from AB and 2·9 m from AC.

†15.5   If axes Ox, Oy, Oz are taken in space, and a body is composed of n masses: m_1 at (x_1, y_1, z_1), m_2 at (x_2, y_2, z_2), etc, then we can derive

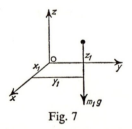

Fig. 7

formulæ for the coordinates of the C.G. similar to the formula given in § 15.3. We first take the xy-plane to be horizontal (Fig. 7). The weights are given by m_1g, m_2g, etc. The moment about the x-axis of a vertical force of m_1g is $m_1g\,y_1$. Therefore

$$\mathscr{M}(x\text{-axis}) \qquad m_1gy_1 + m_2gy_2 + \ldots + m_ngy_n = Mg\bar{y}.$$

Similarly $\bar{x}$ is obtained by taking moments about the y-axis. To get $\bar{z}$, suppose the body to be turned round so that the yz-plane is horizontal, and then take moments about the y-axis.

Dividing through by the common factor g, the formulae for the coordinates of G are found to be

$$\bar{x} = \frac{1}{M}\sum_{r=1}^{n}m_r x_r, \quad \bar{y} = \frac{1}{M}\sum_{r=1}^{n}m_r y_r, \quad \bar{z} = \frac{1}{M}\sum_{r=1}^{n}m_r z_r,$$

where

$$M = \sum_{r=1}^{n}m_r.$$

EXAMPLE 4. *Three rectangular pieces of plywood* $OBPC, OCQA, OARB$, *where* $OA = 1.2$ m, $OB = 1.6$ m, $OC = 1.0$ m *are joined together to form the two sides and the base of a box (see Fig. 8). Find the C.G.*
Let the mass of the plywood be s kg per m^2 of area. Then $OBPC$ has mass

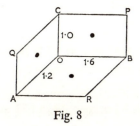

Fig. 8

$1.6s$ kg, and its C.G. is at the centre of the rectangle. Taking OA, OB, OC as axes, this has coordinates $(0, 0.8, 0.5)$. Similarly, the masses of $OCQA$, $OARB$ are $1.2s$ at $(0.6, 0, 0.5)$ and $1.92s$ at $(0.6, 0.8, 0)$. Therefore

$$M = 1.6s + 1.2s + 1.92s = 4.72s,$$

and
$$\bar{x} = (1.6s \times 0 + 1.2s \times 0.6 + 1.92s \times 0.6)/4.72s = 0.4,$$
$$\bar{y} = (1.6s \times 0.8 + 1.2s \times 0 + 1.92s \times 0.8)/4.72s = 0.6,$$
$$\bar{z} = (1.6s \times 0.5 + 1.2s \times 0.5 + 1.92s \times 0)/4.72s = 0.3.$$

The C.G. is 0.4 m from the side $OBPC$, 0.6 m from the side $OCQA$, and 0.3 m above the base $OARB$.

15.6 In some examples the body whose C.G. is required is obtained by subtracting parts from a regular figure, rather than by adding two regular figures together.

EXAMPLE 5. AOB, COD are perpendicular diameters of a circular metal plate of radius 80 mm. Two holes are punched in the plate: one of radius 20 mm with its centre on OB 10 mm from O, and the other of radius 10 mm

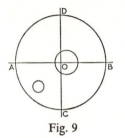

Fig. 9

with its centre 40 mm from OA and 40 mm from OC. Locate the C.G. of the remainder of the plate (Fig. 9).

We find the C.G. by imagining the original un-punched plate to be reconstituted. The metal discs taken from the two holes are replaced; these, together with the remainder whose C.G. is to be found, form the separate components, and the original plate forms the whole body (whose C.G. is known to be at the centre of the circle).

If the mass of the metal is s gm per mm^3 area, the two small discs have masses $(\pi \times 20^2)s = 400\pi s$ gm and $(\pi \times 10^2)s = 100\pi s$ gm. The original plate had a mass $(\pi \times 80^2)s = 6400\pi s$ gm, so that the remaining piece has mass $5900\pi s$ gm. If we take OB, OD as axes, we have:

	SEPARATE MASSES			WHOLE BODY
Mass	$400\pi s$	$100\pi s$	$5900\pi s$	$6400\pi s$
x	10	-40	$\bar{x}$	0
y	0	-40	$\bar{y}$	0

The equations are

$$400\pi s \times 10 + 100\pi s \times (-40) + 5900\pi s \times \bar{x} = 6400\pi s \times 0,$$
$$400\pi s \times 0 + 100\pi s \times (-40) + 5900\pi s \times \bar{y} = 6400\pi s \times 0.$$

These give $\qquad \bar{x} = 0, \quad \bar{y} = \frac{4000}{5900} = 0\cdot68.$

The C.G. is therefore on OD at a distance of 0·68 mm from O.

15.7 The next example illustrates a 'piecemeal' method of finding the C.G. of a body which can sometimes be usefully employed instead of the

Fig 10

'wholesale' method so far described. This uses the fact that the C.G. of masses m_1 at A and m_2 at B is at the point which divides AB in the ratio $m_2 : m_1$ (Fig. 10). For, if G is the C.G., the equation of moments about G is

$$-m_1 g \times AG + m_2 g \times GB = (m_1 + m_2)g \times 0,$$
so that $\qquad AG/GB = m_2/m_1.$

EXAMPLE 6. Find the C.G. of three masses p, q, r placed at the corners of a triangle ABC.

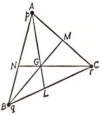

The C.G. of masses p at A and q at B is at a point N on AB such that $AN/NB = q/p$ (Fig. 11). We therefore replace these two masses by a single mass $(p + q)$ at N, so that instead of the original three masses we now have only two. The C.G. of $p + q$ at N and r at C is at a point G on CN such that $CG/GN = (p + q)/r$. This is the C.G. of the three masses.

Fig. 11

Similarly, G is also on AL, where $BL/LC = r/q$ and $AG/GL = (q + r)/p$; and on BM, where $CM/MA = p/r$ and $BG/GM = (p + r)/q$. The reader who is familiar with the theorems of Ceva and Menelaus will be able to verify that AL, BM, CN are in fact concurrent, and that their point of concurrence divides these lines in the ratios stated.

A particularly important case arises when $p = q = r$. Then L, M, N are the mid-points of the sides of the triangle, and AL, BM, CN are medians of the triangle. The point G divides each median in the ratio $2 : 1$. This point is called the *centroid* of the triangle.

EXERCISE 15(b)

1–4. Find the centres of gravity of pieces of cardboard cut into the shapes shown in the diagrams. Verify your results experimentally. The dimensions are given in cm.

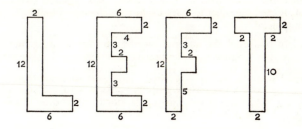

5–8. Find the centres of gravity of lengths of wire bent into the shapes shown in the diagrams above.

In Questions 9–16 find the centres of gravity of the bodies.

9. A board of length 3 m and width 1 m has a square hole, 0·5 m × 0·5 m, cut in it. The centre of the hole is on the longitudinal axis of symmetry, 1 m from one end of the board.

10. A circular plate of radius 120 m has a circular hole of radius 40 m. The centre of the hole is 60 mm from the centre of the plate.

11. *OA*, *OB* are perpendicular radii of a circular metal plate of radius 0·5 m. Studs, each of mass one-eighth that of the plate, are fastened at *A* and at *M*, the mid-point of *OB*.

12. Five straight pieces of wire, each of length 60 mm, are joined to form a pentagon *ABCDE*. Angle *A* = angle *B* = 90°, angle *C* = angle *E* = 150°.

13. A square metal plate of side 16 cm has a rectangular piece measuring 6 cm × 4 cm removed from one corner.

14. *ABCD* is a rectangular sheet of plywood; *AB* = 320 mm and *BC* = 160 mm. *X* is a point in *AB* 80 mm from *B*, *Y* is in *BC* 64 mm from *B*, *Z* is in *CD* 64 mm from *D* and *T* is in *AD* 80 mm from *D*. Rectangular pieces *XBYR*, *DTSZ* are cut away.

15. *OA*, *OB* are perpendicular radii of a circular piece of cardboard of radius 120 mm. Two circular holes are cut; one of radius 30 mm and centre two-thirds of the way from *O* to *A* and the other of radius 40 mm and centre the midpoint of *OB*.

16. Repeat Question 15 with angle *AOB* = 90° + $\bar{\omega}$.

17. A circular metal plate of radius 40 mm has a circular hole of radius 10 mm. Find the position of the hole if the C.G. of the remaining metal is 1·2 mm from the centre of the plate.

18. The plate described in Question 11 has a single stud fastened at *A*. A circular section, centre *M* and radius 125 mm, is cut out. Find the position of the C.G.

19. *ABCD* is a rectangular sheet of metal; *AB* = 100 mm and *BC* = 40 mm. Two circular holes are cut, each of radius 10 mm. One has centre the mid-point of *AC* and the other touches *BC* at its mid-point. Find the C.G. of the remaining metal.

20. Eight uniform cubes are put together to form a larger cube, of edge 2 m, which stands on the floor, and then one of the eight is taken away. Find the distance of the C.G. of the remainder from the floor.

21. A parcel of books measuring 40 cm × 24 cm × 6 cm contains 12 books each 20 cm × 12 cm × 2 cm. One of the books is removed from a corner of the parcel. Find the C.G. of the remainder.

22. In a triangle *ABC*, *D* divides *BC* internally in the ratio 5 : 3 and *G* divides *AD* internally in the ratio 4 : 1. Find the ratio of masses at *A*, *B* and *C* whose centre of gravity is at *G*.

23. Masses p, q and r are placed at the points $(0, 0)$, $(10, 0)$, $(0, 8)$. The centre of gravity of the masses is at $(5, 3)$. Find the ratio $p : q : r$.

†24. Eight uniform cubes each of edge 1 m are placed together to form a cube of edge 2 m. Cube A is on top of cube P, cube B on top of cube Q, cube C on top of cube R and cube D on top of cube S. Find the C.G. of the solid formed by removing cube A and replacing it on top of cube C.

†25. Find the C.G. of the solid formed from the cube in Question 24, if cube A is removed and replaced on top of cube B.

†26. OA, OB, OC are three pieces cut from a uniform length of wire, having lengths 120 mm, 50 mm, 90 mm. They are joined together at O in such a way that each is at right angles to the other two. BC, CA, AB are joined by three more pieces from the same length of wire, so that a skeleton pyramid is formed. Find the distances of its C.G. from the planes of the triangles OBC, OCA, OAB.

Calculus methods

*15.8 For many bodies the calculation of the position of the C.G. requires the methods of calculus. These methods are illustrated by the examples which follow. The reader is advised to try to understand the principles involved, and not to commit to memory a large number of formulae for dealing with problems of various types.

EXAMPLE 7. Find the C.G. of a solid hemisphere of uniform density and radius 1 m.

The hemisphere can be formed by rotating about the x-axis that part of the circle

$$y = \sqrt{(1 - x^2)}$$

for which x is positive (see Fig. 12). The volume of the hemisphere is $\frac{2}{3}\pi \times 1^3 = \frac{2}{3}\pi$ m^3. If the density is q kg m^{-3}, the mass of the hemisphere is $\frac{2}{3}q\pi$ kg. By symmetry, the C.G. will lie on the x-axis; let its coordinate be $\bar{x}$.

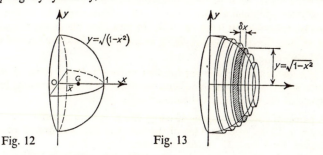

Fig. 12   Fig. 13

Suppose the solid to be cut into a large number of slices by planes parallel to the base (i.e. perpendicular to the x-axis). These slices are approximately in the shape of circular cylindrical discs. We now replace the hemisphere by a new solid (Fig. 13) made up of a number of exactly cylindrical discs; a typical one of these, shown shaded in Fig. 13, has for its base the circular section of the original hemisphere whose x-coordinate is x and a thickness which we denote by δx. The base is therefore a circle of radius $y = \surd(1 - x^2)$, so that the disc has a base area of $\pi y^2 = \pi(1 - x^2)$, a volume of $\pi(1 - x^2)\delta x$ and a mass of $q\pi(1 - x^2)\delta x$.

The C.G. of this new solid, which is made up of a number of discs of this kind, is calculated from the formula (see § 15.3)

$$M\bar{x} = \sum m_r x_r.$$

In this formula, m_r is the mass of one of the discs, and x_r the distance of its C.G. from the y-axis. This C.G. is half-way between the bounding planes of the disc, and therefore has a coordinate $x + \frac{1}{2}\delta x$. For this body, therefore,

$$\sum m_r x_r = \sum \{q\pi(1 - x^2)\delta x \times (x + \frac{1}{2}\delta x)\}$$
$$= \sum q\pi x(1 - x^2)\delta x + \sum \frac{1}{2}q\pi(1 - x^2)(\delta x)^2.$$

We now proceed to a limit by letting the number of discs tend to infinity in such a way that the thickness of every disc tends to zero. Then the solid formed of the discs approximates ever more closely to the hemisphere, and the difference between the masses of the two solids, and between the moments of their weights, tends to zero. In the formula for the C.G., therefore, the mass M of the disc solid tends to $\frac{2}{3}q\pi$, the mass of the hemisphere, and $\bar{x}$ tends to the value of $\bar{x}$ for the hemisphere. We know from the theory of integration that, of the two sums in the expression for $\sum m_r x_r$ found above, the first:

$$\sum q\pi x(1 - x^2)\delta x$$

tends to

$$\int_0^1 q\pi x(1 - x^2)dx,$$

whilst the second:

$$\sum \frac{1}{2}q\pi(1 - x^2)(\delta x)^2$$

tends to zero. It is important to notice in passing that, in the limit, the same result would have been found by taking the C.G. of the disc to have coordinate x instead of $x + \frac{1}{2}\delta x$. That is, small quantities can be neglected in locating the C.G. of the individual discs.

Therefore, proceeding to the limit in the formula

$$M\bar{x} = \sum m_r x_r,$$

we have for the hemisphere

$$\frac{2}{3}q\pi\bar{x} = \int_0^1 q\pi x(1 - x^2)dx$$

$$= \left[q\pi(\frac{1}{2}x^2 - \frac{1}{4}x^4) \right]_0^1$$

$$= \frac{1}{4}q\pi,$$

so that

$$\bar{x} = \frac{3}{8}.$$

The C.G. of the hemisphere is on its axis of symmetry $\frac{3}{8}$ m from the centre

*15.9 Once the method of Example 7 has been understood, the calculation can be simplified, especially by using the fact that small quantities can be neglected in locating the C.G. of the separate thin slices.

EXAMPLE 8. Find the C.G. of a lamina[1] bounded by the axes and parts of the line $x = 1$ and the curve $y = 1 + x^2$ (Fig. 14).

We consider first a lamina composed of a number of rectangles, of which a typical one has width δx and height equal to the height of the curve $y = 1 + x^2$ at the point whose x-coordinate is x. Such a rectangle has an area of $y\,\delta x = (1 + x^2)\delta x$. If the mass of the material is s per unit area, the mass of the rectangle is $s(1 + x^2)\delta x$.

The C.G. of the new lamina is calculated from the formulae

$$M\bar{x} = \sum m_r x_r, \quad M\bar{y} = \sum m_r y_r.$$

In these formulae, (x_r, y_r) is the C.G. of the typical rectangle, which is at $(x + \frac{1}{2}\delta x, \frac{1}{2}y)$. It can, however, be shown as in Example 7 that no error is introduced when we proceed to the limit if this is taken to be $(x, \frac{1}{2}y)$.

The value of M for the lamina composed of rectangles is

$$\sum s(1 + x^2)\delta x.$$

In the limit, when the width of the rectangles tends to zero and the number of rectangles tends to infinity, this tends to

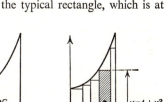

Fig. 14   Fig. 15

$$\int_0^1 s(1 + x^2)dx = \left[s(x + \tfrac{1}{3}x^3)\right]_0^1 = \tfrac{4}{3}s.$$

The other sums in the formulae are

$$\sum m_r x_r = \sum \{s(1 + x^2)\delta x \times x\} = \sum s(x + x^3)\delta x,$$

and

$$\sum m_r y_r = \sum \{s(1 + x^2)\delta x \times \tfrac{1}{2}y\} = \sum \tfrac{1}{2}s(1 + x^2)^2\delta x.$$

In the limit, these tend to

$$\int_0^1 s(x + x^3)dx = \left[s(\tfrac{1}{2}x^2 + \tfrac{1}{4}x^4)\right]_0^1 = \tfrac{3}{4}s,$$

and

$$\int_0^1 \tfrac{1}{2}s(1 + x^2)^2dx = \left[\tfrac{1}{2}s(x + \tfrac{2}{3}x^3 + \tfrac{1}{5}x^5)\right]_0^1 = \tfrac{14}{15}s.$$

The formulae for the C.G. of the lamina in Fig. 14, to which the lamina of rectangles approximates in the limit, is therefore given by the equations

$$\tfrac{4}{3}s\bar{x} = \tfrac{3}{4}s, \quad \text{and} \quad \tfrac{4}{3}s\bar{y} = \tfrac{14}{15}s,$$

so that the coordinates of G are $(\tfrac{9}{16}, \tfrac{7}{10})$.

[1] A lamina is a plane sheet of matter of negligible thickness.

†*EXAMPLE 9. Find the C.G. of a semicircular wire of radius R.*
By symmetry, the C.G. is on the radius at right angles to
the bounding diameter. We take this radius as the x-axis,
and denote the coordinate of G by $\bar{x}$.

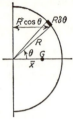

Suppose the wire to be cut into a large number of small
arcs, of which a typical one extends from the radius
making an angle θ radians with the axis, to the radius
making an angle $\theta + \delta\theta$ (see Fig. 16). This arc has length
$R\delta\theta$, and if the mass of the wire is p per unit length the arc
has mass $pR\delta\theta$. Since small quantities can be neglected in
locating the C.G. of this small arc, we take it to be at one
end of the arc, so that its x-coordinate is $R \cos \theta$.

In the formula for the C.G., M is the mass of the whole   Fig. 16
wire, which is $p\pi R$. Also

$$\sum m_r x_r = \sum \{pR\delta\theta \times R \cos \theta\} = \sum pR^2 \cos \theta\delta\theta.$$

In the limit, when the length of the arcs tends to zero and the number of
arcs tends to infinity, this tends to

$$\int_{-\pi/2}^{\pi/2} pR^2 \cos \theta d\theta = \left[pR^2 \sin \theta \right]_{-\pi/2}^{\pi/2} = 2pR^2.$$

(The limits of integration are the values of θ at the two ends of the wire.)
The C.G. of the whole wire is therefore given by

$$p\pi R\bar{x} = 2pR^2,$$

so that

$$\bar{x} = \frac{2R}{\pi}.$$

15.10 The next example uses a similar idea to that used in the last
three examples, but no integration need be performed.

*EXAMPLE 10. Prove that the C.G. of a triangular lamina is at the centroid
of the triangle.*

We require first a simple geometrical result. Let XY be a transversal
parallel to the base BC of a triangle ABC, and let Q be the mid-point of XY
(Fig. 17). Then AQ produced cuts BC at the mid-point of BC.

For, from the similar triangles AXQ, ABL,

$$\frac{XQ}{BL} = \frac{AQ}{AL}.$$

Also, from the triangles AQY, ALC,

$$\frac{QY}{LC} = \frac{AQ}{AL}.$$

Since we are given that $XQ = QY$, it follows that $BL = LC$.

We now prove the main result. We consider first a different lamina composed of a number of rectangles, each having for an axis of symmetry a transversal of the triangle ABC parallel to the base BC (Fig. 18). The C.G. of each of these rectangles is at the mid-point of its axis of symmetry, and

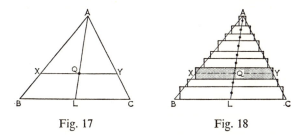

Fig. 17   Fig. 18

we have just proved that this lies on the median AL. Therefore the C.G. of the whole lamina lies on this median.

When we proceed to the limit the lamina of rectangles approximates ever more closely to the given triangular lamina. The masses of the two laminae are, in fact, exactly equal, however many rectangles are taken; and the difference between the moments of their weights about any line tends to zero as the widths of the rectangles tend to zero. We deduce that, in the limit, the C.G. of the triangular lamina lies on AL.

By a similar argument, it follows that G lies on the medians BM and CN. It is therefore at the centroid of the triangle ABC.

It will be noticed that the C.G. of a triangular lamina coincides with the C.G. of three equal masses placed at the corners of the triangles (see § 15.7, Example 6). This cannot, however, be generalized to polygons of more than three sides; for example, the C.G. of a quadrilateral lamina does not in general coincide with the C.G. of four equal masses placed at the four corners.

By an argument similar to that used in Example 10 it can be proved that the C.G. of a solid tetrahedron is on each of the lines joining a vertex to the centroid of the opposite face.

Some important results

15.11 It will be convenient to give a list of the positions of the centre of gravity for bodies of shapes which occur frequently in problems in mechanics. The derivation of these results requires the methods described in §§ 15.8–15.10, and is left to the student.

Solid bodies (of uniform density):

Hemisphere, radius r. On the radius of symmetry, distance $\frac{3}{8}r$ from the centre. (Cf. § 15.8, Example 7.)

Right circular cone, height h. On the axis of symmetry, distance $\frac{1}{4}h$ from the centre of the base.

Pyramid on any base. On the line joining the vertex to the C.G. of the base, one-quarter of the distance up from the base.

Hollow bodies (surfaces of uniform density):

Hemispherical shell, radius r. On the radius of symmetry, distance $\frac{1}{2}r$ from the centre.

Plane areas (laminae of uniform density):

Triangle. At the centroid (see § 15.10, Example 10).

Sector of circle, radius r, with angle 2θ radians at the centre. On the radius of symmetry, distance $\frac{2}{3}r \sin\theta/\theta$ from the centre. In particular, for a semicircle $\theta = \frac{1}{2}\pi$, so that the C.G. is $4r/3\pi$ from the centre.

Linear figures (wires of uniform density):

Arc of circle, radius r, subtending 2θ radians at the centre. On the radius of symmetry, distance $r \sin\theta/\theta$ from the centre. The result for a semicircular arc (see § 15.9, Example 9) is obtained by taking $\theta = \frac{1}{2}\pi$.

EXERCISE 15(c)

In Questions 1–4 find the centres of gravity of the solids formed by the revolution of areas bounded by the given curves and lines.

*1. $y^2 = x$, $y = 0$, $x = 6$; about the x-axis.

*2. $y^2 = x^3$, $y = 0$, $x = 5$; about the x-axis.

*3. $y = 1 - x^2$, $y = 0$, $x = 0$; about the y-axis.

*4. $x^2y = 1$, $y = 0$, $x = 1$, $x = n$; about the x-axis. What is the limiting position of this C.G. as $n \to \infty$?

In questions 5–9 find the centres of gravity of uniform laminae bounded by the given curves and lines.

*5. $y^2 = x$, $x = 6$.

*6. $y^2 = x^3$, $x = 5$.

*7. $y = x^2$, $y = 0$, $x = 1$.

*8. $y = 4 - x^2$, the positive axes.

*9. $x^3y = 1$, $y = 0$, $x = 1$, $x = n$. What is the limiting position of this centre of gravity as $n \to \infty$?

*10. The density of a rod AB of length l varies uniformly along its length, and the density at B is twice that at A. Find the distance of the centre of gravity from A.

11. A sheet of metal is in the shape of a square $ABCD$ with an isosceles triangle EBC described on the side BC. If the side of the square is 0·4 m and the perpendicular from E to BC is 0·3 m, find the distance of the C.G. of the sheet from AD.

12. $ABCD$ is a square sheet of paper, centre O, of side 0·6 m. The corners A and B are folded over so that they coincide at O. Find the position of the C.G. of the folded sheet.

13. A uniform lamina $ABCD$ has $AB = BC = CD = 360$ mm and angle $ABC = $ angle $BCD = 120°$. Find the distance of the C.G. from BC.

14. OAD is a uniform triangular lamina and H is the mid-point of AD. Through the mid-point of OH a line is drawn parallel to AD cutting OA in B and OD in C. Show that the C.G. of the trapezium $ABCD$ is on HO at a distance $\frac{2}{5}HO$ from H.

15. $ABCD$ is a square uniform plate of side 9 cm. AC, BD meet at O, and the triangle AOB is cut out. Find the C.G. of the piece that remains.

16. $ABCD$ is a uniform square lamina of side 1 m. P, Q divide AB, BC in the ratio 2 : 1 and R, S divide CD, DA in the ratio 1 : 2. Find the distance from AB of the C.G. of the lamina $APQCRS$.

17. $ABCD$ is a square of side 100 m, from which a semicircle with AB as diameter is removed. Find the C.G. of the figure remaining.

18. AB and CD are parallel sides of a trapezium, of lengths 60 mm and 90 mm and a distance 150 mm apart. Find the distance of the C.G. from CD. If the weight of the trapezium is W, show that a weight of $\frac{1}{15}W$ must be placed along AB in order that the trapezium may balance about the line parallel to AB and CD and half-way between them.

19. A uniform rod of length 60 mm, with its cross-section a circle, is sharpened at one end, like a pencil, to a conical point, without shortening the axis of the cylinder. If the height of this cone is 10 mm, find the distance the C.G. is shifted by sharpening.

20. Find the C.G. of a uniform solid truncated cone whose plane faces are circles of radii 20 mm and 30 mm at a distance 40 mm apart.

21. The cross-section of a solid right prism is an equilateral triangle of side 60 mm. On one end is fixed a solid triangular pyramid of height 120 mm and base an equilateral triangle of side 60 mm. If the length of the prism is 120 mm, find the C.G. of the solid.

22. A hemispherical bowl of weight W and radius 10 cm is full of liquid whose weight is $4W$. Find the position of the C.G.

23. A wire is bent in the form of a U, the straight sides being x metres long and the curved part being a semicircle of radius 0·2 m. Find the value of x if the C.G. of the wire is on the diameter of the semicircle.

24. A hollow closed vessel consists of a cylinder of base radius 22 mm and height 88 mm, closed at one end by a plane surface and at the other by a hemispherical shell. Find the distance of the C.G. from the plane face.

†**25.** A lamina is in the shape of a sector of a circle of radius 60 mm, the angle at the centre being 60°. The lamina is bound along the curved edge with wire, the mass of the wire per unit length being equal to the mass of the lamina per unit area. Find the distance of the C.G. from the centre.

†**26.** From a solid block in the shape of a right circular cylinder of height h a conical hole is bored out, the base of the cone being coincident with one end of the cylinder and the axis being along that of the cylinder. The volume removed is one-quarter of the volume of the original cylinder. The remaining solid vessel is placed with its axis vertical and the hole uppermost, and the hole is filled with liquid whose density is half that of the material of which the block is made. Find the C.G. of the vessel and liquid combined.

†**27.** $ABCD$ is a quadrilateral with $AB = 3$ cm, $BC = 12$ cm, $CD = 13$ cm, $DA = 4$ cm, $BD = 5$ cm. Find by drawing: (i) the C.G. of a uniform lamina of the shape $ABCD$, and (ii) the C.G. of equal masses placed at A, B, C and D.

†**28.** Explain why the C.G. of masses 1, 6, 5, 6 placed at the vertices A, B, C, D of the quadrilateral in Question 27 coincides with the C.G. of the lamina.

Stable and unstable equilibrium

15.12 If a body is hung up from a single point, or stands with just one point in contact with a supporting surface, there are only two forces acting on it: its weight acting vertically through the C.G. and a force through the point of support. For equilibrium these two forces must act along the same line. It follows that the C.G. must be in the same vertical line as the point of support.

This property is used in locating experimentally the C.G. of a body of irregular shape. If a number of points are taken in the body, and it is suspended from each in turn, then the C.G. is in each case known to be on a vertical line through the point of support. In this way a number of lines can be found in the body on which the C.G. is known to lie, and the point through which they all pass is the C.G.

> *EXAMPLE 11. A closed loop of wire is in the form of a semicircle and its bounding diameter (Fig. 19). It hangs freely, pivoted to a fixed point at one end of its bounding diameter. What angle does this diameter make with the vertical in equilibrium?*

We first find the C.G. of the wire, which is clearly on the radius at right angles to the bounding diameter. Let the radius of the wire be r and the mass p per unit length. We regard the wire as composed of two parts: a straight wire of length $2r$ and a semicircular wire of length πr, whose C.G. was calculated in § 15.9, Example 9.

	SEPARATE PARTS		WHOLE BODY
Mass	$2rp$	πrp	$(2 + \pi)rp$
Distance from AB	0	$2r/\pi$	$\bar{x}$

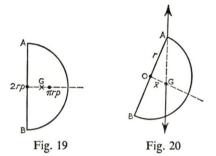

Fig. 19   Fig. 20

The equation is

$$2rp \times 0 + \pi rp \times \frac{2r}{\pi} = (2 + \pi)rp \times \bar{x},$$

which gives

$$\bar{x} = \frac{2r}{2 + \pi}$$

When the wire hangs from its pivot at A it does so with G vertically below A (Fig. 20). Therefore

$$\tan GAO = \frac{\bar{x}}{r} = \frac{2}{2 + \pi},$$

and the required angle GAO is 21°.

15.13 If in Example 11 the wire were slightly displaced from its position of equilibrium, in its own plane, the forces on it would immediately tend to restore it to the position in which G is vertically below A. It would, if the pivot were smooth, oscillate about that position of equilibrium like a pendulum. This kind of equilibrium is said to be STABLE. On the other hand, a pencil balanced on a table by its point, if slightly displaced, would tend to fall farther from the vertical; this is called UNSTABLE EQUILIBRIUM.

A cylinder standing on its base on a level surface is in stable equilibrium, because a small displacement would bring restoring forces into play. Admittedly, if it were displaced too far it would topple right over; but the factor determining its stability is the nature of the forces when it receives a small displacement from its equilibrium position. There are positions of unstable equilibrium with the cylinder standing on points of its rim.

The position of the centre of gravity of a body is often a crucial factor in determining the stability of equilibrium.

EXAMPLE 12. A child's toy consists of a solid hemisphere of radius r and a solid circular cone of height h and radius r, the two parts being of the same material and stuck together at their circular boundaries. Discuss the stability of the position of equilibrium when it stands with its hemispherical surface in contact with a rough, horizontal table.

The C.G. of the composite body is on its axis of symmetry, and may be above or below the centre of the hemisphere. Fig. 21 shows the body slightly displaced from the vertical position when the C.G. is above the centre of the

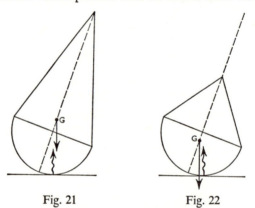

Fig. 21   Fig. 22

hemisphere. By moments about the point of contact with the table it appears that the body will tend to turn clockwise, and therefore farther from the vertical position; this is therefore a position of unstable equilibrium. If the C.G. is below the centre of the hemisphere, as in Fig. 22, the weight of the toy has an anticlockwise, i.e. a restoring, moment about the point of contact, so that equilibrium is stable.

The C.G. of the toy can simply be found in terms of r and h, since the C.G. of a hemisphere and of a cone are known (see § 15.11). If the material has density q, we have:

	SEPARATE PARTS		WHOLE BODY
Mass	$\frac{2}{3}\pi q r^3$	$\frac{1}{3}\pi q r^2 h$	$\frac{1}{3}\pi q r^2 (2r + h)$
Height above centre	$-\frac{3}{8}r$	$\frac{1}{4}h$	$\bar{x}$

Therefore

$$-\tfrac{2}{3}\pi q r^3 \times \tfrac{3}{8}r + \tfrac{1}{3}\pi q r^2 h \times \tfrac{1}{4}h = \tfrac{1}{3}\pi q r^2(2r + h) \times \bar{x},$$

$$\bar{x} = \frac{h^2 - 3r^2}{4(2r + h)}.$$

Equilibrium is unstable if G is above the centre, so that $\bar{x}$ is positive. This occurs if $h^2 - 3r^2$ is positive, i.e. if $h > r\sqrt{3}$. Equilibrium is stable if $h < r\sqrt{3}$.

It is interesting to consider what happens when $h = r\sqrt{3}$. The toy can then rest in equilibrium with any point of the hemisphere in contact with the table, since the weight always acts through the point of contact. A small displacement from the vertical position then produces no tendency either to restore the toy to its vertical position or to make it tilt farther. This is described as NEUTRAL EQUILIBRIUM.

If the conical part of the toy is reasonably tall, there are other positions of neutral equilibrium for this toy, lying on its side with a generator of the cone in contact with the table.

EXERCISE 15(d)

1. The wire pentagon described in Question 12, Exercise 15(b), is hung up from A. Find the angle between AB and the vertical.

2. The sheet of carboard described in Question 15 of Exercise 15(b) is suspended from A. Find the angle between OA and the vertical.

3. An L-shaped uniform wire ABC is suspended from A. If $AB : BC = 5 : 3$, find the angle between AB and the vertical.

4. A uniform lamina ABC in the form of a triangle in which the angles A, B, C are 90°, 60°, 30° is suspended from A and has a particle attached at one corner so that it rests with BC horizontal. Show that its mass must be two-thirds that of the lamina. To which corner must it be attached?

5. $ABCD$ is a square uniform lamina; M, N, O are the mid-points of AB, BC, BD. The square $BNOM$ is cut away. The remaining lamina is stood on the edge AM on a rough inclined plane, AM being along a line of greatest slope, with M above A. What is the greatest possible angle of inclination of the plane if the lamina is not to topple over?

6. A uniform square lamina $ABCD$ suspended from A is in equilibrium in a vertical plane, AC being vertical. X, Y are the mid-points of AB, BC, and the triangular portion BXY is cut away. In the new position of equilibrium, what angle does AC make with the vertical?

7. The cross-section of a uniform right prism is a rhombus $PQRS$, in which $PQ = 120$ mm, $SQ = 80$ mm. The prism rests with PQ on a rough plane, which is tilted about a line perpendicular to PQ so that the cross-section remains vertical and P rises above Q. What will be the inclination of the plane when the prism topples over?

8. A thin, uniform metal plate in the form of a regular hexagon $PQRSTV$, of side a, has the triangular portion PTV removed. Find the C.G. of the remainder. If this portion is now suspended freely from P, find to the nearest degree the angle which PQ makes with the vertical.

9. The figure shows an end-face $ABQP$ of a prism. The other end is $A'B'Q'P'$, and the edges AA', BB', QQ', PP' are all perpendicular to the end-faces. $ABQP$ is formed by cutting an isosceles right-angled triangle PQC

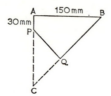

from an isosceles right-angled triangle ABC. $AB = AC = 150$ mm, angle $PAB =$ angle $PQB = 90°$, angle $ABQ = 45°$, $AP = 30$ mm. Find the distances of the C.G. of the prism: (i) from the face $ABB'A'$, (ii) from the face $APP'A'$.

The prism is placed with its face $PQQ'P'$ in contact with a very rough plane of angle $45°$; all the edges AA', BB', QQ', PP' are horizontal. Can it rest in this position: (i) with PP' higher than QQ', (ii) with QQ' higher than PP'?

10. $ABCD$ is a non-uniform rectangular sheet of metal in which $AB = 70$ mm and $AD = 50$ mm. When the sheet is suspended from A, AB makes an angle of $45°$ with the vertical, and when it is suspended from B, BA makes an angle $\bar{\omega}$ with the vertical. Find the position of the C.G. and the angle made by AB with the vertical when the sheet is suspended from D.

11. When a square wooden board $ABCD$ is suspended from A, the angle between AB and the vertical is $\tan^{-1} \frac{1}{2}$. When the board is suspended from C, the angle between CB and the vertical is $\tan^{-1} \frac{1}{3}$. Find the angle between DA and the vertical when the board is suspended from D.

12. A frustum of a right circular cone of height h and semi-vertical angle θ is obtained by cutting the cone by a plane parallel to the base at a distance $\frac{1}{2}h$ from the vertex. If the frustum is placed on its slant side on a horizontal plane, prove that it will not topple over if $\cos^2 \theta > \frac{28}{45}$.

13. A toy consists of a solid circular cylinder of radius r, with a heavy hemispherical base of the same radius fixed to one end. The density of the hemisphere is 8 times that of the cylinder. Find the greatest possible height of the cylinder if the toy will always return to the vertical when displaced.

14. A hollow vessel is in the form of a circular cylinder of height h and radius r closed at one end by a hemispherical shell of radius r. Discuss the stability of the position of equilibrium in which the vessel stands with its axis vertical and its curved surface touching a horizontal plane.

†15. A child's toy consists of a hemispherical shell of radius 2 cm and mass 5 gm, attached to a rod of mass 2 gm per cm length. One end of the rod is fastened to the inside of the hemisphere, and the rod is perpendicular to the plane of the rim and passes through its centre. Find how long the rod may be if the toy is to rest in stable equilibrium on a horizontal plane.

†16. $ABCD$ is a square non-uniform lamina of side 100 mm. Experiments are carried out by standing the lamina, on an edge, on a line of greatest slope of a plane of angle $\bar{\omega}$. It is found that the lamina will stand on the edge AB with A below B, and also on the edge CD with C below D. If placed on the edge DA with D below A it topples over. Prove that the C.G. must lie within a certain trapezium, and find the area of this trapezium.

†17. An isosceles triangle is cut from a corner of a uniform square lamina. Show that the remainder can stand vertically on a shortened edge if the part cut off is 0·5 of an edge, but not if it is 0·6 of an edge.

†18. C is the centre of a uniform solid sphere of radius 100 mm, having in it two spherical holes of centres A and B and radii 10 mm and 20 mm, so situated that $CA = CB = 75$ mm and $AB = 90$ mm. Show that when the sphere rests in equilibrium on a horizontal plane the line AB makes an angle of $\tan^{-1}\left(\frac{12}{7}\right)$ with the vertical.

CHAPTER 16

ENERGY AND POWER

Work and kinetic energy

16.1 When a body moves under the action of certain forces, we sometimes wish to know how much use a particular force has been in this motion. This depends not only on the size of the force but also on the distance through which it has moved its point of application. It is desirable to have a measure of this 'usefulness' of a force; if a force moves its point of application through a certain distance in its own direction we define the *work done by the force* as the quantity

force × distance.

For example, if a luggage-truck is pulled along a platform by applying a force of 20 N to a handle, and if the truck is moved a distance of 150 m, the work done is 3000 units.

We shall now see how this quantity enters into a dynamical equation. It will be remembered that in § 13.2 (p. 167) we considered the effect of a force in increasing the speed of a body from u to v in time t. The following calculation is on similar lines, but we are now concerned with the distance that the body covers while accelerating, rather than the time which it takes.

If the acceleration is uniform, and the body moves a distance s in a straight line while its velocity changes from u to v, the acceleration is found from the formula

$$v^2 = u^2 + 2as.$$

This gives
$$as = \tfrac{1}{2}v^2 - \tfrac{1}{2}u^2.$$

The force required to produce this acceleration is found from the equation of motion

$$F = ma.$$

The work done by this force is Fs. From the foregoing equations we find that

$$Fs = mas = m(\tfrac{1}{2}v^2 - \tfrac{1}{2}u^2),$$

so that
$$Fs = \tfrac{1}{2}mv^2 - \tfrac{1}{2}mu^2. \tag{1}$$

It is useful to give a name to the quantities appearing on the right side of this equation.

DEFINITION. *When a body is in motion, the expression*

$$\tfrac{1}{2} \textit{ mass } \times \textit{ (velocity)}^2$$

is called the KINETIC ENERGY *of the body.*

We shall use the abbreviation K.E. for kinetic energy.
With these definitions, equation (1) can be written:

work done by force = K.E. at end − K.E. at start,

or *work done by force = increase of K.E.*

16.2 To maintain coherence in the system of units, we take the unit of work to be the amount of work done when a force of 1 N is applied through a distance of 1 m. This quantity is of such importance in physics that the unit has a special name – the *joule*[1] (J); and since it is convenient to measure all the quantities appearing as terms of an equation in the same unit, kinetic energy is also measured in joules. (In the alternative form of the metric system based on the centimetre, gramme and second as fundamental units (see § 3.9) the corresponding unit of work and energy was called an *erg*.)

This definition suggests that we might write

$$(1 \text{ N}) \times (1 \text{ m}) = (1 \text{ J});$$

but it will be recalled that we have already written (see § 6.14)

$$(1 \text{ N}) \times (1 \text{ m}) = (1 \text{ N m}),$$

where the newton metre is a unit of moment and not of work – a quite different physical quantity. This brings out an important point that, whilst it is sometimes useful to extend the operations of algebra to allow the multiplication and division of physical quantities, common sense must always be used in interpreting the results.

EXAMPLE 1. A car of mass 1200 kg starts from rest and is observed to reach a speed of 20 m s⁻¹ after it has travelled 250 m. Neglecting resistances, find the driving force, assumed to be constant.
There is no K.E. at the start, and the K.E. at the end is

$$\tfrac{1}{2}mv^2 = \tfrac{1}{2} \times 1200 \times 20^2 = 240\,000 \text{ joules.}$$

If the driving force is F newtons, the work done by this force is

$$F \times 250 \text{ joules.}$$

Therefore $\qquad\qquad 250F = 240\,000,$

so that $\qquad\qquad\qquad F = 960.$

[1] After James Joule (1818–89), who first developed the modern concept of energy.

16.3 In § 16.1 the equation

$$Fs = \tfrac{1}{2}mv^2 - \tfrac{1}{2}mu^2$$

was obtained by supposing that there was a single force F accelerating the body. If there were in addition a resistance to motion R, the term F in the equation of motion would have to be replaced by $F - R$, and the final equation would become

$$Fs - Rs = \tfrac{1}{2}mv^2 - \tfrac{1}{2}mu^2. \tag{2}$$

The additional term appearing in equation (2), the product of the resistance and the distance over which it acts, is called the *work done against the resistance*. It will be observed that the effect of this term is to reduce the final amount of kinetic energy.

Equation (2) may be written:

work done by accelerating force — work done against resistance
= increase of K.E.

EXAMPLE 2. *The driver of a car of mass* 800 *kg travelling at* 36 *km h⁻¹ sees an obstruction in the road. He applies his brakes immediately, but does not use the clutch to disengage the engine until he has travelled a further* 10 *m. He finally comes to rest at a distance of* 30 *m after the brakes were applied. If the engine was exerting a forward thrust of* 140 *N, find the retarding force due to the brakes.*

One advantage of using the energy method to solve this problem is that the whole motion can be considered at once rather than in two stages. For, during the first stage before the clutch is disengaged,

work done by driving force — work done against resistance = gain of K.E.;

or, more conveniently since the car is slowing down,

work done against resistance — work done by driving force = loss of K.E.

In the second stage the engine makes no contribution, so that

work done against resistance = loss of K.E.

Adding these last two equations, we have for the complete motion

total work done against resistance

— work done by driving force in first stage = total loss of K.E.

In order to calculate the K.E. at the start, the speed of 36 km h⁻¹ must first be written as 10 m s⁻¹. We then have

$$\tfrac{1}{2}mu^2 = \tfrac{1}{2} \times 800 \times 10^2 = 40\,000.$$

Since there is no K.E. at the end, the loss in K.E. is 40 000 J.

The work done by the driving force over the 10 m for which it acts is

$$140 \times 10 = 1400 \text{ J}.$$

If the resistance is R newtons, the work done against this resistance over the distance of 30 m is

$$(R \times 30) \text{ J}.$$

Therefore $30R - 1400 = 40\,000$,

so that $R = 1380$.

The force due to the brakes is therefore 1380 N.

16.4 In § 16.1 it was supposed that the force F was acting along the line in which the body was moving. It often happens, however, that a body is accelerated along one straight line by a force acting in some other direction. This may occur, for example, when a bead is pulled along a wire, or a truck along rails. If the force makes an angle θ with the line of motion, the term F in the equation of motion must be replaced by $F\cos\theta$, the resolved part of the force. Equation (1) of § 16.1 then becomes

$$Fs\cos\theta = \tfrac{1}{2}mv^2 - \tfrac{1}{2}mu^2. \tag{3}$$

The work done by the force must therefore be taken as $Fs\cos\theta$.

DEFINITION. *If a force F moves its point of application in a straight line from A to B, where AB is of length s and F is at an angle θ to AB, the* WORK DONE BY THE FORCE *is Fs cos θ.*

This definition is illustrated in Fig. 1. Since $s\cos\theta$ is equal to AC,

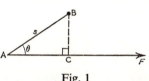

Fig. 1

the amount of movement in the direction of F, the work done by the force can still be regarded as:

force $\times$ distance moved by point of application in direction of force.

It should be noticed that the only forces which contribute terms to the work–energy equation (3) are those which have a resolved part in the direction of motion. In an example such as the bead pulled along a straight wire by a force at an angle to the wire there is also a normal contact force from the wire on the bead at right angles to the direction of motion. Such a force is called a FORCE OF CONSTRAINT. Since it has no resolved part along the wire, it does no work in the motion.

*The definition of work given above must be modified when the force is not constant. It will be shown in Volume 2 that the formula should then be $\int F\cos\theta\,ds$.

16.5 It should be observed that the work done by a force and the K.E. of a body are scalar quantities (see § 7.3) and not vector quantities. The kinetic energy of a body moving with speed v is always $\frac{1}{2}mv^2$, whatever the direction of its velocity. In particular, kinetic energy is never negative. In this respect these quantities should be contrasted with the impulse of a force and the momentum of a body, which were shown in § 13.9 to be vector quantities.

For example, two identical trains passing each other with speeds of 100 km h^{-1} have the same kinetic energy, whereas the momentum of one is minus the momentum of the other. Two men pushing lawn mowers through a certain distance in different directions may do the same amount of work, but they exert different impulses.

EXAMPLE 3. A bead of mass 6 gm is threaded onto a smooth circular wire, centre O and radius 4·8 m, which is fixed in a horizontal plane. A and B are two points on the wire such that angle AOB is 60°. The bead runs round

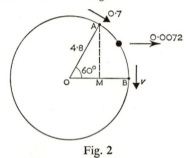

Fig. 2

the wire, and when it reaches A it is moving at 0·7 m s^{-1}. Between A and B it is acted on only by a constant force of 0·0072 N in a direction parallel to the radius OB. With what speed will it reach B? (Fig. 2).

Of the three forces which act on the bead, two – its weight acting vertically and the normal contact force from the wire – are always at right angles to the direction of motion, and therefore do no work. To find the work done by the third force we shall suppose that the formula

force × distance moved in the direction of the force

remains valid even when the body does not move in a straight line. This gives the work done by the force of 0·0072 N as

$$0{\cdot}0072 \times MB = 0{\cdot}0072 \times (4{\cdot}8 - 4{\cdot}8 \cos 60°) = 0{\cdot}017\,28 \text{ J}.$$

The K.E. at A is

$$\tfrac{1}{2} \times 0{\cdot}006 \times 0{\cdot}7^2 = 0{\cdot}001\,47 \text{ J};$$

and, if the speed at B in m s^{-1} is v, the K.E. at B is

$$\tfrac{1}{2} \times 0{\cdot}006 \times v^2 = 0{\cdot}003\,v^2 \text{ J}.$$

Since K.E. is a scalar quantity, the gain in K.E. can be found simply as the difference between these two numbers. Therefore

$$0{\cdot}017\,28 = 0{\cdot}003v^2 - 0{\cdot}001\,47$$

which gives $v = 2{\cdot}5.$

The bead reaches B with a speed of $2{\cdot}5$ m s^{-1}.

The proof of the assumption made in this example, that even when the motion is not in a straight line the work done is still the product of the force and the distance moved in the direction of the force, must be left for a later volume. It makes use of techniques of calculus which may be as yet unfamiliar to the student.

EXERCISE 16(a)

1. Compare the K.E. of the following: a sprinter of mass 70 kg running at 10 m s^{-1}, a bullet of mass 30 gm moving at 550 m s^{-1}, a truck of mass 2000 kg moving at 20 m s^{-1} and a ship of mass 1000 tonnes moving at $0{\cdot}3$ m s^{-1}. (See Exercise 13(a), Question 1.)

2. What is the K.E. of a 10 kg mass, originally at rest, when it has moved a distance of 4 m under the action of a force of 20 N? What speed does it acquire?

3. A waiter pushes a trolley of mass 40 kg across a room. When it has moved 3 m it has a speed of $1{\cdot}5$ m s^{-1}. With what force does he push it?

4. A constant force of 3×10^{-4} N acting on a 15 gm mass originally at rest gives it a velocity of $0{\cdot}1$ m s^{-1}. Through what distance has the force acted?

5. The velocity of a body of mass 8 kg increases from 4 m s^{-1} to 6 m s^{-1} while the body moves in a straight line through a distance of 5 m. What force (in the direction of the line) acts on the body?

6. A 10 kg body is moving with a speed of 5 m s^{-1}. It is brought to rest by a constant force of 100 N acting in the direction opposite to the direction of motion. How far does the body move while the force is being applied?

7. A stone is sliding across the ice. If it slides 25 m after it has a speed of 5 m s^{-1}, find the coefficient of friction.

8. If the braking force on a car can bring it to rest in a distance of 12 m from a speed of 50 km h^{-1}, what distance is needed to stop from 100 kmh^{-1}? From what speed can the car be stopped in 27 m?

9. A car of mass 1000 kg accelerates from a standstill to 54 km h^{-1} while covering a distance of 50 m. Assuming that the resistance to motion is 150 N, find the driving force.

10. The resistance to motion of a motor boat of mass 780 kg is 120 N, and the driving force from the propellers is 250 N. What distance does it cover while increasing speed from 2 to 3 m s^{-1}?

11. A sledge of mass 32 kg starts from rest and is pulled with a force of 50 N against a resistance of 30 N for a distance of $9{\cdot}8$ m. How fast is it then going?

12. A 50 000 tonne liner slows down from 36 knots to 24 knots with engines stopped in a distance of 900 m. Taking 1 knot to equal 0.5 m s^{-1} and assuming the resistance of the sea to be constant, calculate this resistance.

13. Find the tractive force needed to accelerate a train of mass 400 tonnes from 40 to 70 km h^{-1} in a distance of 2 km, assuming that the resistance to motion is 40 N per tonne.

14. The total resistance to motion of a car with brakes on is $\frac{4}{5}$ of the weight of the car. Show that the car can be stopped in about 12 m from a speed of 50 km h^{-1}.

15. The mass of a cyclist and his machine is 80 kg. He starts from rest and exerts a constant forward force of 70 N until he has travelled 32 m. He then applies his brakes until he has gone a further 3 m. If there is throughout a constant resistance to motion of 20 N, and if the braking force is 180 N, find his final speed.

16. A man wishes to drive a car from A to B, a distance of 100 m, starting from rest at A and using the engine as little as possible. If the resistance is 250 N and the driving force 1250 N, how far from A does he stop using his engine?

17. If the car in Question 16 has a mass of 750 kg, and if the man stops using his engine half-way from A to B, with what speed will he pass B?

18. The tractive force on a car of mass 1200 kg when driven in first gear is 3000 N and when driven in second gear is 1500 N. The resistance is 300 N. Find the speed attained if a man starts from rest, drives 10 m in first gear and then changes into second gear for a further 30 m.

19. A boy on a toboggan is sliding on horizontal ground towards a wall 30 m away at a speed of 10 m s^{-1}. Calculating that the frictional resistance of 75 N is insufficient, he digs in his heels, producing an additional resistance of 125 N, and stops just before he hits the wall. If the mass of the boy and toboggan together is 70 kg, how far is he from the wall when he digs in his heels?

20. A man pulls a dog with a lead inclined at $\bar{\omega}$ to the horizontal. If the tension in the lead is 25 N, how much work does the man do when the dog is moved 4 m along the ground?

21. A woman pushes a pram of mass 20 kg from rest with a force of 40 N inclined at $60°$ to the horizontal. If frictional resistances amount to 11 N, find the speed of the pram after it has gone 2.5 m.

Other forms of energy

16.6 Consider the motion of a stone falling vertically under the action of gravity. Suppose that when it is at a height h_1 above the ground its velocity is v_1, and that when it has fallen to a height h_2 its velocity has increased to v_2. If the mass of the stone is m, the force acting on it is its weight mg, and the work done by this force as the stone falls is

$mg(h_1 - h_2)$. This is equal to the gain in the K.E. of the stone, so that

$$mgh_1 - mgh_2 = \tfrac{1}{2}mv_2{}^2 - \tfrac{1}{2}mv_1{}^2. \tag{4}$$

This equation can be rearranged in the form

$$mgh_1 + \tfrac{1}{2}mv_1{}^2 = mgh_2 + \tfrac{1}{2}mv_2{}^2. \tag{5}$$

(These equations could also be obtained by using the equation

$$v^2 = u^2 + 2as$$

with $u = v_1$, $v = v_2$, $s = h_1 - h_2$, $a = g$, and multiplying by $\tfrac{1}{2}m$.)

The quantities mgh_1, mgh_2 which occur in equations (4) and (5) are examples of what we call potential energy. It will be noticed that mgh_1 is equal to the work which would be done by the weight of the stone if it fell from a height h_1 to the ground.

DEFINITION. *The* (GRAVITATIONAL) POTENTIAL ENERGY *of a body in a given position is the work which would be done by its weight if it were to move from that position to a point at some fixed level.*

We shall often use the abbreviation P.E. for potential energy. The fixed level may be taken to be at any convenient height, provided that the same level is used throughout the solution of a particular problem.

We have seen that the P.E. of a body is measued by *mgh*, i.e.

weight of body × *height above fixed level.*

(This formula only holds on the assumption that the weight of a body does not vary with its height. This point is discussed more fully in Volume 2.)

Equation (4) can now be written

loss of P.E. = gain in K.E.,

and equation (5) as

(K.E. + P.E.) at start = (K.E. + P.E.) at end.

That is, as the stone falls the sum of its kinetic energy and its potential energy remains constant.

16.7 Two quantities have now been introduced to which we have given the name 'energy' – kinetic energy and gravitational potential energy. We shall now discuss what is meant by energy in more general terms.

A body which is moving is, by virtue of its movement, capable of doing work as it loses its speed. For example, a railway engine which runs into a buffer will compress the buffer; it is thereby doing work, since the force compressing the buffer is moving its point of application.

A body which is capable of doing work is said to possess energy. Broadly speaking, energy is something which can be fed into a machine or an engine to produce useful results. For example, in a windmill the kinetic energy of the air is used to drive the sails; in a hydro-electric plant the potential energy of a mass of water at a height is used to drive a dynamo.

Energy appears in many different forms. Heat and electricity are forms of energy. A mass of gas under compression possesses energy. Certain substances possess energy which can be released when they undergo chemical change; these substances are called fuels. Within the individual atoms of matter is stored a vast latent quantity of nuclear energy.

Energy is continually changing from one form into another. For example, the chemical energy of coal may be used to heat the water in a boiler. Some of this water is turned into steam, part of whose energy is due to its state of compression. This may be used to drive a piston in a cylinder, thereby creating kinetic energy. This kinetic energy can in turn be used to drive a dynamo and create electrical energy.

The quantity of energy involved in these changes is governed by a very important principle, first enunciated by Joule, known as the principle of the CONSERVATION OF ENERGY. This states that, despite the changes which its form undergoes, energy is neither created nor destroyed. In any system out of which and into which no energy passes the total amount of energy remains unaltered.

A simple illustration of this principle is that of the stone moving vertically under gravity, discussed in § 16.6. The stone possesses two types of energy, kinetic and potential; while the stone is in the air the amounts of energy of each kind vary in such a way that their sum remains constant.

16.8 If a body of mass m is raised vertically at a constant speed, there is an upward force on it equal to its weight mg. The work done by this force in raising the body through a height h is mgh, which is equal to the potential energy of the body. Thus the potential energy may be regarded either as the amount of work the weight of the body does as it falls or as the amount of work needed to raise it to the given height.

Similarly, the kinetic energy of a moving body may be regarded either as the work which it can do as its speed decreases to zero or as the work which must be done on it to produce its speed.

16.9 We shall now show from first principles, using the equation of motion, that the equation

$$\text{K.E.} + \text{P.E.} = \text{constant},$$

derived in § 16.6 for a body moving vertically, is still true if it moves down a path inclined to the vertical.

Consider a particle of mass m sliding from rest down a smooth slope of angle θ (Fig. 3). The equation of motion is

$\mathscr{R}$ (down the plane) $mg \sin \theta = ma,$

so that $a = g \sin \theta.$

If the particle moves through a *vertical* distance h, the distance that it has moved down the plane is $h/\sin \theta$. It therefore acquires a velocity v given by

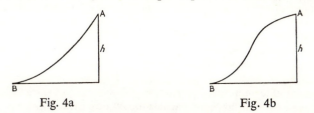

$$v^2 = 2as$$

$$= 2g \sin \theta \times \frac{h}{\sin \theta}$$

$$= 2gh.$$

Hence, multiplying by $\frac{1}{2}m$,

Fig. 3

$$mgh = \tfrac{1}{2}mv^2. \tag{6}$$

At the top of the slope the particle has no kinetic energy and has potential energy mgh (taking the level of the foot of the slope as the fixed level from which P.E. is measured). At the bottom it has no potential energy and has acquired kinetic energy $\frac{1}{2}mv^2$. The sum of the two types of energy is therefore the same at the end as at the beginning.

Equation (6) can also be interpreted as

work done by weight = gain in K.E.

since h is the distance moved by the point of application of the weight in the direction of the weight. The only other force on the particle is the normal force N. This force does no work, since the motion is perpendicular to N.

It can be proved that equation (6) still holds when the particle slides down from A to B by a curved path, provided that the surface is

Fig. 4a	Fig. 4b

smooth, h being the difference in height between A and B (see Figs. 4a and 4b). The result does not depend on the form of the curve AB. This fact is used in the next example.

EXAMPLE 4. A string of length 0·5 m is attached to a fixed point A and carries a 20 gm mass at its lower end. The mass is pulled aside until the string makes an angle $\bar{\omega}$ with the vertical, and it is then allowed to swing freely as a pendulum. With what speed does it pass through the lowest point of its path? (Fig. 5.)

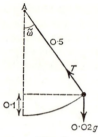

Fig. 5

When it is pulled aside, the mass of 0·02 kg rises to a height of

$$0·5 - 0·5 \cos \tilde{\omega} = 0·1 \text{ m}$$

above the lowest point. It therefore has P.E. of amount

$$0·02g \times 0·1 = 0·0196 \text{ joules,}$$

taking the lowest point of the path as the fixed level and using the value $g = 9·8$ m s^{-2}. As it swings down it loses this potential energy, and gains kinetic energy

$$\tfrac{1}{2} \times 0·2 \times v^2 = 0·01v^2 \text{ joules,}$$

where v is the speed in m s^{-1} at the lowest point.

Therefore
$$0·0196 = 0·01v^2,$$
$$v = 1·4.$$

Its speed at the lowest point is 1·4 m s^{-1}.

The tension in the string is another example of a force of constraint (see § 16.4); because of this force the mass is constrained to move in a circular path. Since at each instant the tension is at right angles to the direction of motion, this force does no work.

16.10 We return now to the problem of the particle sliding down the slope discussed at the beginning of § 16.9. Had the slope been rough, with coefficient of friction μ ($< \tan \theta$), an additional term

$$-\mu N = -\mu mg \cos \theta$$

would have appeared in the equation of motion, giving an acceleration of only

$$g \sin \theta - \mu g \cos \theta.$$

The final equation would then have taken the form

$$mgh - \mu mg \cos \theta \times \frac{h}{\sin \theta} = \tfrac{1}{2}mv^2.$$

The second term in this equation, which is equal to the friction force multiplied by the distance the particle moves down the slope, represents the work done against the resistance (see § 16.3). We therefore have:

P.E. lost — work done against resistance = K.E. gained.

At first sight it may seem that this is not in accordance with the principle of conservation of energy. In fact, however, although the total amount of mechanical energy (K.E. and P.E.) is reduced, the amount of energy in other forms (such as heat) increases so as to redress the balance.

16.11 In more general problems there may be some factors tending to increase the total amount of mechanical energy, such as the action of an engine or the exertion of bodily energy, and others tending to reduce it, such as frictional resistances. From the physical point of view it remains true that no energy is being created and none destroyed. Although an engine produces additional mechanical energy, it cannot do so without consuming fuel and thus reducing the total amount of chemical energy. Friction produces a local rise in temperature at the sliding surfaces, a certain amount of noise, and often some permanent deformation of the bodies involved, and these represent an increase of energy of non-mechanical kinds to offset the loss of mechanical energy.

For the student of mechanics, however, these other forms of energy are of no concern, and instead of the principle of conservation of energy the following is used:

The Work–Energy Principle. *The work done by the forces acting on a body is equal to the increase in its mechanical energy (K.E. + P.E.).*

In applying this, the work done *by* a resistance is a negative quantity, equal to

$$- \text{ the resistance} \times \text{the distance over which it acts.}$$

This should not be confused with the work done *against* a resistance, which is the corresponding positive quantity.

EXAMPLE 5. A cyclist reaches the top of a hill with a speed of 3 m s^{-1}. He descends 30 m and then rises 20 m on the other side, reaching the top of the next rise with a speed of 2·5 m s^{-1}. The total mass of the cyclist and his machine is 120 kg, the road and air resistances amount to 20 N and the road distance between the two points is 800 m. Find the work done by the cyclist during this stretch.

At the start the K.E. is

$$\tfrac{1}{2} \times 120 \times 3^2 = 540 \text{ J,}$$

and at the end it is

$$\tfrac{1}{2} \times 120 \times 2{\cdot}5^2 = 375 \text{ J.}$$

In calculating the P.E., take as the fixed level that of the point at the end of his ride. He starts at a height of 30 m − 20 m = 10 m above this; his weight is $120 \times 9{\cdot}8 = 1176$ N, so that

$$\text{P.E. at start} = 1176 \times 10 = 11\,760 \text{ J,}$$

and the P.E. at the end is zero.

The work done against the resistance is

$$20 \times 800 = 16\,000 \text{ J.}$$

The work–energy principle takes the form:

(K.E. + P.E.) at start + work done by cyclist
— work done against resistance = (K.E. + P.E.) at end.

Therefore

540 + 11 760 + work done by cyclist − 16 000 = 375 + 0,

so that the work done by the cyclist is 4075 J.

EXERCISE 16(b)

1. The rise in elevation from the Atlantic Ocean to the highest level of the Panama Canal is made by three steps at Gatun locks. If the height gained at each lock is 9 m, find the change in P.E. of a 20 000 tonne ship when it passes through the locks.

2. A long rectangular block of stone has mass 100 kg, and its cross-section is a square with each side 1 m. It is placed with one of its long faces on the level ground, and is gradually pushed over, so that it turns about one of the long edges, until it balances on that edge. Find the work done.

3. What is the K.E. of a 2 kg body that has fallen 3·6 m from rest? What is then its velocity? (Take $g = 9·8$ m s^{-2}.)

4. Find the K.E. acquired by a 3 kg body that has fallen from rest through a height of 20 m. How much more is acquired in falling through the next 20 m?

5. A stone of mass 0·75 kg is dropped from a height of 1·6 m into a pond. The stone begins to sink in the water with a velocity of 2·4 m s^{-1}. What is the energy lost in striking the water?

6. A railway truck of mass 10 tonnes runs freely for 400 m down an incline of 0·5% (1 in 200). Calculate the K.E. acquired and hence the final velocity of the truck.

7. A mass of 2 kg falls from rest for a distance of 3 m through water which exerts a constant resistance to motion of 8 newtons. Find its K.E.

8. A block of mass $\frac{1}{2}$ kg slides down a groove 16 m long on a slope of 1 in 20. At the end it has attained a speed of 3 m s^{-1}. How much energy has been lost, and what is the resisting force, assumed constant?

9. A cyclist starting from rest freewheels for 120 m down a slope of 1 in 30. At the bottom of the slope the road becomes horizontal, and the cyclist stops without using his brakes after going a further 40 m. If the total mass of the bicycle and rider is 72 kg, find the resisting force, assuming it to be constant throughout.

10. A bead of mass 15 gm slides for 480 mm down a wire inclined at $\bar{\omega}$ to the horizontal. If the force of friction opposing the motion is 8·2 mN, and if the bead has a velocity of 0·8 m s^{-1} at the top of the slope, calculate its velocity at the bottom. (Take $g = 9·8$ m s^{-2}.)

11. The approach to a ski-jump is 25 m long, the difference in vertical height between the start and take-off being 10 m. If there is a resisting force equal to one-fifteenth of his weight acting on a jumper while he is sliding down the approach, find his speed when he lands 8 m below the take-off point.

12. A body slides down a sloping chute into a swimming-bath. If he starts from rest at a vertical height of 5 m above the water and if the chute is perfectly smooth, prove that the velocity with which he enters the water is about 10 m s^{-1}. If the chute is not smooth and if the boy of mass 50 kg dissipates 1600 J of energy in overcoming the friction of the chute, find the magnitude of the velocity with which he enters the water. (Take $g = 10 \text{ m s}^{-2}$.)

13. A string of length 1·25 m is attached to a fixed point and carries a mass of 2 kg at its other end. The mass is held so that the string is horizontal and taut, and is then allowed to swing. Find its maximum velocity.

14. A body of mass 5 kg is suspended from a hook by means of a light string of length 4 m. The body is drawn aside until the string makes an angle of 45° with the vertical. Find the increase in the P.E. of the body. The body is released and swings back. Neglecting the friction at the hook, find the velocity of the body as it passes through its first position (i.e. vertically under the hook).

15. A mass of 8 gm hangs vertically from a string of length 0·3 m, whose other end is attached to a fixed point. It is projected horizontally with a velocity of 1·4 m s^{-1}. What is the greatest angle that the string makes with the vertical in the ensuing motion?

16. One end of a string of length 1·8 m is attached to a fixed point and the other end carries a mass of 2 kg. The mass is held so that the string is horizontal and taut, and is then projected vertically downwards with a velocity of 10 m s^{-1}. Find the velocity of the mass at the highest point of its circular path. (Take $g = 10 \text{ m s}^{-2}$.)

17. Two particles each of mass 0·1 kg are falling vertically with a velocity of 1 m s^{-1}, and are connected by a straight horizontal string of length 0·5 m. The mid-point of the string comes into contact with a fixed horizontal peg. Find the velocities of the particles just before they collide.

18. A mass of 10 gm hangs by a string of length 0·2 m from a fixed point A. The mass is drawn aside so that the string makes an angle of 30° with the vertical, and is then let go. There is a small fixed horizontal peg 80 mm vertically below A. Find the angle between the vertical and the lower part of the string when the mass is again momentarily at rest.

19. Masses of 3 kg and 5 kg hang one on either end of a string which passes over a smooth peg. The masses are initially at rest, and motion is then allowed to take place. When the masses have each moved through a distance of 1·6 m, find: (i) the gain of P.E. of the smaller mass, and (ii) the loss of P.E. of the larger mass. Assuming that the total gain in K.E. of the system is equal to the total loss of P.E., find the speed with which the masses are moving.

20. A mass of 3 kg rests on a smooth table 2 m from the edge. It is connected by a string which runs perpendicular to the edge of the table to a 5 kg mass which hangs vertically. If motion is allowed to take place, use the principle of the conservation of energy to find the speed of the masses just before the 3 kg mass reaches the edge of the table.

21. A particle of mass 2 gm lies on a smooth plane of angle 30°. It is attached to one end of a string, which passes up the plane and over a smooth pulley at the top, and has attached to its other end a particle of mass 6 gm which hangs vertically. Find the speed of the particles when they have moved 0·64 m from rest.

†**22.** A bead of mass 10 gm can slide on a fixed smooth vertical wire. It is attached to one end of a string, which passes over a smooth peg at A, distant 0·2 m from the wire, and carries at its other end a mass of 30 gm. The bead is held at the same horizontal level as A, with the string taut, and is then let go. Find how far the bead falls before it comes momentarily to rest.

†**23.** A light string of length $2b$, supporting at each end a particle of mass m, passes over two smooth pegs which are $2a$ apart in a horizontal line, the mid-point of the string being mid-way between the pegs. A particle of mass M is now attached to the mid-point of the string. Show that the particles of mass m begin to rise. Find an expression for the P.E. of the three particles when the parts of the string between the pegs make an angle of θ with the horizontal. If the system comes to instantaneous rest while the masses at the ends of the string are below the pegs, prove that this occurs when $\tan \frac{1}{2}\theta = M/(2m)$.

Power

16.12 Consider two cranes, each lifting a load of weight 20 kN to a height of 25 m; suppose that the first does this in 5 s, and that the other takes 20 s. Then each crane does $20\,000 \times 25 = 500\,000$ joules of work, but the first crane works at a faster rate than the other. We say that it is more 'powerful'.

We define POWER as the rate at which work is done. The first crane does 500 kJ of work in 5 s; we say that its power is 100 kJ s^{-1}. The power of the second crane is only 25 kJ s^{-1}.

The standard unit of power is a rate of working of 1 joule per second (1 J s^{-1}); this is given a special name, the *watt* (W).[1] As with other units we also use prefixes to denote multiples and submultiples of the watt. In particular, since the watt is a fairly small unit for many purposes, the kilowatt (1 kW = 10^3 W = 1 kJ s^{-1}) and the megawatt (1 MW = 10^6 W = 1 MJ s^{-1}) are in common use. For example, the cranes in the example above are working at rates of 100 kW and 25 kW respectively.

The watt is, of course, familiar in everyday life as a unit of electrical

[1] After James Watt (1736–1819), best known for his work on the steam engine.

power – a reminder that mechanical and electrical energy are two interchangeable forms of the same fundamental physical quantity.

It should be noticed that if an engine has a rating of 30 kW, this does not mean that it works always at this rate, but only that this is its maximum rate of working. A man running upstairs may develop $\frac{1}{2}$ kW for a short time, but he would soon exhaust himself if he worked as hard as this continuously.

Another unit of power, which has kept a place in some contexts in both metric and non-metric countries since the 19th century, is the horse-power. As its name suggests, this unit (whose size is about $\frac{3}{4}$ of a kilowatt) was an estimate of the output of a working horse at a time when this animal provided an important source of power for many purposes.

EXAMPLE 6. A force of 2000 *N pulls a truck up a slope at a constant speed of* 5 *m s^{-1}. Find the power developed.*

In 1 s the force moves its point of application through a distance of 5 m. The work done per second is therefore (2000 N) $\times$ (5 m) = 10 000 J. It follows that the power developed is 10 000 J s^{-1} = 10 000 W, or 10 kW.

EXAMPLE 7. Find the power developed by a pump which raises water at a rate of 400 *l per minute through a vertical distance of* 4 *m and delivers it in a fountain with a speed of* 1·5 *m s^{-1}.*

The pump is creating both potential and kinetic energy, since the water is not only being raised but also is given a certain speed. Since a litre of water has a mass of about 1 kg, the mass of water discharged per minute is 400 kg. The P.E. thus created is

$$(400 \times 9 \cdot 8 \text{ N}) \times 4 \text{ m} = 15\ 680 \text{ J},$$

and the K.E. is

$$\tfrac{1}{2} \times 400 \times 1 \cdot 5^2 \text{ J} = 450 \text{ J}.$$

The power developed is therefore

$$(15\ 680 + 450) \text{ J} \div 60 \text{ s} = 269 \text{ W}.$$

16.13 If the engine of a vehicle is producing a force of F newtons, and the vehicle travels s metres in t seconds, the rate of working is Fs joules in t seconds, or Fs/t watts. Since s/t is equal to v, the speed of the vehicle, the power developed by the engine is given by

$$Fv \text{ watts.}$$

This formula holds even if the vehicle is not travelling at a constant speed. For if in time δt seconds it moves δs metres, the average power is

$$\frac{F\delta s}{\delta t} = F\frac{\delta s}{\delta t},$$

and this tends to Fv as $\delta t \rightarrow 0$.

EXAMPLE 8. A car of mass 1000 kg, whose engine is working at 21 kW, climbs a hill. (i) When the slope of the hill is 10% (1 in 10) the car maintains a steady speed of 15 m s⁻¹. Find the resistance to motion. (ii) If the slope

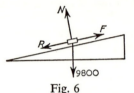

Fig. 6

flattens out to 4% (1 in 25), the speed of the car still being at first 15 m s⁻¹, find the initial acceleration (supposing that the resistance remains the same).
The power of the engine, 21 000 W, is equal to the product of the force and the speed. Therefore, if the tractive force of the engine is F newtons,

$$F \times 15 = 21\,000,$$
so that $$F = 1400.$$

(i) By a slope of 10% we mean a slope of angle θ, where $\sin \theta = 0.1$. The resolved part of the weight down the hill is

$$1000 \times 9.8 \times \sin \theta = 9800 \times 0.1 = 980 \text{ N}.$$

Let the resistance be R newtons. Then, since there is no acceleration,

$\mathcal{R}$ (up the hill) $\qquad 1400 - R - 980 = 0,$
so that $$R = 420.$$

The resistance is 420 N.

(ii) When the slope is 4%, the resolved part of the weight down the hill is

$$9800 \times 0.04 = 392 \text{ N}.$$

The tractive force is still 1400 N, and the resistance 420 N. Therefore, if the acceleration in m s⁻² is a,

$\mathcal{R}$ (up the hill) $\qquad 1400 - 420 - 392 = 1000a,$
which gives $$a = 0.59.$$

It should be noticed that this is only the initial acceleration. If the power, which equals the force times the speed, remains constant, the tractive force must decrease as the speed increases, so that the acceleration also decreases. To maintain the acceleration of 0·59 m s⁻² the power developed would have to increase as the speed increases.

EXERCISE 16(c)

1. A mountaineer of mass (with equipment) 100 kg climbs 360 m in an hour. At what average rate must he work to overcome the force of gravity?

2. A crane raises a 5000 kg casting at a rate of 0·8 m s⁻¹. At what rate is the engine working?

3. A pit cage has a mass of 500 kg. If it rises 800 m to the surface in a minute, and the engine is working at an average rate of 180 kW, how many 85 kg miners is it carrying? (Take $g = 10$ m s^{-2}.)

4. A sailor of mass 75 kg ascends a rope ladder 16 m high in 20 s. Find his rate of working.

5. A motor whose output is 3·5 kW raises a load of 400 kg through a height of 20 m. How long does it take?

6. A car travelling on a level road at 108 km h^{-1} experiences resistances of 750 N. Find the power which the engine must develop to maintain this constant speed.

7. Find the power needed to keep a train of mass 450 tonnes going at a steady speed of 90 km h^{-1} against resistances amounting to 100 N per tonne.

8. When a racing car is travelling at its maximum speed of 324 km h^{-1} its engine is developing 225 kW. Find the resistance to motion.

9. The engines of a liner travelling at 45 km h^{-1} are developing 120 MW. Find the resistance of the water.

10. A snow-plough experiences a resistance to motion of 15 kN. At what speed (in km h^{-1}) can it clear a path if its engine is developing 20 kW?

11. What power must be supplied by the electric motor of a trolley-bus travelling at 48 km h^{-1} if the resistance to motion is 600 N?

12. A blacksmith wields an 8 kg hammer, delivering 25 blows a minute onto an iron bar. The speed of the hammer just before each blow is 12 m s^{-1}, and the hammer is brought to rest by the blow. Find the rate at which the man is working.

13. An engine discharges 4000 l of water per minute with a speed of 15 m s^{-1}. What power is it developing?

14. A pump raises 4000 l of water per minute through a height of 15 m. What power is necessary to do this?

15. Find the power needed to raise water 3 m from a tank and to discharge it through a nozzle of cross-sectional area 300 mm^2 at 10 m s^{-1}.

16. Electricity is usually charged for in kilowatt-hours (kWh). How much energy in joules does this unit represent?

17. A 300 tonne train is pulled up a slope of 0·5% (1 in 200) at 45 km h^{-1}; the frictional resistances amount to 60 N per tonne. At what rate is the engine working?

18. A car of mass 1500 kg climbs a hill of slope 10% (1 in 10) at 36 km h^{-1}, the frictional resistances being 300 N. What power is the engine developing?

19. At 54 km h^{-1} in top gear the engine of a car of mass 1500 kg can develop 27·5 kW. If the friction resistances are 200 N, what is the steepest hill that the car can climb at this speed? (Take $g = 9·8$ m s^{-2}.)

20. The engine of a 5000 kg lorry can develop 30 kW, and its maximum speed on a level road is 90 km h^{-1}. Assuming that the friction resistance is constant, calculate its value; deduce the greatest steady speed at which the lorry can climb a hill of 4% (1 in 25).

21. The engine of a 5000 kg motor coach can work at 40 kW. If the resistance to motion is 1500 N, find the maximum speed along the level and up a slope of angle $\sin^{-1}$ ($\frac{1}{98}$). (Take $g = 9.8$ m s^{-2}.)

22. A train of mass 500 tonnes experiences a resistance of 80 kN when moving at 90 km h^{-1} on the level. If the power developed and the resistance remain unchanged when it descends a slope of 1 in 245, at what constant speed will it then travel? (Take $g = 9.8$ m s^{-2}.)

23. A machine is driven by a rope drive. There are six ropes moving at 20 m s^{-1}, and the tensions in each on either side of the wheel are 15 kN and 2 kN. Find the power transmitted.

24. A belt drive transmitting 60 kW runs at 15 m s^{-1}. Find the difference in tension of the belt on the two sides of the wheel.

25. A belt drive transmitting 20 kW runs at 20 m s^{-1}. If the tension on the slack side of the pulley is 800 N, what is the tension on the taut side?

26. A train of mass 100 tonnes acquires a speed of 54 km h^{-1} uniformly from rest in 450 m. Assuming a resistance of 40 N per tonne mass of the train, find the maximum power at which the engine is working during the 450 m run.

†27. A train of mass 200 tonnes starts from rest on a slope of 1 in 196. Until the velocity reaches 6 m s^{-1} the engine exerts a constant pull of 60 kN, and there is a constant resistance of 10 kN. In what time will the speed of 6 m s^{-1} be attained, and at what rate will the engine then be working? (Take $g = 9.8$ m s^{-2}).

†28. At 108 km h^{-1} a car of mass 1250 kg experiences a resistance of 750 N. If the engine can develop 30 kW at this speed, find the maximum acceleration of which it is then capable.

†29. A load of 3000 kg is being hauled by a rope up a railway line which rises 1 in 140. The friction force is 590 N. At a certain instant the velocity is 4 m s^{-1} and the acceleration 0.5 m s^{-2}. Find the pull in the rope and the power being developed at this instant. (Take $g = 9.8$ m s^{-2}.)

†30. A train of mass 200 tonnes is ascending an incline of 1 in 196 at a steady speed of 90 km h^{-1}. If the friction and wind resistance amount to 100 N per tonne, find the power developed by the engine. Prove that when the track becomes level the acceleration will be 0.05 m s^{-2}. (Take $g = 9.8$ m s^{-2}.)

†31. The resistance to motion of a car of mass 1500 kg is given by the formula $(400 + v^2)$ newtons, where v is the speed in m s^{-1}. The power developed by the engine in top gear is given by the formula $1.3v$ kW. Find the maximum speed of the car, and its maximum acceleration when travelling at 15 m s^{-1}.

Energy and momentum

16.14 In §§ 13.5 to 13.7 (pp. 170–173) it was shown that when two bodies change their velocity simply as a result of the interaction between them, the total momentum of the two bodies remains unaltered. We shall show that in these circumstances there may be a change in the total mechanical energy of the system.

Consider Example 5 of § 13.7 (p. 172). Before the two toboggans collided the first of mass 80 kg has a speed of 8 m s⁻¹, and therefore K.E. of amount

$$\tfrac{1}{2} \times 80 \times 8^2 = 2560 \text{ joules;}$$

the second of mass 60 kg moving at 1 m s⁻¹ had K.E.

$$\tfrac{1}{2} \times 60 \times 1^2 = 30 \text{ joules.}$$

After the collision the toboggans had a common speed of 5 m s⁻¹, and the total K.E. is

$$\tfrac{1}{2} \times 80 \times 5^2 + \tfrac{1}{2} \times 60 \times 5^2 = \tfrac{1}{2} \times 140 \times 5^2 = 1750 \text{ joules.}$$

The total amount of K.E. has therefore decreased from 2590 to 1750 joules as a result of the impact. The remaining 840 joules has been converted into non-mechanical forms of energy.

Again, in Example 6 of § 13.7, there is a change in the total mechanical energy. Before the shot is fired neither the gun nor the shell has any K.E. Afterwards the shell has K.E. of amount

$$\tfrac{1}{2} \times 8 \times 1000^2 = 4 \times 10^6 \text{ joules,}$$

and the gun has K.E. of amount

$$\tfrac{1}{2} \times 400 \times 20^2 = 8 \times 10^4 \text{ joules.}$$

Therefore, although the system has acquired no total momentum, the mechanical energy has increased. The source of this energy is the chemical energy originally possessed by the explosive.

16.15 Although the formulae for K.E. and work, on the one hand, and momentum and impulse, on the other, look much the same, it will be noticed that the types of problem in which these quantities are usefully applied are quite different. It is comparatively rare for there to be two alternative methods of solving a problem, one using energy and the other using momentum.

The equations of momentum are especially useful when we are dealing with impacts between two or more bodies. Since energy is almost always lost (converted into non-mechanical forms) when an impact occurs, it is not usually possible to make use of equations involving energy in such examples. On the other hand, we have seen that the equations of energy are especially useful when bodies move along curved paths, in which case some of the external forces may act at right angles to the direction of motion and so do no work. Since momentum is a vector quantity, the equations of momentum cannot often be used in solving problems of this kind.

There are, however, some problems which are solved partly by using the concept of energy and partly by momentum. The two examples which follow are typical.

EXAMPLE 9. The speed of an air-gun pellet is measured by means of the following experiment. The pellet is fired horizontally into a lump of plasticine, which hangs from a fixed point by a vertical string, and which has a mass 49 times that of the pellet. It is found that the plasticine (with the pellet inside it) swings so that it rises a vertical distance of 0·1 metres. What was the speed of the pellet? (Fig. 7).

The motion is in two stages:

(i) *The impact.* We suppose that the pellet comes to rest in the plasticine instantaneously. The principle of the conservation of momentum governs this stage of the motion; the external forces – the weights and the tension in the string – act vertically and have no horizontal impulse.

(ii) *The swing.* This is most easily discussed by the principle of energy. Of the external forces, the tension in the string does no work, since it is at

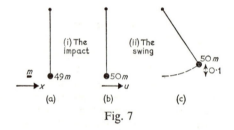

Fig. 7

right angles to the direction of motion. Potential energy is gained, and an equal amount of kinetic energy lost.

It is easier in this example to do the calculations for the second stage first. If the pellet has a mass of m kg, the plasticine has a mass of $49m$ kg, and the combined mass is $50m$ kg. Let the velocity in m s^{-1} at the beginning of the swing be u; its kinetic energy is then $\frac{1}{2}(50m)u^2$ joules. The mass rises 0·1 metres, so that this K.E. is converted into P.E. of amount

$$(50m) \times 9\cdot8 \times 0\cdot1 = 49m \text{ joules.}$$

Therefore
$$25mu^2 = 49m,$$
$$u = 1\cdot4.$$

We can now perform the calculations for the first stage. If the velocity in m s^{-1} of the pellet when fired is x, its momentum is mx. The momentum of the plasticine before the impact is zero, since it is hanging at rest. After the impact the combined mass has momentum of amount $(50m)u = 70m$. Therefore

$$mx = 70m,$$
$$x = 70.$$

The pellet was fired at 70 m s^{-1}.

EXAMPLE 10. Luggage unloaded from an air liner is tumbled onto a conveyor belt moving at 0·5 m s⁻¹. The luggage for 60 passengers, averaging 15 kg per passenger, is delivered on the belt in 20 seconds. What extra power is needed to drive the belt during this period?

As each suitcase drops on the belt, its speed is increased by 0·5 m s⁻¹. In all, 900 kg of luggage has its speed raised by this amount, gaining momentum of $900 \times 0.5 = 450$ N s. This momentum is produced by the impulse of a force acting for 20 s, so the magnitude of the force is $450 \div 20 = 22.5$ N.

The principle of momentum was used in this part of the problem, since we have here essentially an 'impact' situation. The nature of the force which gives a velocity to the luggage is friction between the belt and the suitcases, and some sliding – with consequent loss of energy – takes place in the process. Since we do not know how much energy is lost in this way, we cannot find the force by equating the work done by the motor to the gain in K.E. of the luggage.

To find the power required to drive the belt, we observe that a force of 22·5 N has to be applied at a speed of 0·5 m s⁻¹. This gives a rate of working of 22.5×0.5 W, or about 11 W.

EXERCISE 16(*d*)

1. A car of mass 810 kg is travelling at 50 km h⁻¹. What force is required to stop it: (i) in 10 s, (ii) in a distance of 50 m?

2. A mass of 3 kg moving with a velocity of 10 m s⁻¹ overtakes a mass of 2 kg moving with a velocity of 2 m s⁻¹ in the same direction. After impact the 2 kg mass moves on with a velocity of 8 m s⁻¹. What is the velocity of the 3 kg mass? How much energy has been lost in the impact?

3. Two laden trucks, one of mass 6000 kg moving at 3 m s⁻¹ and the other of mass 4000 kg moving at 2 m s⁻¹, are travelling along the same track. They collide, and move on together. Find the loss of energy at the impact, if they are originally moving: (i) in the same direction, (ii) in opposite directions.

4. Masses of 7 gm and 3 gm are connected by a string which is originally slack. The 3 gm mass is struck with an impulse of $2 \cdot 1 \times 10^{-3}$ N s in a direction away from the other. Find the energy lost by the system when the string tightens. Repeat the question when it is the 7 gm mass that is struck.

5. A truck of mass 1000 kg moving at 1·2 m s⁻¹ strikes a stationary truck of mass 3000 kg. If the momentum of the first truck after the collision is one-quarter of what it was before, find the speeds of the two trucks after the collision and the total loss of energy of the system.

6. A truck of mass 1000 kg moving at 1·2 m s⁻¹ strikes a stationary truck of mass 3000 kg. If the energy of the first truck after the collision is one-quarter of what it was before, find the speeds of the two trucks after the collision and the total loss of energy of the system.

7. A mass of 2 kg moving at 5 m s⁻¹ strikes a mass of 4 kg moving at 1 m s⁻¹ in the same direction along the same line. If the energy lost at the impact is 8 J, find the speeds after the impact.

8. A gun fires a shell of mass 10 kg with a muzzle velocity of 600 m s^{-1}. If the recoiling parts of the gun have a mass of 1200 kg, find: (i) the energy created by the burning of the charge, (ii) the constant force needed to bring the recoiling parts to rest in 1·5 m.

9. A shell of mass 15 kg is moving horizontally with a speed of 60 m s^{-1} when it explodes into two parts. One part has a mass of 5 kg and travels after the explosion at 300 m s^{-1} in the original direction of motion of the shell. Find the energy created by the explosion.

10. Particles of masses m and $2m$ are connected by a string and lie on a smooth table with the string slack. The mass m is projected away from the other along the table with velocity u. Find the energy lost when the string becomes taut.

11. A ball of mass 3 kg hanging vertically from a fixed point by a string receives a horizontal blow from a club, and rises a vertical height of 0·9 m. What was the impulse of the blow? (Take $g = 9·8$ m s^{-2}.)

12. A block of wood of mass 6 kg is suspended by a number of vertical strings each 3 m long attached to points in the ceiling. A bullet of mass 60 gm is fired horizontally into the block and remains embedded. The block starts to move with a speed of 4 m s^{-1}. What was the speed of the bullet? Through what angle with the vertical will the strings swing?

13. A ball of mass 90 gm is tied to the end B of a string AB 0·9 m long. The end A is fixed so that the ball can swing above and just clear of a horizontal table. Another ball of mass 150 gm is now placed on the table immediately below the point of suspension of the first one, and the 90 gm ball is pulled aside so that the string is horizontal and taut. The 90 gm ball now swings down, strikes the 150 gm ball and rises again on the other side. If the 150 gm ball thus acquires a speed of 2·1 m s^{-1} along the table, find the speed of the swinging ball (i) before, and (ii) after the impact, and the angle through which the string swings afterwards. (Take $g = 9·8$ m s^{-2}.)

14. Two small masses, of 3 gm and 4 gm respectively, hang side by side by strings of equal length 0·2 m from the same point. The 3 gm mass is now pulled aside until its string makes 60° with the vertical, and released. It strikes the 4 gm mass at the lowest point of its swing, and is brought to rest by the impact. Through what angle does the 4 gm mass swing?

15. A 10 gm bullet is fired into a wooden block of mass 990 gm which hangs by long vertical strings. After the bullet enters the block the strings swing through an angle such that the block rises a vertical distance of 1·25 m. At what speed did the bullet enter the block?

16. A puck of mass 400 gm is struck with an impulse of 2 N s across ice which offers a resistance of 0·25 N. How far will it travel?

17. A conveyor belt is running light at a speed of 2 m s^{-1}. Coal is now fed onto it at a rate of 40 kg per second. Find the additional force which the motor must produce and the additional power required if the belt is still to run at the same speed.

18. A steam train is travelling at 20 m s^{-1} when it starts to pick up water from a trough. If it takes up 1500 l over a distance of 300 m, find what additional power will be required if the train is not to slacken speed. Show also that if the speed of the train were twice as great, eight times as much additional power would be needed.

19. 100 kg of lead shot is fed every second onto a belt running at 3 m s^{-1}. How much more power is needed than when it is running light? How much of this power is used in giving kinetic energy to the lead shot? What happens to the rest?

20. A conveyor belt is running at 3 m s^{-1}. Coal is fed on to the belt at the rate of 100 kg per second, so that when it runs on to the belt it already has a horizontal speed of 1 m s^{-1}. Find the power needed to drive the belt.

21. A stake of mass 3 kg is driven vertically into the ground by a sledge hammer whose head has a mass of 5 kg. The hammer hits the stake with a speed of 4 m s^{-1}. Assuming that after the impact the hammer and the stake instantaneously acquire the same speed, and that they then remain in contact until the stake has come to rest, find what this speed is, and find the resistance of the ground (assumed constant) if the stake penetrates a distance of 10 mm.

22. A nail of mass 15 gm is knocked horizontally into a wall with a hammer whose head has a mass of 1 kg. Before the impact the hammer has a speed of 4 m s^{-1}. If the resistance of the wall to penetration is 3000 N, find how far the nail goes in.

23. A pile driver of mass 2000 kg is allowed to fall onto a pile of mass 500 kg. The earth offers a resistance of 385 kN, and the pile penetrates a distance of 0·5 m. Taking g to be 10 m s^{-2}, find to the nearest metre the height through which the pile driver falls freely.

†**24.** A body of mass 2 kg moving at 7 m s^{-1} on a horizontal table strikes a body of mass 1 kg moving at 1 m s^{-1} in the same direction along the same line. Find the velocities after impact if the loss of energy is to be: (i) as large as possible, (ii) as small as possible.

†**25.** A mass $2M$, initially at rest, suddenly bursts into two parts of masses $M + m$, $M - m$ by an internal explosion of energy E. Find the relative velocity of the parts.

†**26.** A boy standing on the ground can throw a ball of mass m horizontally with a speed u. If he stands on a trolley which is free to move in the direction in which the ball is thrown, and uses as much energy as before in throwing the ball, prove that he can throw it only with a speed

$$u\sqrt{\frac{M}{M + m}},$$

where M is the combined mass of the boy and the trolley.

†**27.** A ball of mass 125 gm is moving with a velocity of 6 m s^{-1} due N. It is then struck, and in consequence its velocity becomes 8 m s^{-1} due E. Find: (i) the increase in K.E., (ii) the change in momentum. Assuming that this change was caused by a constant force acting for 0·01 s, find this force. Find also the distance that the force moves its point of application in its own direction.

†28. A body of mass 5 kg is moving due N with a speed of 7 m s^{-1}. A constant force acts on it for $\frac{1}{2}$ s in a fixed direction. At the end of this time it is moving at 8 m s^{-1} in a direction S60°E. Find the force, the direction in which it acts, and the distance it moves its point of application in that direction.

CHAPTER 17

MACHINES

17.1 Many devices exist for converting energy from one form to another. Those in which electrical energy is produced from some other kind of energy (e.g. the chemical energy of fuel or the potential energy of a mass of water) are called *dynamos* or *generators*. If the object of the convertor is to produce mechanical energy, it is called a *motor* or an *engine*. If both input and output energies are electrical, we have a *transformer*, whereas if both input and output are mechanical we have a *machine*.

In all these devices the principle of the conservation of energy is applicable; but inevitably some of the energy put in fails to be converted in the desired manner, and this energy is useless in the final application. For example, no one has yet designed a steam engine in which a proportion of the chemical energy of the fuel consumed is not wasted in the form of heat energy which is thrown away – emitted through the funnel and dissipated in the atmosphere. For this reason the output energy is always smaller than the input energy.

The ratio of the output energy to the input energy is called the EFFICIENCY of the convertor. This is usually expressed as a percentage.

If the convertor is running steadily, without building up reserves of energy within itself or using stored-up energy, the efficiency can also be expressed as the ratio of the energy delivered in a unit of time to the energy put in in the same time – that is, the ratio of the power output to the power input.

EXAMPLE 1. A hydro-electric plant generating 50 MW uses 70 000 kg of water per second, falling through a height of 90 m. Find its efficiency.
The P.E. used by the generator in 1 second is
$$70\,000 \times 9\!\cdot\!8 \times 90 \text{ J},$$
so that the power input is $70\,000 \times 9\!\cdot\!8 \times 90$ W. The power output is 50 000 000 W. Therefore the efficiency is
$$\frac{50\,000\,000}{70\,000 \times 9\!\cdot\!8 \times 90}$$
$$= 0\!\cdot\!81, \text{ or } 81\%.$$

17.2 In the rest of this chapter we shall be concerned only with machines in which both input and output are mechanical. The purpose of a machine is usually to produce a large force (e.g. to raise a heavy load, or to make a cable taut) by applying a smaller force to the machine. The student will be familiar with many devices which fulfil this function, such as levers, pulley systems, jacks and so on.

The object of this chapter is to discuss some of the more elementary principles of the theory of machines, and to illustrate their application by means of a few simple examples. It does not set out to describe a large number of machines in great detail, although most of the commoner varieties receive mention either in the text or in the exercises. For a fuller treatment the reader must be referred to one of the books written for engineers specifically devoted to this branch of applied mechanics.

17.3 In a machine the power output and the power input are both measured as a force multiplied by the speed with which it is applied. If the input is a force F_i applied at a speed v_i, and the output a force F_o applied at a speed v_o, we have:

$$\text{Efficiency} = \frac{F_o v_o}{F_i v_i}.$$

Since the efficiency is always less than 1, $F_o v_o$ is always smaller than $F_i v_i$. Nevertheless, machines can be devised to make F_o much larger than F_i; a large force which it is humanly impossible to exert can be produced from a machine operated manually. With a suitable machine a casting weighing 5000 N can be lifted by a force of only 50 N.

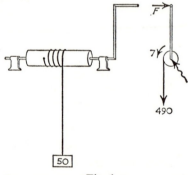

Fig. 1

EXAMPLE 2. A mass of 50 kg is attached to a light rope, whose other end is wound round and fixed to an axle of radius 50 mm. This axle is mounted horizontally between bearings, and is turned by a handle fixed to the axle which moves round the same axis in a circle of radius 350 mm. The bearings

produce a friction couple of limiting magnitude 7 N m. Find the force
needed to raise the load, and the efficiency. (This machine is called a
windlass, see Fig. 1.)

Let F be the force in newtons which must be applied to the handle to raise
the mass at constant speed. The forces on the system are in equilibrium when
the machine is running steadily, and the tension in the rope is equal to the
weight of the load, which (using the value $g = 9.8$ m s^{-2}) is 490 N. Working
in newton-metre units,

$\mathcal{M}$(axis) $F \times 0.35 - 490 \times 0.05 - 7 = 0$

so that $F = 90.$

Thus a load whose weight is 490 N can be raised by a force of only 90 N.
   Since $F_o = 490$, $F_i = 90$, the efficiency is given by

$$\frac{490 v_o}{90 v_i}.$$

Now the handle moves in a circle of radius 7 times that of the axle, so that
the handle must be moved at 7 times the speed at which the load rises.
Therefore

$$\frac{v_o}{v_i} = \frac{1}{7},$$

and the efficiency is $\dfrac{490}{90 \times 7} = 0.78$, or 78%.

It should be noticed that the force is calculated for the time when
the machine is running steadily. A rather larger force would be necessary to produce the initial acceleration to start the load in motion.
When the speed of running is constant the forces can be calculated by
methods that are essentially statical.

17.4 The quantity F_o/F_i, expressing the number of times the force
put into the machine is magnified, is called the MECHANICAL ADVANTAGE
of the machine. For example, the mechanical advantage of the machine
discussed in Example 2 for a load of 50 kg is $490 \div 90 = 5.4$.

   The mechanical advantage of a machine is not always the same for
all loads. The machine in Example 2 is a case in point; if the load were
increased to 100 kg it would be found that the force would need to be
increased only to 160 N, so that the mechanical advantage would be
$980 \div 160 = 6.1$ for this load. The reason for this is that when the
load is larger the friction does not, according to the data of this example,
become greater in proportion.

   Nearly all machines have a mechanical advantage which is greater
than 1 – that is to say, they are used to create a large output force from
a smaller input force. This is not, however, true of a machine such as

the clockwork motor, in which the spring produces a larger force than is required at the output end. Another exception is the bicycle.

> *EXAMPLE 3. A loaded trolley of mass* 200 *kg is pulled up onto a station platform by means of a ramp at an angle of* 7° *to the horizontal. An additional force of* 50 *N has to be exerted to overcome the friction of the bearings in the trolley. Regarding the ramp as a machine for raising the trolley, find the mechanical advantage.*

When the trolley is being pulled at a steady speed, the force with which it is pulled must counteract the resolved part of the weight down the ramp, which is $200 \times 9\cdot8 \times \sin 7° \approx 240$ N, and the friction. The input force F_i is therefore

$$240 \text{ N} + 50 \text{ N} = 290 \text{ N}.$$

Since the object of the machine is to raise the load through a certain vertical height, the output force F_o must be regarded as the weight of the trolley – the force which would be needed to achieve the same object without the aid of a machine. This is $200 \times 9\cdot8 = 1960$ N. Therefore the mechanical advantage is

$$\frac{F_o}{F_i} = \frac{1960}{290} = 6\cdot8.$$

17.5 Since the efficiency of a machine, given by $F_o v_o / F_i v_i$, is always less than 1, $F_o v_o$ is smaller than $F_i v_i$. If the machine has a mechanical advantage greater than 1, so that F_o is larger than F_i, it follows that v_o must be smaller than v_i.

This is a feature common to all machines which are used to produce a large force from a smaller one; the speed with which the output force can be applied is smaller than the speed with which the input force has to be exerted. In Example 2 the handle moves in a circle of radius 7 times that of the axle on which the load is wound up. It must therefore move at 7 times the speed with which the load rises.

The quantity v_i / v_o is called the VELOCITY RATIO of a machine. Thus the velocity ratio of the machine in Example 2 is 7.

It is useful to notice that the ratio of the two velocities is equal to the ratio of the distances through which the two forces act in a given time; this is often a more convenient way of calculating this quantity. In Example 3 the velocity ratio is

$$\frac{\text{distance moved up the ramp by the trolley}}{\text{vertical height gained}}$$

which is easily seen to be cosec 7°, or 8·2.

Machines such as the clockwork motor and the bicycle have velocity ratios which are smaller than 1. In the clockwork motor the spring unwinds very slowly, which means that the machine is able to run for a long time, although producing a very small force.

17.6 It is useful to observe that

$$\text{efficiency} = \frac{F_o v_o}{F_i v_i} = \frac{(F_o/F_i)}{(v_i/v_o)} = \frac{\text{mechanical advantage}}{\text{velocity ratio}}.$$

Thus in Example 3 we have seen that the mechanical advantage is 6·8, the velocity ratio 8·2, so that the efficiency is 6·8/8·2 = 0·83, or 83%.

The velocity ratio of a machine is determined solely by its geometrical configuration, and is therefore the same for all loads. We saw in § 17.4, on the other hand, that the mechanical advantage may vary with different loads. The relation given above then shows that the efficiency may also vary with different loads.

Also, since the efficiency is always less than 1, it follows that the mechanical advantage will always be smaller than the velocity ratio.

EXAMPLE 4. A cable is tightened by means of a block and tackle (see Figs. 2 and 3). A block of three pulleys is fastened to the cable, and another block of two pulleys is firmly anchored. The rope is attached to the anchored block, passes round all the pulleys, and the free end comes off a pulley on the

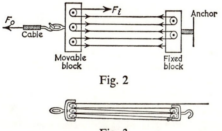

Fig. 2

Fig. 3

block attached to the cable. Owing to the friction of the pulleys, the tension in the rope decreases by 5% each time it passes over a pulley. Find the mechanical advantage, velocity ratio and efficiency of the machine.

(Fig. 2 is merely a diagram to illustrate the mechanical principles. In practice, the pulleys in each block would all be mounted on the same axle, as shown in Fig. 3.)

The output force F_o is the tension in the cable, and the input force F_i the tension in the free end of the rope. Because of the friction, the tension in the next portion of the rope is only $0.95F_i$, and the tension in the next portion is 0·95 of this, i.e. $(0.95)^2 F_i$, and so on. After the rope has passed round all the pulleys, the tension in the last portion of rope, which is fixed to the anchored block, is $(0.95)^5 F_i$.

Resolving for the forces on the movable block,

$$F_o - F_i - (0.95)F_i - (0.95)^2 F_i - \ldots - (0.95)^5 F_i = 0,$$

so that
$$F_o = F_i(1 + 0.95 + 0.95^2 + 0.95^3 + 0.95^4 + 0.95^5)$$
$$= F_i(1 + 0.95 + 0.902 + 0.857 + 0.814 + 0.774)$$
$$= 5.30F_i.$$

[The reader who is familiar with the theory of geometrical progressions will know that the expression in brackets can be calculated as

$$(1 - 0.95^6)/(1 - 0.95) = 5.30.]$$

The mechanical advantage F_o/F_i is therefore equal to 5·30.

Some care is needed in calculating the velocity ratio. Suppose that the blocks move closer together by a distance of 1 unit. Then each of the five ropes joining the blocks is shortened by 1 unit, so that the length of the free part of the rope is shortened by 5 units. But the pulley over which the free end passes is on the movable block, and this also moves a distance of 1 unit. The free end of the rope therefore moves a total distance of 6 units, which is 6 times the distance through which the end of the cable is pulled. The velocity ratio of the machine is therefore 6.

We deduce that the efficiency of the machine is 5·30 ÷ 6 = 0·88, or 88%.

17.7 Large mechanical advantages can sometimes be achieved by the use of differential mechanisms. For instance, the load, instead of being suspended by a single rope wound over a pulley or an axle, can be slung from a continuous loop of rope which winds back on to another pulley. This second pulley is mounted on the same axis and rotates together with the original pulley, but it has a smaller radius.

EXAMPLE 5. The machine of example 2 is modified by slinging the 50 kg load from a smooth, light pulley; the rope passes round the pulley and its

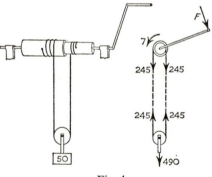

Fig. 4

free end runs round an axle of radius 40 mm, which is rigidly connected to the 50 mm axle and turns with it about the same axis. Find the velocity ratio, mechanical advantage and efficiency. (Fig. 4.)

To find the velocity ratio, consider one complete revolution of the handle. The handle moves through a distance of 700π mm, and 100π mm of rope are wound on to the 50 mm axle, while 80π mm are wound off the 40 mm axle. The hanging rope therefore shortens by 20π mm. Since this rope is in two vertical portions, each shortens by only 10π mm, and this is the distance through which the load rises. The velocity ratio is therefore $700\pi \div 10\pi = 70$.

Since the load is slung from a smooth, light pulley, the tension in the rope is only 245 N. Supposing the friction couple to be still 7 N m,

$$\mathscr{M}(\text{axis}) \quad F \times 0.35 - 245 \times 0.05 + 245 \times 0.04 - 7 = 0,$$

so that
$$F = 27.$$

The mechanical advantage is therefore $490 \div 27 = 18.2$, and the efficiency is $18.2 \div 70 = 0.26$, or 26%.

EXERCISE 17(a)

1. A man is inflating a tyre by means of a bicycle pump. The piston has to push against a pressure of 40 kN m^{-2}, the cross-sectional area of the piston being 300 mm^2 and the length of each stroke 0·3 m. If he pumps at a rate of 80 strokes a minute and the efficiency of the pump is 20%, at what rate is he working?

2. By turning a handle attached to a dynamo a man keeps a 15 watt bulb alight. If the handle has a radius of 100 mm and is turned round 40 times a minute with a force of 50 N, find the efficiency of the dynamo.

3. A car dynamo is driven by a belt running at 1 m s^{-1}. If the dynamo is 80% efficient and generates 88 watts, what is the difference in tension of the belt on either side of the wheel?

4. In burning 1 litre of diesel fuel the equivalent of 2.5×10^7 joules of energy is created. How much fuel is used in hauling a train of total mass 500 tonnes for 1 km up a gradient of 1 in 98 against frictional resistances of 20 kN if the engine has an efficiency of 28%? (Take $g = 9.8$ m s^{-2}.)

5. A garage hand jacks up the rear axle of a car, for which a force of 4000 N is required. He exerts a force of 250 N through a distance of 0·6 m and raises the car 25 mm. Find the velocity ratio, mechanical advantage and efficiency of the jack.

6. In a machine whose velocity ratio is 12 the relation between the input force and the load (the output force) in newtons is

$$F_i = 0.1F_o + 75.$$

Calculate the mechanical advantage of this machine for various loads from 0 to 2500 N, and display these results on a graph. For what loads does the efficiency of the machine exceed 60%?

7. For a certain machine the load, L newtons, and the effort, E newtons, are connected by a formula

$$E = aL + b,$$

where a, b are constants. When $L = 220$, $E = 14$, and when $L = 550$, $E = 29$. Find a and b. If the velocity ratio of the machine is 25, calculate its mechanical advantage and efficiency for a load of 440 newtons.

8. The equation connecting the input force F newtons and the mass M kg raised by a certain machine is of the form $F = a + bM$. A force of 250 N is needed to raise a load of 1000 kg. When the load is 250 kg the mechanical advantage is 25. Find a and b. If the efficiency when raising 375 kg is 50%, find the velocity ratio, and deduce the efficiency when raising 750 kg. (Take $g = 10$ m s^{-2}.)

The windlass

9. In a windlass (see Example 2, p. 248) the handle has a length of 0·3 m, and the rope carrying the load winds onto an axle of radius 30 mm. What is the velocity ratio? If there is a friction couple of 6 N m at the bearings, what load can be lifted by exerting a force of 150 N on the handle? What is the efficiency for this load? (Take $g = 10$ m s^{-2}.)

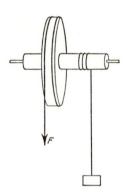

10. For the windlass described in Question 9, find an equation connecting the weight (W newtons) of the load and the force F newtons needed to raise it.

The wheel and axle

The force is applied to a rope wound onto the wheel, which is rigidly fixed to the axle.

11. If the radius of the wheel is 6 times that of the axle, and if 10% of the work done is wasted in overcoming friction, find the force needed to raise a load of mass 150 kg. At what speed can a man working at 80 W raise a load of mass 100 kg with the machine?

The vice

12. In a vice the force applied to the handle acts round a circle of radius 100 mm. The pitch of the screw (i.e. the distance the jaws move for one revolution of the handle) is 5 mm. If the efficiency of the vice is 40%, what force do the jaws exert when a force of 50 N is applied to the handle?

13. What force would have to be applied to the handle of the vice in Question 12 to grip a block of wood so that a force of 300 N is needed to pull it out, the coefficient of friction between the jaws and the block being 0·3?

The screw

14. A nut is tightened against a spring by means of a spanner 75 mm long. The screw-thread has a pitch of 5 mm. If a force of 250 N is exerted on the spring, and the screw is 20% efficient, find the force applied to the spanner.

15. A hexagonal nut is tightened by applying a single force of 100 N at the end of a spanner 120 mm long. Find the work done in one complete turn of the nut. If the pitch of the screw is 1 mm, and the efficiency is 30%, find the thrust of the nut in the direction of its axis.

Pulley systems

16. Find the velocity ratio of the pulley system (*a*). Find the force needed to raise a load of 60 kg if the lower pulley has a mass of 1 kg and (i) if there is no friction at the pulleys, (ii) if in order to overcome friction there is a difference in tension of 10 N each time the rope passes round a pulley.

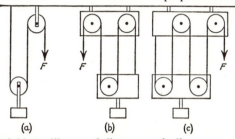

(a)   (b)   (c)

17. In (*b*) and (*c*) are illustrated diagrammatically two arrangements of a block-and-tackle system. By considering the effect of raising the lower block by 1 m, find the velocity ratios of the systems. Ignoring the effect of friction and the weight of the lower block, find the mass of the greatest load that can be raised by a 70 kg man with each machine.

18. Find the efficiency of the system (*b*) in raising a load of mass 50 kg if the lower block has mass 1 kg and the tension in the rope decreases by 2·5 N each time it passes round a pulley.

19. Find the load that can be lifted by a force of 250 N using the system (*c*) if the tension in the rope decreases by 10% each time it passes round a pulley, and the lower block has mass 1 kg. Find also the mechanical advantage and efficiency for this load.

20. If in (*c*) the lower block is of mass 2 kg and the tension decreases by 10 N in passing round each pulley, find the relation connecting the force *F* newtons and the weight *W* newtons. (Take $g = 10$ m s^{-2}.)

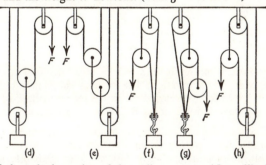

(d)   (e)   (f)   (g)   (h)

21. Find the velocity ratios of the pulley systems (*d*) to (*h*). (In (*f*) and (*g*) takes all the strings to be vertical.) Find also the mechanical advantage and efficiency if the systems are used to raise a load of mass 100 kg, taking each pulley to have mass 1 kg and, in (*f*) and (*g*), the tackle to which the load is attached to have mass 5 kg. Ignore the effect of friction.

The Weston differential pulley

The upper pulleys are fixed to each other so that both rotate together. The chain engages in cog teeth on the pulleys, the number of teeth being proportional to the radii of the pulleys.

22. Find the velocity ratio of the machine if the radii of the upper pulleys are 80 mm and 75 mm. Find the force needed to raise a load of mass 150 kg if the lower pulley has a mass of 2 kg and there is a friction couple of 6 N m at the upper pulleys. Find also the efficiency for this load.

†**23.** If friction and the weight of the lower block are neglected, and if the radii of the upper pulleys are a and b (where $a > b$), show (by independent methods) that the mechanical advantage and velocity ratio are both $2a/(a - b)$.

The differential wheel and axle

The rope carrying the load winds off an axle of smaller radius than that onto which it rewinds.

24. The radii of the wheel and the two axles are 300 mm, 50 mm, 45 mm. There is a friction couple of 10 N m at the bearings. Draw graphs showing the force required and the efficiency of the machine for loads up to 500 kg.

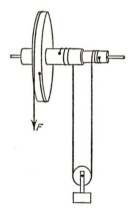

The bicycle

25. A cyclist exerts on the forward pedal a force of 100 N at right angles to the crank, which is 150 mm long. The two cog wheels have radii 100 mm and 40 mm. Find the force exerted at the rim of the rear wheel, whose radius is 300 mm: (i) if there is no friction, (ii) if there are friction couples of 1 N m at the hub and at the crankshaft.

26. A cyclist is riding along a level road at 5 m s⁻¹. His bicycle is geared so that for each revolution of the pedals it advances a distance equal to the circumference of a wheel of diameter 2 m, and the length of the cranks is 0·2 m. If the resistance to his motion is 32 N and the efficiency of the machine is 80%, find the thrust which he must exert on the pedals at right angles to the crank, and the rate at which he works.

The wedge

†**27.** A pillar free to move smoothly up and down is raised by a wedge of angle θ and negligible weight driven by a horizontal force. If the angle of friction between the pillar and the wedge, and also between the wedge and the ground, is λ, show that the mechanical advantage is

$$\frac{\cos(\theta + \lambda)\cos\lambda}{\sin(\theta + 2\lambda)}.$$

17.8 In some machines either the input or the output, or both, has the form of a couple rather than an ordinary force. Examples of this are afforded by screws and gear mechanisms. (A screw may be regarded as a ramp arranged in the form of a spiral staircase, so that the rotation eliminates the translatory effect.)

To estimate the efficiency of such machines, it is necessary to be able to calculate the work done by a couple when the body on which it acts turns through a certain angle. To do this, suppose that the body rotates about a point O through an angle θ, and that one of the forces making up the couple acts at a point X, where $OX = r$ (Fig. 5). If θ is measured in radians, the point X moves through a distance $r\theta$.

If the force at X is regarded as the sum of two components in perpendicular directions, P at right angles to OX and Q along OX, the force P does work of amount $P \times (r\theta)$ and the force Q does no work, since it acts always at right angles to the direction of motion of X. The total work done by the force is therefore $P \times (r\theta)$, which can be written also in the form $(Pr) \times \theta$. Now Pr is the moment about O of the force at X, since Q has no moment about O, so that the work done by the force is equal to the moment of the force multiplied by the angle through which the body turns.

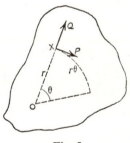

Fig. 5

This applies to each of the forces composing the couple. We deduce that:

work done by couple
    = moment of couple × angle through which body turns,

the angle being measured in radians.

Moreover, if the rate of rotation of the body is measured by the number of radians through which it turns in unit time (this is known as the *angular velocity* of the body), we have:

power developed by couple = moment of couple × angular velocity.

EXAMPLE 6. One wheel of a car is jacked up by a screw jack; the load on this wheel is 2000 N. *The handle is turned by a couple of* 5 N m, *and* 20 *turns of the handle are needed to raise the car* 0·1 m. *What is the efficiency of the jack?*

In raising the car 0·1 m, the handle is turned through 40π radians, so that the work done is $5 \times 40\pi = 200\pi$ N m. The amount of useful work done is $(2000 \text{ N}) \times (0\cdot1 \text{ m}) = 200$ N m, so that the efficiency of the machine is

$$200 \div (200\pi) = 0\cdot32, \text{ or } 32\%.$$

If, as in this example, the input has the form of a couple and the output that of a force, no meaning can be given to the terms mechanical advantage and velocity ratio.

17.9 In a gear mechanicsm both input and output have the form of couples. Consider two parallel shafts geared together by a pair of spur gears (Fig. 6). Suppose that a torque of moment L_t is applied to the driving shaft, and let its gear have a radius or r_t. Let the mating gear on the driven (output) shaft have radius r_o, and let the torque transmitted to this shaft be L_o.

The torque is transmitted by the normal contact force N of the teeth in contact. If the perpendiculars from the axes of the shafts onto the line of action of this force are p_i and p_o, the equation of moments for the input shaft gives

$$\mathcal{M} \text{ (axis)} \qquad\qquad L_t - Np_i = 0.$$

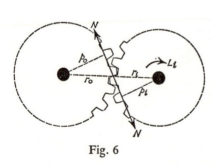

The torque transmitted to the output shaft is equal to the moment of N about the axis of that shaft, and is given by

$$L_o = Np_o.$$

It follows that $\dfrac{L_o}{p_o} = \dfrac{L_t}{p_i}$.

But, by similar triangles

$$\frac{p_o}{r_o} = \frac{p_i}{r_t}.$$

Therefore $\qquad \dfrac{L_o}{r_o} = \dfrac{L_t}{r_t}; \qquad (1)$

Fig. 6

that is, the torque is proportional to the radius of the gear. This equation ignores the effect of friction forces.

In order for the gears to fit, the points of contact of the teeth on both wheels must move at the same speed. If the driving shaft rotates at a rate of ω_i radians per second, the teeth of its gear move a distance of $r_i\omega_i$ in each second. Similarly, the speed of the teeth on the mating gear is $r_o\omega_o$, where ω_o is the rate of rotation of the output shaft. Therefore

$$r_o\omega_o = r_i\omega_i; \qquad (2)$$

that is, the angular velocities of the shafts are inversely proportional to the radii of their gears.

If we multiply together equations (1) and (2), we obtain

$$L_o\omega_o = L_i\omega_i,$$

an equation which states that the power output is equal to the power input. This is impossible to achieve in practice, because of friction; nevertheless, spur gears can be a very efficient method of transmitting power.

Geometrical considerations limit the ratios of radii which can be used in spur gears. To obtain high angular velocity ratios and mechanical advantages, however, a train of gears of this type can be used. (A familiar use of such a train is in clock mechanisms; in this case the velocity ratio is less than 1, and a very small fraction is desirable.)

17.10 In most machines a high degree of efficiency is desirable, so that the energy losses are made as small as possible. There are, however, some kinds of machine (such as jacks, wedges, etc) in which it is advantageous to have friction forces large enough to prevent the machine from running back of its own accord when the driving force is removed. The technical name for this is *overhauling*. (This tendency to run back can also be prevented, of course, by a locking device, such as a ratchet.)

As an example, compare the two machines discussed in Examples 2 and 5. In Example 2 (p. 248), when the force F is removed, there remains a moment of 24·5 N m anticlockwise about the axis from the weight of the load. The friction couple will tend to oppose this, but since its limiting value is only 7 N m, it will be insufficient to prevent the load from falling back again, and some form of locking mechanism will have to be incorporated in the machine.

In Example 5 (p. 252), when the force F is removed, the tensions in both parts of the rope have moments about the axis. Since these tensions are each 245 N, the moments are $245 \times 0·05 = 12·25$ N m anticlockwise and $245 \times 0·04 = 9·8$ N m clockwise. A couple of only 2·45 N m is needed to maintain equilibrium, and this is less than the limiting friction couple. The machine does not therefore run back.

With many kinds of machine the critical efficiency above which overhauling occurs is 50%. For, when the machine is being used to raise a load,

work done by input force
$$= \text{work done on load} + \text{work done against friction.}$$

When the input force is removed and the machine overhauls, it will gain kinetic energy as it falls. Therefore

work done by load in falling > work done against friction.

Now the work done in raising the load is equal to the work done by the weight of the load as it falls through the same distance when the machine runs back. Also, for many machines the friction forces are merely reversed in direction and have the same magnitude when the machine reverses, so that the work done against the friction is the same in both directions. It follows that, if the machine is to run back when the input force is removed,

work done by input force < 2 × work done in raising load,

i.e. the efficiency is greater than 50%.

This criterion does not apply if an appreciable amount of the work put in is used in raising some of the working parts of the machine itself, as for example when the load hangs from a heavy pulley block.

EXERCISE 17(b)

1. When a couple of moment 4 N m is applied to a screw which has a pitch of 5 mm, a force of 700 N results. What is the efficiency of the screw?

2. A surface is polished by contact with a disc which rotates at 5 revolutions per second, the rotation being resisted by a couple of moment 0·45 N m. The disc is rotated by a handle, of length 150 mm and turned at a rate of 1 revolution every 2 seconds. If the efficiency of the machine is 75%, what force must be applied to the handle?

3. A wing-nut is tightened against a spring. If the pitch of the screw-thread is 3 mm and a force of 200 N is applied against the spring, and if the efficiency is 25%, what couple must be applied to the nut?

4. A bolt is screwed into a hole; the screw has a pitch of 4 mm and the efficiency of the screw is 10%. What force in the direction of the axis of the bolt is produced by applying a couple of 2 N m to the head?

5. A bacon slicer is operated by a force of 3 N applied to a handle which turns in a circle of radius 200 mm. The cutting wheel rotates 6 times as fast as the handle, and the efficiency is 80%. Find the average resisting couple exerted by the bacon on the cutting wheel.

Gears

In the figure the wheels *B* and *C* rotate together on the same shaft. *A* has radius 20 mm and 24 teeth, *B* 50 mm and 60 teeth, *C* 15 mm and 18 teeth, *D* 60 mm and 72 teeth.

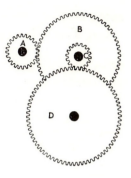

6. Find the ratio of the angular velocities of *A* and *D*. Do these wheels rotate in the same or in opposite senses? If a torque of 50 N m is applied to the shaft *A*, and there is a friction couple of 1 N m at the shaft of *B* and *C*, find the torque transmitted to the shaft *D*. Find also the efficiency of the system.

7. With the same friction couple as in Question 6, find the efficiency for torques of 10 and 100 N m applied to the shaft *A*.

8. If the gear train is used the other way round, find the torque that must be applied to the shaft *D* in order that a torque of 20 N m should be transmitted to the shaft *A*, the friction couple being the same as in Question 6. If the shaft *A* is run at 2000 revolutions per minute, what power must be supplied to the shaft *D*?

9. A car of mass 1200 kg can climb a hill of 1 in 12 in top gear, the friction resistances being 250 N. The gear ratio in top gear is 1 : 5 (5 revolutions of the engine to one of the back axle). What is the gear ratio in third gear if the car can climb 1 in 8, assuming the force from the engine is the same? What gradients can it climb in a second gear of 1 : 12 and a bottom gear of 1 : 20? (Neglect friction within the gearbox.)

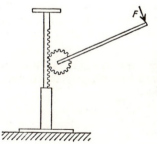

The rack and pinion

10. A jack is worked by a rack and pinion. The cogs are 10 mm apart and there are 15 cogs on the wheel. The crank handle is 0·5 m long and turns the wheel about a fixed centre. What thrust is produced by an effort of 150 N if the efficiency is 35%? (Take $\pi = \frac{22}{7}$.)

11. A press is worked by a rack and pinion. The cogs are 15 mm apart and there are 12 cogs on the wheel or pinion. The crank handle is 0·6 m long. If the efficiency is 60%, what thrust is produced by an effort of 250 N?

The worm gear

12. A gun barrel is elevated by means of a worm gear which is 40% efficient. If the mating gear has 80 teeth and the torque applied to the worm wheel is 8 N m, find the torque transmitted by the gear.

13. The output shaft of an electric motor is geared to the armature by means of a worm drive. If the mating gear has 60 teeth, what is the ratio of the angular velocities of the two shafts? If the armature turns at 3000 revolutions per minute and if the power transmitted by the motor is 20 kW, what is the average torque on the armature if the worm gear is 60% efficient?

The screw jack

14. The small bevel gear fixed to the handle has 7 teeth, and the large one on the collar with which it engages has 18. A screw whose pitch is 5 mm passes through the collar. How many turns of the handle are needed to raise the car 10 mm? If the efficiency of the jack is 15% and the load on the axle of the car is 4000 N, find the couple that must be applied to the handle of the jack.

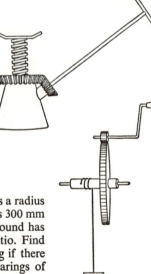

The winch

15. In the figure the small cog-wheel has a radius $\frac{1}{8}$ of that of the large wheel. The handle is 300 mm long and the axle onto which the rope is wound has a radius of 30 mm. Find the velocity ratio. Find the force needed to raise a load of 250 kg if there is a friction couple of 5 N m in the bearings of both shafts. Deduce the efficiency for this load.

16. For the machine described in Question 15, find the critical load below which the winch will not overhaul when the handle is released. What force would be needed to *lower* a load of 100 kg?

17. The working parts of the winch of a crane are as follows: A drum of diameter 0·3 m, round which the hauling rope is wound. At the end of this drum and rigidly fixed to it, a cog-wheel with 80 teeth. A second cog-wheel, working on the first, with 10 teeth and turned by a handle 0·3 m long.

Find against what load at the end of the rope the machine can be used by a man who can exert a force of 500 N on the handle, if the efficiency of the machine is 80%.

The grinding-wheel

18. The gear-wheels have 80 and 20 teeth respectively. The handle is 70 mm long and the grinding-stone has a radius of 120 mm. If there are friction couples of 0·5 N m at the bearings of both shafts, and if when grinding there is an additional force of 5 N at the rim of the grinding-wheel, find the force that must be applied to the handle. Find the speed at the rim of the grinding-wheel if the handle makes 70 turns a minute.

The Weston differential pulley (see Exercise 17(a), Question 22–23)

19. If the radii of the two upper pulleys are 70 mm and 60 mm, what friction couple is necessary at the bearings of these pulleys if the machine is not to run back with a load of mass 200 kg? (Ignore the mass of the lower pulley.)

20. If the two upper pulleys have radii of 70 mm and 60 mm and there is a friction couple of 8·7 N m, and if the lower pulley has mass 5 kg, prove that the machine will run back with a load of mass 175 kg but that the efficiency is less than 50%. Why does the criterion given in § 17.10 break down? (Take $g = 9·8$ m s^{-2}.)

MISCELLANEOUS EXERCISE D

In purely statical questions use the approximation $g = 10 \, m \, s^{-2}$. *In dynamical questions indication is given where necessary if one particular value is preferred.*

1. A liner is moving directly forward under tow from the bow by two tugs A and B. The tension T in the cable to the tug B is half that in the cable to the tug A. The cable to the tug A is inclined at $20°$ to the direction of motion of the liner. Calculate the direction of the cable to the tug B. What is the resultant force moving the liner?

2. A rock of mass 200 kg falls over a precipice; what is its kinetic energy when it has fallen 45 m?

If it continues to fall umimpeded, how much kinetic energy is added to it in the next second? (Take $g = 10 \, m \, s^{-2}$.)

3. An engine working at 165 kW draws a train of mass 100 tons up a slope which rises 1 m for every 280 m measured along the slope. The train travels with constant velocity. If the frictional resistance to the motion is 75 N per tonne mass, find the velocity of the train in km h⁻¹. (Take $g = 9 \cdot 8 \, m \, s^{-2}$.)

4. Two racing cars A and B pass the same point at the same instant. A is moving at a steady speed of 30 m s⁻¹; B then has a speed of 25 m s⁻¹, but maintains a uniform acceleration of 0·05 m s⁻². Find after what time B will overtake A, and what B's speed will then be.

Show also that, whatever B's uniform acceleration may be, his speed on overtaking A will be the same.

5. A uniform ladder, $6\frac{1}{2}$ m long and of mass 40 kg, leans against a smooth vertical wall and reaches a point 6 m above the level ground. The ground is rough, the coefficient of friction being $\frac{1}{3}$. Find the smallest force which, acting horizontally against the bottom of the ladder, would enable a man of mass 70 kg to stand on the top of the ladder without his causing it to slip.

6. A circular metal disc, of uniform thickness and radius 90 mm, has a circular hole of radius 30 mm bored in it. The centre of the hole is 40 mm from the centre of the disc. Find the position of the centre of gravity of the remainder.

7. A sphere of wood with centre C and mass 500 gm is suspended from a fixed point A. AC is 1 m. A bullet of mass 15 gm, moving with a velocity of 30 m s⁻¹, enters and embeds itself in the wood. With what velocity will the sphere begin to move and to what height will it rise?

8. A set of pulleys is used to raise a block of stone of mass 750 kg. The effort required to raise the block is 250 N, and the efficiency of the system is 45%. Through what distance will the effort have to be applied to raise the block 3 m, and how much work is wasted?

9. A sledge of mass 10 kg is dragged along the rough level ground by a force of 40 N inclined to the horizontal at an angle of 30°. Calculate the vertical reaction between the sledge and the ground.

If the coefficient of friction between the sledge and the ground is 0·3, find the work done in overcoming friction while the sledge is moving through 4 m.

10. A ship A is sailing NE at 20 km h^{-1} while a ship B is sailing W at 16 km h^{-1}. What is the relative velocity of B with respect to A?

At noon B is 60 km E of A. At what instant will A and B be nearest to one another, and what will be their distance apart at that moment?

11. A lamina is in the shape of an equilateral triangle ABC. A force of 10 N acts along BA, one of 4 N along AC and one of 12 N along CB. Find the magnitude of the resultant of these forces and the angle its direction makes with CB.

12. A cyclist working at 75 W rides at 50 km h^{-1} down a slope of inclination θ, where $\sin \theta = \frac{1}{100}$. If the total mass of the rider and his machine is 66 kg, show that the frictional force opposing his motion is about 12 N.

The lowest speed at which the cyclist can ride without falling off is 5 km h^{-1}. Calculate the inclination of the steepest slope up which he can ride, assuming that he works at the same rate as before and that frictional resistance remains unchanged. (Take $g = 10$ m s^{-2}.)

13. A marble weighing 30 gm was dropped from rest at a height of 2·5 m onto a horizontal floor. Calculate the kinetic energy and the momentum it had acquired on reaching the ground, specifying your units.

The marble was observed to rebound to a height of 1·6 m. Calculate the loss of kinetic energy at the impact, and the total change of momentum. Assuming contact with the floor lasted for 0·1 s, find the average force between the marble and floor during that time. (Take $g = 9·8$ m s^{-2}.)

14. A rifle is fired at 100 m range at a circular target whose centre is at the same level as the rifle. If the rifle is held with the barrel horizontal and the bullet has a muzzle velocity of 500 m s^{-1}, find how much below the centre the bullet hits the target.

Prove that the barrel of the rifle must be elevated through an angle of about $\frac{1}{2} \sin^{-1} (0·004)$ for the bullet to hit the target in the centre.

15. You are given that, when a spring is stretched, the tension is directly proportional to the amount by which its stretched length exceeds its unstretched length. (This is known as *Hooke's law*.)

AP, BP and CP are three springs of identical mechanical properties and the same unstretched lengths. They are attached to fixed points at A, B and C. When stretched their lengths are a, b and c and the angles APB and BPC are 90° and $(90 + \theta)°$. Find the unstretched length of the springs in terms of b, c and θ, and deduce that

$$c(\cos \theta - \sin \theta) = a(1 - \sin \theta) - b(1 - \cos \theta).$$

16. A thin, uniform flat plate is in the shape of a square *ABCD* of side 1 m with an isosceles triangle *CDE* described externally on the side *CD*; the angle *CED* = 90°. Find the distance of the centre of gravity of the plate from *AB*.

If the plate hangs from *B* in equilibrium under gravity, find the inclination of *BA* to the downward vertical.

17. A pump raises 810 litres of water per minute from a depth of 20 m; the water is delivered at a speed of 10 m s⁻¹. Find (i) the potential energy, (ii) the kinetic energy, gained by the water delivered each second. Show that, neglecting frictional losses, the pump is working at about 3·3 kW.

18. A 50 kg bag of flour is hoisted vertically through 8 m in 1 min by a man working a pulley system. In this time the man working the machine does 4500 J of work. What is the efficiency of the pulley system and at what rate is the man working?

If the velocity ratio is 5, what average force is the man exerting?

19. A rod *AB*, 3 m in length and of mass 10 kg, whose centre of gravity is at a point 1 m from *A*, is suspended in a horizontal position by two strings from *A* and *B*, each inclined outwards so that their continued directions meet at a point below *AB*. The string from *A* is inclined at 60° to the horizontal. Find the inclination to the horizontal of the string from *B*, and the tension in it.

20. The figure shows diagrammatically an arrangement of three light coplanar bars, forming a linkage; they are pin-jointed to each other at *B* and *C*, and to the ground at *A* and *D*. A load of 100 N is applied perpendicular to the bar *BC* 2 m from *B*, and the linkage is held in equilibrium by a force *P*

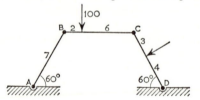

applied perpendicular to *CD* 3 m from *C*. (i) By considering the equilibrium of *BC*, determine the direction and magnitude of the reaction at *C*. (ii) By considering the equilibrium of *CD*, find the magnitude of *P* and the direction and magnitude of the reaction on the ground at *D*.

21. The straight line *AK* is perpendicular to the straight line *ABCD*; *AK* = 20 mm, and *AB* = *BC* = *CD* = 10 mm. At *K* four forces act, represented in magnitude and direction by *KA*, *KB*, *KC*, *KD* on a scale of 1 N to 10 mm. Find the magnitude of the resultant, and the moment of this resultant about *A*.

22. A mass of 10 kg hanging by a string of length 1 m from a point *P* is pulled 0·25 m away from the vertical line through *P* by another string attached to the mass and held at rest in this position with the second string at right angles to the first. Find the tension in each string.

If the second string is suddenly cut so that the mass is free to swing, find its velocity at the lowest point. (Take *g* = 10 m s⁻².)

23. A railway truck of mass 12 tonnes starts from rest at the top of a slope of length 135 m and of inclination α, where $\sin \alpha = \frac{1}{294}$. Neglecting frictional resistances, show that, when the truck reaches the bottom of the slope, its speed is 3 m s^{-1}.

Just after reaching the bottom of the slope the truck collides with a stationary truck of mass 6 tonnes. If the trucks move on together after the impact, find their common velocity. Find also the loss of kinetic energy due to the impact. (Take $g = 9.8$ m s^{-2}.)

24. The banks of a frozen pond are inclined to the horizontal at an angle of 30°. A uniform plank is placed with one end on the ice and the other end on a bank, the vertical plane through the plank cutting the bank in a line of greatest slope. Assuming the ice to be perfectly smooth and the plank to be just on the point of slipping, find the coefficient of limiting friction between the plank and the bank.

If the plank has mass 10 kg and a man of mass 60 kg stands on it at a distance from the bank equal to $\frac{3}{4}$ of the length of the plank, find the reactions at the two ends.

25. A smooth pulley is fixed to the roof of a lift, and over it there passes a rope with masses of 10 kg and 6 kg at its ends; the 10 kg mass rests on the floor of the lift. Find the contact force between this mass and the floor when the lift is moving downwards at 7 m s^{-1} with a retardation of 1.5 m s^{-2}.

26. A uniform circular disc, centre O, has a diameter AOB. The part of the disc within the circle on AO as diameter is cut out and placed so as to make double thickness on the circle of diameter OB. Find the centre of gravity of the material of the disc in this new arrangement.

27. A nail of mass 50 gm is driven horizontally into a fixed block of wood by a hammer of mass 1 kg. Just before the impact the hammer is moving with a speed of 6.3 m s^{-1}. Assuming that the hammer does not rebound, find the common speed of the nail and the hammer just after impact and the loss of kinetic energy.

If the nail penetrates the wood to a depth of 45 mm, find the time during which the nail is brought to rest. Show also that the resistance of the wood to penetration, assumed to be constant, is about 430 N.

28. A screw-jack, operated by two equal forces each acting at a radius of 100 mm, has a screw with a pitch of 5 mm. Calculate the velocity ratio of the screw jack.

If equal forces of 50 N are needed to raise a load of 250 kg, find the efficiency of the screw-jack at this load.

29. After a train has started from rest the times at which it passes certain fixed points are noted. These times, and the distances of the points from the start are:

Distance (m)	0	5	20	80	320	800	1280
Time (s)	0	4.5	10.5	27.0	75.0	162.0	240.0

Using these figures, plot a graph relating the speed and the time; deduce from it the acceleration of the train at a speed of 3 m s^{-1}.

30. A uniform rectangular paving stone, $ABCD$, has mass 50 kg; AB is 0·9 m and BC is 0·6 m. It is lying on a level surface when an upward vertical force is applied to it at a point on AB which is 75 mm from A. How great must the force be in order to start lifting the stone? About which side will the stone turn?

In order to make the stone turn about the other side through C a vertical force is also applied at the other end of this side. How great must this force be, and how great must the lifting force then be?

31. $ABCD$ is a square and Y is the mid-point of BC. Forces are represented in magnitude and position by the lines AY, YD, BD. Find the magnitude of their resultant and the angle which its line of action makes with AB.

If X is the mid-point of AB, and a force represented in magnitude and position by the line DX is added to the other three, show that the resultant of these four forces passes through C.

32. A train is drawn by its engine up an incline of 1 in 80. At a certain instant the speed is 30 km h⁻¹ and the acceleration 0·1 m s⁻². If the resistance to motion is 75 N per tonne mass of train and the total mass of the train is 400 tonnes, calculate the tractive force exerted by the engine, and the power at which it is working at this instant.

If this represents the maximum power of the engine, what is the greatest steady speed the train can have up this incline, frictional resistance remaining constant? (Take $g = 10$ m s⁻².)

33. A gun, of mass 2000 kg and free to recoil horizontally, fires a cannon ball of mass 50 kg with a speed of 60 m s⁻¹. Find the speed of recoil of the gun and show that the kinetic energy of the cannon ball is 40 times that of the gun.

If the cannon ball strikes a fixed block of wood and penetrates it to a depth of 0·6 m, show that the cannon ball comes to rest 0·02 s after striking the wood. Show also that the resistance of the wood to penetration, assumed to be constant, is 150 kN.

34. A boat is to travel due E in a current which is running $\theta°$ N of E. If the speed of the boat in still water is 5 knots and the speed of the current is 3 knots, what is the greatest value of θ for which the speed of the boat to the east will exceed 5 knots?

35. A uniform rod AB of length $2a$ and weight W is hinged at A and rests in contact with a smooth horizontal peg so that AB is inclined at an angle of 60° to the downward vertical through A. Find the distance of the peg from A if the reaction at A is horizontal, and find the magnitude of this reaction and also the force on the peg.

36. A uniform rectangular box is of mass 3 kg, and has a base of interior measurement 320 mm by 240 mm. It is tightly packed with 12 cylindrical tins, each of diameter 80 mm and of mass (with contents) 2 kg, standing upright in 3 rows of 4. If a corner tin be now taken out, find how far the centre of gravity of the whole will be shifted: (i) towards a shorter side of the box, (ii) towards a longer side.

37. Calculate the power of an engine which raises the water in a pipe of cross-section 0.01 m² to a height of 10 m and then delivers it at this height at 100 litres per second.

38. A pulley system consists of two blocks; the upper block has 3 sheaves and the lower has 2, and the same rope passes continuously round all the pulleys, one end being made fast to one of the blocks. What is the velocity ratio of the system? To lift a load of mass 200 kg an effort of 450 N is required. Calculate the mechanical advantage of the system and its efficiency.

39. A golf ball is hit from ground level and just clears an obstacle of height a at a horizontal distance of $3a$. It reaches the ground again at the same level as the point of projection and a distance $4a$ from it. Find the tangent of the angle of projection and the greatest height attained.

40. A uniform circular cylinder, of height 8 cm and diameter 6 cm, rests with its circular base on a rough horizontal plane. Find through what angle the plane can be tilted before the cylinder upsets, and find the least value of the coefficient of friction for this to be possible.

*41. If a body moves with constant acceleration, prove that the space-average of the velocity over any distance is
$$\frac{2(u^2 + uv + v^2)}{3(u + v)}.$$
Is this greater or less than the time-average?

42. A string has one end fixed at A and, passing under a movable pulley of mass M at B and over a fixed pulley at C, carries a mass M' at D. Each part of the string is vertical. Show that M descends with acceleration
$$\frac{(M - 2M')g}{M + 4M'}.$$

43. A truck starting from rest has an acceleration a for a time t and then continues at uniform speed. A case of mass m rests on the floor of the truck, at a distance d from the back edge. Find relations between a, t, d, μ and g: (i) if the case is not to move on the truck, (ii) if the case is not to fall off the truck.

44. Whilst a train is travelling at 21 m s⁻¹ an orange is thrown out of a carriage window horizontally with a velocity relative to the train of 7 m s⁻¹ at right angles to the track. It is thrown from a height of 2.5 m above the track. Find the distance of the point where it lands (measured horizontally): (i) from the train, (ii) from the point of projection. (Take $g = 9.8$ m s⁻².)

45. ABC is a triangle with $a = 100$ mm, $b = 90$ mm, $c = 80$ mm. A particle inside the triangle is attracted towards A, B and C by forces of 5, 7 and 6 N. Find, by drawing, the distances of the particle from the vertices in the equilibrium position.

46. A rectangular block of mass 100 kg stands on rough ground with one face close to and parallel to a vertical wall. A light 45° wedge is forced between the block and the wall, the coefficients of friction between the wedge and the wall, the wedge and the block and the block and the ground all being $\frac{1}{3}$. Find the vertical force that must be applied to the wedge to move the block.

47. A 50 gm bullet striking a fixed block horizontally when travelling at 30 m s⁻¹ penetrates it to a depth of 150 mm. Find the resistance, assumed to be constant. If the block of mass 5 kg is free to move on a smooth horizontal surface, and the resistance is the same as before, find how far the bullet will penetrate.

48. To one end of a uniform rod of length l and mass M are attached a mass M and one end of a string of length $3l$. The other end of the string is attached to a smooth wall against which the other end of the rod rests. If in equilibrium the rod makes an angle θ with the horizontal, prove that $\tan^2 \theta = \frac{8}{7}$.

49. A mass m kg is to be raised through a vertical height of h metres, starting from rest and coming to rest under gravity, by a light chain whose tension is not to exceed P newtons. Prove that the shortest time in which this can be done is

$$\sqrt{\left\{ \frac{2hP}{g(P - mg)} \right\}} \text{ seconds.}$$

*If a large amount of material is to be raised, prove that the total time occupied by the upward journeys will be as short as possible if the material is sent up in loads of $(2P/3g)$ kg.

50. A ball is dropped vertically on to a paved yard from a height of 4·9 m. Every time that it hits the paving its speed just after the impact is $\frac{3}{4}$ of its speed just before. Find the time that elapses before it stops bouncing, and the total distance that it covers before coming to rest. (Take $g = 9·8$ m s⁻².)

51. Two particles are projected simultaneously from the same point with the same speed in the same vertical plane. Their initial directions of motion make angles α and β with the horizontal. Prove that during their flight through the air the line joining the particles makes a constant angle with the horizontal. Find this angle in terms of α and β.

52. A bus of mass 2500 kg has its centre of gravity 1 m above the ground, and its axles are 7 m apart. When standing on level ground, $\frac{2}{3}$ of the weight is borne by the rear axle. The bus is parked on a hill of inclination $\tan^{-1}(\frac{7}{24})$, facing downhill. Find the coefficient of friction necessary between the tyres and the ground if it is not to slip down the hill: (i) if all wheels are locked, (ii) if the rear wheels are locked, (iii) if the front wheels are locked.

53. Two smooth cylinders of unequal radii are in contact, with their axes horizontal. The first rests on a plane inclined at an angle α to the horizontal, the second on a plane at an angle β. Show that in equilibrium the plane containing the axes of the cylinders makes with the vertical an angle θ, where

$$\cot \theta = \frac{W_2 \cot \alpha \sim W_1 \cot \beta}{W_1 + W_2},$$

W_1 and W_2 being the weights of the cylinders.

54. A horizontal jet of water of cross-section 7000 mm² impinges with a velocity of 40 m s⁻¹ on a fixed vertical plate. Find: (i) the horse-power necessary to project the water, and (ii) the steady force on the plate, assuming that the water does not rebound from it.

55. A rope of length 7 m is attached to two hooks in the ceiling 5 m apart. A light, smooth ring is free to slide along this rope, and from this ring hangs a load of mass 30 kg. Find the magnitude and direction of the smallest force which, applied to the ring, can keep the ring at a point on the rope 3 m from one hook and 4 m from the other. Find also the tension in the rope in this position.

56. To the end A of a uniform rod AB is attached one end of a string whose length is equal to that of the rod. The other end is fixed to a hook on a rough vertical wall, and the rod is in equilibrium with the end B in contact with the wall. Prove that the inclination of the rod to the wall cannot be less than $\cot^{-1}(\frac{1}{3}\mu)$. Show also that for varying inclinations of the rod the tension in the string is less when friction is limiting than when it is not limiting.

57. Two bodies of masses M and $M - m_1$ are connected by a string passing over a smooth peg. On the second body is placed a third of mass $m_1 + m_2$. The system is released from rest, and after it has moved through a distance h the added mass $m_1 + m_2$ is left behind on a ring through which the second body just passes. Show that the latter will descend a further distance

$$\frac{hm_2(2M - m_1)}{m_1(2M + m_2)}.$$

58. A cylindrical tin without a lid is 120 mm high and 30 mm in radius. The centre of gravity is on the axis 40 mm from the centre of the base. Thin biscuits of radius 30 mm are put into the tin. When the tin is full the weight of the biscuits is 4 times that of the tin.

Find the height (h mm) of the centre of gravity of the whole above the base when the depth of biscuits is x mm. Draw a graph of h for values of x between 0 and 120.

The tin is now placed on a plane rough enough to prevent sliding whose inclination is $\tan^{-1}(\frac{5}{6})$. Find between what limits the depth of biscuits must lie in order that the tin may not upset.

59. A shot of mass m penetrates a thickness t of a fixed plate of mass M; if M were free to move, and the resistance were uniform and the same as when the plate is fixed, show that the thickness penetrated would be $Mt/(M + m)$.

60. Two bodies, of masses M, m, are connected by a string. The mass M is placed on a board inclined at an angle α to the horizontal, and the string runs up the board parallel to a line of greatest slope, over the smooth edge at the top of the board; the mass m hangs vertically. The coefficient of friction μ between the mass M and the board is less than $\tan \alpha$. Prove that no motion ensues if

$$M(\sin \alpha + \mu \cos \alpha) > m > M(\sin \alpha - \mu \cos \alpha).$$

Find the acceleration of the masses: (i) if $m > M(\sin \alpha + \mu \cos \alpha)$, (ii) if $m < M(\sin \alpha - \mu \cos \alpha)$.

INDEX

273

ANSWERS

Most answers are given to some degree of approximation. For example, many angles are given to the nearest degree and many numbers to two or three significant figures. Answers to questions involving g have usually been based on the approximation $g = 9\cdot8$ m s^{-2}, unless the value 10 m s^{-2} has been suggested in the exercise; students who have used the less accurate value must expect some discrepancy in the final figure of their answers.

EXERCISE 1(a)

1. 10 800 km h^{-1}.   2. 55·6 min.   3. 48·2 km h^{-1}.   4. 500 s.
5. 0·6 m s^{-1}, $\frac{1}{3}$ m s^{-1} forwards.   6. 15 km h^{-1}, 7·5 km h^{-1}.
7. In m s^{-1}: (i) 4·6, (ii) 7·5, (iii) 14·3, (iv) 41, (v) 10·4, (vi) 13, (vii) 8, 11, 16, 48.
8. 4·5 m s^{-1}, 7 m s^{-1}.   9. (i) 34·3 s; (ii) 45, 60, 66 m s^{-1}.
10. (i) 24, -12, 60 mm s^{-1}; (ii) $t = 1$, $s = 11$, $t = 4$, $s = -16$.
11. 100 m, 5 m s^{-1}, 5 s, 101 m.   12. 25 m s^{-1}, 750 m.   13. 20 s, 55·5 m.
14. (i) 14 m s^{-1}; (ii) $t = 11$; (iii) $t = 20$.

EXERCISE 1(b)

1. $1\cdot27 \times 10^5$ km h^{-2}.   2. $1/129\cdot6 = 0\cdot0077$.   3. 2250 km h^{-2}, 0·17 m s^{-2}.
4. 5 s.   5. 175 m.   6. 0·75 km.   7. 20 s, 400 m.   8. $6\frac{2}{3}$ km.
9. $9\frac{1}{3}$ km, 42 km h^{-1} per minute $= 2520$ km h^{-2}.   10. 3·2 min.
11. 2 m s^{-2}, 16 m.   12. 22 m s^{-1}, 0·73 m s^{-2}.   13. $\frac{1}{22}$ m s^{-2}.
14. $14\frac{1}{2}$ s, 116 m.   15. (i) 0·7 m s^{-2}; (ii) 0·2 m s^{-2}; (iii) 70 m.
16. (i) 1 m s^{-2}; (ii) 61 m.   17. 4·1, 2·3 m s^{-2}; 200 m.   18. 13·5 m s^{-1}.
19. 9 m s^{-1}, -12 m s^{-2}, and 0 m s^{-1}, 6 m s^{-2}; 2 m, -3 m s^{-1}, 0 m s^{-2}.
20. 150 m; 0·4, 1·6 m s^{-2}.   21. 3325 cm; -12 or -36 cm s^{-2}.
22. 6 s; 60 m.   23. 22·9 s.   25. $nv/(n + 2)$.   26. $(n - 1)v/n$.   27. $s = 6$.

EXERCISE 1(c)

1. 135 m, 1·1 m s^{-2}.   2. 81 cm; $\frac{1}{2}$ cm s^{-2}.
3. 5 min; 480 km h^{-2} $= 0\cdot037$ m s^{-2}.   4. 24·5 m.   5. 1125 m.
6. 10 s; 275 m.   7. 18 m s^{-1}.   8. 70 km h^{-1}.   9. 5 m s^{-1} $= 18$ km h^{-1}.
10. 2·5 m s^{-2}.   11. 225 m.   12. 31 m.   13. 8 m s^{-1}.   14. 20 s; 9 m s^{-1}.
15. 1·2 km.   16. 120 m; 5 m s^{-1}.   17. 18·5 m s^{-1}; 1·6 s.
18. 2 s; after 4 s; 9 cm to right of O, 6 cm s^{-1} to right; 9 cm to right of O, 6 cm s^{-1} to left; 15 cm to left of O, 18 cm s^{-1} to left.
20. 300 m; 9 m s^{-1} $= 32\cdot4$ km h^{-1}.   21. 480 m; 12 s.
22. 8·5 m s^{-1}; 80, 53·3 s; 3120 m.   23. 14 m s^{-1}.   24. 2 cm s^{-2}; 80 cm s^{-1}.
26. 1 m s^{-2}. 0·1 m s^{-2}; 79·2 m.   27. 81 m; 30 s.   28. $u^2/2(a_1 + a_2)$.

EXERCISE 1(*d*)

1. 0·5 s; 5 m s⁻¹.   **2.** 65 m.   **3.** 120 m.   **4.** 0·4 s and 2 s; 8 m s⁻¹.
5. 10 m s⁻¹.   **6.** 2 s.   **7.** 60 m.   **8.** 45 m s⁻¹.   **9.** 1·6 s.
10. 2·4 s; 10 m.   **11.** 180 m.   **12.** 15 m s⁻¹; 25 m s⁻¹; 1 s and 2 s; 3·7 s.
14. 830 m.

EXERCISE 3(*a*)

1. 5·4, 10⁻¹⁴ N.   **2.** 0·11 N.   **3.** 240 N.   **4.** 60 kg.   **5.** 200 m s⁻².
6. 0·8 m s⁻².   **7.** 100 kg.   **8.** 0·042 m s⁻².   **9.** 40 N.   **10.** 25 N.
11. 60 000 N.   **12.** 1·6 × 10⁶ N; 0·08 m s⁻²; 2½ min.   **13.** 30 kg.
15. 0·2 m s⁻².   **16.** 225 N.   **17.** 0·138 N.   **18.** 2000 N.   **19.** 400 000 N.
20. 8500 N.   **22.** 52 N.

EXERCISE 3(*b*)

1. 13·6 N.   **2.** (i) 9400 N; (ii) 9800 N; (iii) 10 400 N.   **3.** 2·6 N.
4. 520 N.   **5.** 70·2 m s⁻².
6. Either descending and accelerating, or ascending and retarding, at
0·8 m s⁻².
7. 1000 kg.   **8.** 5 kg, 5·3 kg.   **10.** $(g - f')/(g - f)$.   **11.** 0·068.

EXERCISE 3(*c*)

1. 8 kN, 48 kN.   **2.** 140 N; 0·2 m s⁻².   **3.** 1 m s⁻²; 60 kN, 36 kN.
4. 42·3 kN, 28·2 kN, 14·1 kN.   **5.** 4800 N, 660 N.   **6.** 0·2 m s⁻²; 3 N.
8. 480 N; 40 kg.   **9.** 60 kg.   **10.** 0·5 m s⁻².   **11.** 200 N; 120 N.
12. 85 N; 1·5 m s⁻².   **13.** 1·4 m s⁻², 33·6 mN.   **15.** 1 kg; ½g
16. 7·6 N.   **17.** 1·25 s.   **18.** 1·4 m s⁻².   **19.** ⅓g; 2 s.
20. After 12 s; 59 m.   **21.** 2·2, 1·8 m s⁻²; 0·24 N.

EXERCISE 4

1. 36 N.   **2.** 45 N.   **3.** 72 N.   **4.** 44 N, 108 N.   **5.** 6 m s⁻²; 12 m.
6. 1·5 m.   **7.** 9 m s⁻².   **8.** 6 m s⁻².   **9.** 7·5 N.   **10.** 6 N.
11. 10 N, 17 N.   **12.** 45°; 14 N.   **13.** 27°; 11 N.   **14.** 30°; 8·7 N.
15. 0·9 m s⁻².   **16.** 14°.   **17.** 2·4 N.   **18.** 0·2 m s⁻².   **19.** 28 N.
20. 58 N, N31° E.   **21.** 79 mN; 29°.   **22.** 100 kN, S33° E.
23. 188 N, 197 N.   **24.** 90°, 57 N or 28°, 27 N.

EXERCISE 5

1. 0·4.   **2.** 98 N.   **3.** 360 N.   **4.** 98 N.   **5.** 163 N.   **6.** 8 m s⁻¹.
7. 0·15.   **8.** 36 N; 2 m.   **9.** 3·45 m s⁻².   **10.** 82 N.   **11.** 40 N.
12. More than 460 N.   **13.** 0·62 m s⁻².   **14.** 540 N.
16. 0·7; (i) 8 N, (ii) 2·5 N.   **17.** 7·9 N.   **18.** 320 N.   **20.** tan⁻¹ (3μ).
21. $g \sec \alpha \sin (\beta - \alpha)$.

Page 70 MISCELLANEOUS EXERCISE A

1. 10 m s⁻¹, 23·3 m s⁻¹; $\frac{1}{9}$ m s⁻². **2.** 0·08 m s⁻²; 3·9 km. **3.** 0·2 m s⁻².
4. 2·5 m s⁻²; 0·4 s. **5.** $\frac{5}{49}W$, $\frac{25}{49}W$. **6.** 40·2 km h⁻¹; 80 N.
7. After 1·5 s; 34 m up. **8.** 0·37 m s⁻²; 5·4 m. **9.** 8·8 m s⁻².
10. (i) 15 m s⁻¹; (ii) 420 m. **11.** 27, 78, 140, 190, 240, 260, 260, 260 mm s⁻².
12. 0·19 m s⁻²; 14·8 m s⁻¹; 67 N. **13.** 4·9 m s⁻²; 9·8 N. **14.** 4 m s⁻²; 64 m.
15. 1·8 m. **17.** (i) 2 m s⁻²; (ii) 3 N, 5 N. **18.** 1500 N; 25 m. **19.** 250 m.
20. (i) 95 N; (ii) 140 N. **21.** 1·56 m s⁻². **22.** 0·5 m s⁻²; 17 s.
23. 12 m s⁻¹; 9 m. **24.** 10 N; 1·28 kg. **25.** 73 N. **26.** 10 s; 10 s.
27. 4·3 N; 2·8 m s⁻²; **28.** (i) 100 N; (ii) 70 N. **29.** 18 N; 1 m s⁻²; 1·4 s.
30. 15°; 510 N. **31.** 2·5 m s⁻²; 93s. **32.** 12 m s⁻¹; 7·2 m. **33.** 9 N; 15 N.
34. 24 N; 16 N, 12 N. **35.** 58 N. **36.** 0·8 m s⁻²; 17 m.
37. 15 m s⁻¹; $\frac{1}{3}$, $\frac{1}{2}$ m s⁻². **38.** 0·1 m s⁻²; 500 m. **39.** 34 m. **40.** 280.
41. 0·15 m s⁻². **42.** After 45 s. **43.** 0·4. **44.** (i) 0·84; (ii) 22 N.
45. (i) 25 N, (ii) 20 N; 7·2 m. **46.** 1125 m; 75 s. **47.** 984 N; 0·15.
48. (i) 0·15 m s⁻²; (ii) 69 kN; (iii) 90 kN. **49.** 2 m s⁻². **50.** 59 N.
51. $\frac{2}{3}$ m s⁻²; 180 m; 11½ s later. **52.** 0·4 m s⁻² down; 200 kg.
53. 2 s; 6 m. **54.** 0·28 s.
55. (i) 49 N; (ii) 28 N; (iii) 7·7 m s⁻², 2·1 m s⁻².
56. 1, 1·25 m s⁻²; 46½ s. **57.** 32 m. **58.** (i) 6 N; (ii) 7 m s⁻².
60. (i) 8·5 N; (ii) 38·5 N; (iii) 19·4 N; (iv) 19·4 N.

Page 82 EXERCISE 6(a)

1. 8. **2.** 4$\frac{5}{6}$. **3.** 4. **4.** 3. **5.** 100 N; 300 N. **6.** 650 N.
7. 0·81 m from pivot. **8.** 2250 N. **9.** 1$\frac{1}{6}$ m from pivot. **10.** 6, 6·4 N.
11. 40, 70 kN. **12.** 1 m; 17·5 kg. **13.** 2$\frac{1}{3}$ m from A. **14.** 90 kg.
15. Within 2 m of other end. **16.** 3, 4·5, 3 kN. **17.** 350 N.

Page 87 EXERCISE 6(b)

1. 50 N. **2.** 100 N. **3.** 2500 N. **4.** 600 N. **5.** 800√3 ≈ 1400 N.
6. 300 N. **7.** 480 N, 70 N. **8.** 80 N, 40 N; $\frac{1}{2}$.
9. $\frac{1}{6}$√3 ≈ 0·29; 50√3 ≈ 87 N. **11.** 20 N; 12 N.
12. 0·05 N at C perpendicular to AC. **19.** $W(\sqrt{2} - 1)$.

Page 92 EXERCISE 6(c)

2. 45 N, 75 N, 60 N. **3.** 32 N m. **4.** 0·25 N m.
5. Between 1·54 and 1·66 m from pivot. **6.** 11·7 N, 20·4 N.
7. 15 N m; 50 N. **9.** $\frac{1}{5}Wa$.

Page 99 EXERCISE 7(a)

1. 1·35 km S10°E. **2.** 5·41 km S34°W, 5·41 km N34°E.
3. 38·6 km S65°W. **4.** 157 m S1°W.
5. 13 u. N67°E; 13 u. N67°W; 13 u. S67°E; 24·5 u. N78°E; 75 u. N53°E;
   41·2 u. N61°W.
6. 7·43 km h⁻¹ N73°W; 3·58 km h⁻¹ N54°E; 17·6 km h⁻¹ N69°W;
   8·16 km h⁻¹ N75°E.

EXERCISE 7(a) continued

7. 26·5 u. S2°E; 17·6 u. S24°E; 25·3 u. S74°W.
8. 8·15 u., 9·21 u. **9.** 11·3 m s⁻¹, 56·5 m s⁻¹.
10. 16, 22·6; 0, 11·3 units. **11.** 24·6 km, 6·1 km; 19·7 km, −14·1 km.
12. 15·3 knots, 12·9 knots; 15·3 knots, 12·9 knots.
13. 102 nautical miles, N20°E. **14.** 349 km S23°W.
15. 5 km h⁻¹ N27°E. **16.** 15 units $\bar{\omega}$ E of N. **17.** 5·94 m, N0°19′W.
19. 9 units, bearing N60°E, elevation 26°
        9 units, bearing N60°E, depression 26°
20. 8·7 m, bearing N28°W, elevation 20°.

PAGE 103   EXERCISE 7(b)

1. 50 km h⁻¹ from S60°W. **2.** 12 knots due S. **3.** 5 knots N42°E.
4. 32°. **5.** 2090 km h⁻¹ S35½°W.
6. −6 or −54 km s⁻¹, 0°; 38 km s⁻¹, 141°; angles being given to direction
    of motion of earth.
7. N87°E. **8.** 3⅓. **9.** 25 km h⁻¹; 66 km h⁻¹ from S49°W.
10. SW. **11.** S57°E. **12.** S26°E or S26°W (the former giving the shorter
    flight).
14. S53°W, 630 km h⁻¹. **15.** 3 hr 28 min. **16.** 12 : 13.
18. from S75°W. **19.** 18 knots from N61°E.

PAGE 108   EXERCISE 7(c)

1. 64 min; 6 km. **2.** 117 km h⁻¹; $\frac{9}{13}$ km. **3.** N44½°W; 37 min.
4. N64°W; 16 min. **5.** 14·3 knots, S51°W; 3·1 nautical miles.
6. 0·175 nautical miles; 4·56 min. **7.** 56½° to GW.
8. 12½ min; 53½° to bank upstream. **9.** 5·6 m s⁻¹.
10 11·3 h after destroyer leaves harbour.
11. 22½ min; 1·88 nautical miles; 12 knots, N62°W. **12.** S67°E.
14. Between N12°E and N41°W. **15.** 10 m s⁻². **16.** S60°W.

PAGE 114   EXERCISE 8(a)

2. 100 m; 0·2 m. **3.** 44 m; 60 m. **4.** 650 m; 31 m. **5.** $\frac{3}{7}$ s; 0·9 m.
6. 41 m. **7.** 2·4 s; 36 m. **8.** 2 s; 60 m. **9.** 630 m.
10. 15 m s⁻¹; 0·8 m. **11.** 0·4 s; 5 m s⁻¹. **12.** 1·4 m s⁻¹. **13.** 31 m s⁻¹.
14. 3 s. **15.** 24 m s⁻¹, 4·8 m. **16.** 20 m s⁻¹.

PAGE 118   EXERCISE 8(b)

2. 6 m along, 5·5 m up; 6° to horizontal. **3.** 8 s; 34° to horizontal.
4. 5 s; 75 m. **5.** 125 m; 160 m. **6.** 17 m s⁻¹, 28°; 0·8 s; 4·3 m.
7. 8·4 m. **8.** 2 m. **9.** 2 s; 5 m; 35 m. **10.** 8·4 m s⁻¹; $\frac{6}{7}$ s; 17°.
11. 6 m s⁻¹; 14·4 m. **12.** 25 km. **13.** 11 m; 60 m. **14.** 4·3 m.
15. 4·6 m away; 80° to horizontal; 59° below horizontal. **16.** 830 m s⁻¹.
17. 3·4 m. **18.** Ratio 16 : 9. **19.** 43 m; 46 m s⁻¹ at 79° to horizontal.
20. 10 s later; 430 m further on. **21.** 37° to horizontal; 23 m s⁻¹.
23. $V^2 \sin^2 \theta/2g$; $2V \sin \theta/g$; $V^2 \sin 2\theta/g$.

PAGE 123   EXERCISE 9(*a*)

1. 6·1 newtons, 35° with *P*.   **2.** 3·6 N, N19°W.
3. 4·6 N, N38°W.   **4.** 11·3 kN, 2° with line of ship.
5. 172 N, N15½°E.   **6.** 3200 N, S54°W.
7. 74° to line of prongs, 560 m s⁻².   **8.** 23, N43°E.
9. 2·6 N, N11°E.

PAGE 127   EXERCISE 9(*b*)

1. 36 N.   **2.** 45 N.   **3.** 72 N.   **4.** 38 N, 11 N.   **6.** 45°; 14 N.
7. 27°; 11 N.   **8.** 30°; 8·7 N.   **9.** 90° − $\bar{\omega}$, $\bar{\omega}$.   **10.** 320 N, 600 N.
11. 1·7 units, N58°E.   **12.** 10 kN, 6·2 kN.   **13.** 7·5 N.   **14.** 6 N.
15. 10 N, 17 N.   **16.** 28 N.   **17.** 58 N, N31°E.   **18.** 79 mN; 29°.
19. 100 kN, S33°E.   **20.** 188 N, 197 N.   **21.** 90°, 57 N or 28°, 27 N.
22. 0·5 N perpendicular to rod.   **23.** 35°.
24. 64° above or 4° below horizontal.   **25.** 78 N, 91 N.   **26.** 80°, 69°.
27. 28°, 20°.   **28.** 1 N parallel to the wire.   **29.** 33·4 N, 31·5 N.

PAGE 132   EXERCISE 9(*c*)

1. 130 N, 23° with vertical.   **2.** 128 N, 21° with vertical.
3. 108 N, 14° with vertical.   **4.** 103 N, 16° with vertical.
5. 60 N vertically.   **7.** 5000 N, $\bar{\omega}$ to vertical.
8. 520 N, 5½° with horizontal.   **9.** 340 N.   **10.** 21, 21, 75, 75 N.
11. 60 N ⊥ to rod, 57 N at 32° to vertical.
12. $\frac{1}{2}W\sqrt{3}$ at 60° to line of greatest slope.

PAGE 133   MISCELLANEOUS EXERCISE B

1. 24 m s⁻¹; 1470 m; 28 min.   **2.** 2 m s⁻²; 2 m s⁻¹; 1·2 m.
3. $\frac{7}{16}l$ from the 4 kg mass.   **4.** 7·4 m s⁻¹ from S74°E.   **5.** 2 km.
6. 33 min 44 s; 44 min 32 s.   **7.** 57 N; 0·58.   **8.** 0·5 kg; 2·5 kg.
9. N24°E, 13 min.   **10.** (i) 25 m s⁻¹; (ii) 2 s; (iii) 3·8 m.
11. (i) 2, 4; (ii) 6*t* − 18; (iii) *t* > 3; (iv) 28 m.   **12.** 360 N.
13. 840, 660 N; 66 kg.   **14.** 50$\sqrt{2}$ ≈ 71 km h⁻¹; 50 km h⁻¹ due N.
15. 45 m; 312 m; 4 s.
16. 4 m s⁻¹; 1·6 m.   **18.** 35 N; 12 m.   **19.** 26·5 m s⁻¹, N41°E.
20. (i) 7 m s⁻¹; (ii) $\frac{5}{7}$ s; (iii) 24 m s⁻¹; (iv) 25 m s⁻¹.
21. 14 m s⁻¹; 146 m from *L*; (*a*) 8 m s⁻¹, (*b*) 16 m s⁻¹.   **22.** 1$\frac{2}{3}$ kg.
23. $\bar{\omega}$.   **24.** 0·57 sea miles.   **25.** 4·3 s.
26. 4·6, 11·8, 19·0, 23·6 m s⁻¹; both 0·433 m s⁻².   **27.** 0·50.   **28.** 3; 14$\frac{1}{4}$.
29. 47 min.   **30.** 0·2*v* s; 0·4*v*² m; 20 m.
31. 10·5 m s⁻¹, 52 m from *O*; 6·5 m s⁻¹; 3 s and 9 s after *A* passes *O*; 51 m.
32. (i) 0·2 m s⁻²; (ii) 360 m; (iii) 12 m s⁻¹.   **33.** $\frac{3}{13}\sqrt{3}$ ≈ 0·4.
34. N28°W; due N; 2 min.   **35.** 6·9 m from wall.   **36.** 3·19 m; 410 N.
37. 91 km h⁻¹, 0·061 m s⁻².   **38.** 11$\frac{1}{4}$ kg; 8$\frac{1}{4}$ kg.   **39.** 33°; 53 knots.
40. 220 m s⁻¹; 5000 m.

PAGE 144 **EXERCISE 10**

1. 65, 25 N. **2.** 0·5 m.
3. 400 N horizontally, 500 N at $\tilde{\omega}$ to horizontal.
4. 174 N. **5.** 3 : 1. **6.** 30°. **7.** 16°. **8.** 50 N. **9.** 2500 N.
10. $800\sqrt{3} \approx 1400$ N. **11.** 300 N.
12. 10 cm, 16 cm from the ends; 63°; 2·2 N.
13. 1·8 m from one end. **14.** 1·7 m, 1 m; 43 N, 25 N.
15. 3·3 m. **16.** 20 N; 30 N at $\tilde{\omega}$ to horizontal.
17. 1·15 m from *B*; 1740 N, 4400 N. **23.** 1·5 m and 3 m; $\frac{1}{4}$; 158 N; 23°.

PAGE 150 **EXERCISE 11**

1. 200 N. **2.** 1·1 N. **3.** 160 N. **4.** 10 N. **5.** (i) 16 N; (ii) 30 N.
6. 30°. **10.** 3200 N, 44°. **11.** 20°. **12.** 100 N[1]. **13.** 360 N[1].
14. 100 N[1]. **15.** 170 N[1]. **16.** 84 N[1]. **17.** 40 N. **18.** More than 460 N.
19. 0·7; (i) 8 N, (ii) 2·5 N. **20.** 8·1 N[1]. **21.** 18°.
22. 150 N at 17° to horizontal.
23. (i) 940 N; (ii) 170 N. Both at 40° to the slope.
24. 25° to horizontal; 20 N. **25.** 8°. **26.** 27°. **27.** 2 kg.

PAGE 156 **EXERCISE 12(*a*)**

4. 39; 270 N. **5.** 18°, 14°, 27°; 63, 41, 22N. **6.** 160 N, 200 N.
7. $\frac{2}{3}$ m from *B* along *BC*. **8.** Within 2 m of *C*. **9.** 100 N. **10.** 1, $\frac{1}{3}$, $\frac{1}{9}$.
11. Both 45°, 0·21 N. **12.** 27 N. **13.** 0·29. **14.** 40°, 14°, 8°.
16. $3W\sqrt{3}$, $\frac{8}{9}a$ from *B*; *W* at 30° to horizontal.
18. On *BC* at *B* and *C*, 180 N at 74° to vertical; on *AB* at *B* and *AC* at *C*, 300 N at 35° to vertical; on *AB* and *BC* at *A*, 390 N at 26° to vertical.

PAGE 163 **EXERCISE 12(*b*)**

5. 1·8 m beyond cliff. **6.** 66 N at 11° to horizontal. **7.** 110, 200 N.
8. 320 N at 51° to horizontal. **9.** 320 N at 18° to horizontal.
10. 320 N at 18° to horizontal. **11.** Horizontal, 45° to horizontal.
12. 43 N horizontal. **13.** Greater than 0·57. **14.** 0·35 m; 1 m. **15.** $5l/4$.
16. $AD = 0{\cdot}48\,AB$; 3·7 *W* at 63° to horizontal, 1·8 *W* at 24° to horizontal.

PAGE 166 **EXERCISE 12(*c*)**

All answers are in kN. + indicates a tension, − a thrust.
1. *BC* +3·5, *AB* −1·7, *AC* −6.
2. *BC* +3·5, *AB* −1·7, *AC* −2, *CD* +4, *AD* −2·3.
3. *BC* and *CD* $+2\frac{1}{2}$, *AB* and *AD* $+3\frac{1}{3}$, *BD* $-4\frac{1}{6}$.
4. *BC* and *CD* −1·7, *AB* and *AD* +1, *AC* +3.
5. *BC* and *AB* +1, *CD* and *AE* +0·62, *BD* and *BE* −0·62, *DE* +0·38.
6. *AB* −5·2, *BC* +2·6, *AC*, *AE*, *ED* −1·7, *CE* +1·7, *CD* +0·9.

[1] Slight differences from the answers given to Exercise 5 are accounted for by the use of the approximation $g = 10$ m s^{-2}.

EXERCISE 13(*a*)

2. 0·036 N s; 1·8 m s⁻¹.   **3.** 200 N.   **4.** 0·78 N s.   **5.** 32 N.
6. 11 250 N s; 3750 N.   **7.** 6 m s⁻¹.   **8.** 2·5 s.   **9.** 0·45 N s.
10. 2·88 N s.   **11.** 6 s.   **12.** 10·8 N s.   **13.** 172 kN.   **14.** 4 s.
15. 300 N.   **16.** 4800 N.   **17.** 0·4.

EXERCISE 13(*b*)

1. 3 m s⁻¹.   **2.** 3 m s⁻¹.   **3.** 5 cm s⁻¹.   **4.** 10 gm.   **5.** 3 m s⁻¹.
6. 2 m s⁻¹.   **7.** 1·25 kg.   **8.** 0·4 m s⁻¹; 0·15 m s⁻¹.   **9.** 0·15 m s⁻¹.
10. 0·15 m s⁻¹.   **11.** 10 m s⁻¹.   **12.** 0·3 m s⁻¹.   **13.** 600 m s⁻¹.
14. 50 m s⁻¹ in opposite direction.
15. 0·75 m s⁻¹ in same direction as before.   **16.** 1 m s⁻¹; 600 N s.
17. Unchanged, 2 m s⁻¹.   **18.** 0·5, 0·4 m s⁻¹.   **20.** 1 m s⁻¹.

21. $\frac{9}{7}$ s; 2·4 × 10⁻³ N s; 60 cm s⁻¹.   **22.** $\dfrac{\sqrt{\{2Fl(2M + m)\}}}{M + 2m}.$

EXERCISE 13(*c*)

1. 75 N.   **2.** 0·06 N.   **3.** 150 N.   **4.** 4000 N.   **5.** 27 N m.   **6.** 75 N.
7. 90 N.   **8.** 0·2 N.   **9.** 10 N.   **10.** 0·3 m.   **11.** 0·6 m.
12. 5 N s at (90° − *ω̄*).   **13.** 6·9 N s at 44°.   **14.** 3 N s at 60°.   **15.** 120 N.
16. 4·2 m s⁻¹ E.   **17.** 10⁷ m s⁻¹ at *ω̄* to original direction.

MISCELLANEOUS EXERCISE C

1. (i) 0·08 m; (ii) 50 N; 30 N; 50 N.
2. (i) 80 N; (ii) 94·3 N; (iii) 78·5 N.   **3.** 5 m s⁻¹; 25 kN.
4. 17 N; 8, 15 N.
5. 31 m; 2 s after second body is projected; 15 m s⁻¹ downwards, 0.
6. 1 m; 10 kg.   **7.** 8 N.   **8.** (i) 29 N, 27°; (ii) 120°.   **9.** 4 N s; 40 N.
11. 94°.   **12.** 89 N; 0·5.   **13.** 4·2 N, S18°W.   **14.** 89 N; 36°.
15. N10°E; 11·4 km.   **16.** 72 N; 68°, 44°.
17. Tensions of 50 N in *AD*, *BC*; thrusts of 71 N in *AB*, *DC*; thrust of
141 N in *AC*.
18. 25 m s⁻¹; 20 m.   **19.** 50 N.   **20.** $\frac{5}{4}$ W; $\frac{3}{4}$ W.   **21.** 2·14 : 1.   **22.** 23°.
23. 25 m s⁻¹.   **24.** 132 m; 17 m s⁻¹.   **25.** 2·35 m s⁻¹, 0·87 m s⁻¹.
26. (i) 130 N; (ii) 53°.   **27.** (i) 41°; (ii) 130 N.   **28.** 17 N.
29. 8·7 N; 1·1 s.   **30.** 15√6 ≈ 37 N.   **31.** 5 N, 29 N.
32. 10°; horizontally.   **33.** 2·5 m s⁻²; 37 N; 3·3 m s⁻¹.
34.   (i) 9*N* + 2*F* = 300, *F* ≤ 15, 33⅓ ≥ *N* ≥ 30.
          (ii) 11*N* + 8*F* = 1200, *F* ≤ 40, 109$\frac{1}{11}$ ≥ *N* ≥ 80.
          (iii) 5*N* + 6*F* = 900, 42$\frac{6}{7}$ ≤ *F* ≤ 56$\frac{1}{4}$, 128$\frac{4}{7}$ ≥ *N* ≥ 112½.

35. $\dfrac{d(u^2 - v^2)}{2\sqrt{(u^2 - v^2 \sin^2 \theta)}}.$ **36.** 32 N, 43 N.

37. 62·5 N; 72·2 N thrust, 36·1 N tension, 14·4 N tension.
38. 0·1 s; 250 m s⁻¹; 196 mm.   **39.** 8·4 m s⁻¹.   **40.** 2λ.

EXERCISE 14(*a*)

1. 430 N at 69° with *BA*; mid-point.
2. 390 N at 75° with *BA*; 1·4 m from *A*.
3. 710 N at 83° with *AB*; 1 m from *A*.
4. 126 N at 61° with *BC*; 94 mm along *BC*.
5. 92 N at 48° with *BC*; 130 mm along *CB*.
6. 42 mm beyond *B*.
8. 21**XY**, where *BX* : *XC* = 2 : 1 and *CY* : *YA* = 3 : 4.
9. Dividing *AC* in ratio 3 : 1.
11. *AX* : *XB* = 1 : 2 and *AY* : *YC* = 2 : 3.
14. Dividing *BC* externally in ratio 5 : 2.
15. *P* $\sqrt{3}$ at 30° to *BC*, meeting *BC* a distance 3*BC* from *B*.
17. 6**PG**, where *G* is the mid-point of the line joining *C* to a point of trisection of *AB*.

EXERCISE 14(*b*)

1. 11·3 newtons, S45°E. **2.** 5·5 newtons, N19°E.
3. 7·8 newtons, N64°E. **4.** 5·7, 45°, *AX* : *XB* = 1 : 3.
5. 2·2, 63°, *BX* : *AX* = 7 : 5. **6.** 4·5, 27°, mid-point.
7. 2, 90°, *BX* : *AX* = 3 : 1. **10.** 1·7 at 30° with *BC*, *CX* : *BX* = 2 : 1.
11. 19·2 N at 81° with *AB*, 17 mm from *B*.
12. *P* $\sqrt{3}$ at right angles to *AB*, dividing *BA* externally in ratio 3 : 2.
13. 1 N at 60° to *AB*. On *AB* produced, 15 *AB* from *B*.
14. 112 N, 71 N. **15.** 0·11 m from *B*, 106 N at 48° with *AB*.
16. 7·75 N, 12·2 N, 26° with *AB*. **17.** 18 N at 34° to *AB*, 1·45 m from *A*.
18. 14$\frac{1}{8}$ N along *BC*, 9$\frac{1}{2}$ N along *DC*, 1$\frac{7}{8}$ N along *DB*.
19. 6 kN, 11 m from *A*. **20.** 2 kN, 3 m from *C*. **21.** 19·5 m from bow.

EXERCISE 14(*c*)

1. 41. **2.** 9·6 N m. **3.** *b*. **4.** 3, 1, 12 N m. **5.** 500 N.
6. 2·04 N m. **7.** 10. **8.** 5 N at $\bar{\omega}$ to *AD*, 14 N m.
9. $\sqrt{3}$ N m, $\frac{5}{8}$ m from *B*.

EXERCISE 15(*a*)

1. 4·7. **2.** 3·24. **3.** 0. **4.** 9. **5.** −1·4. **6.** 6 gm. **7.** 10 kg.
8. 100 mm from end. **9.** 67 mm from end. **10.** 0·87 m above ground.
11. 0·29 from end of handle. **12.** 0·88 m from butt.
13. 36·7 mm above floor. **14.** 66·5 mm. **15.** 11·7 mm above base.
16. 21·7 mm above base. **17.** 1$\frac{1}{6}$ cm above base. **18.** 135, 90 gm.

24. $\dfrac{n^2 + n + 1}{2n(2n + 1)}$. **25.** 0·54 m from top of handle.

EXERCISE 15(b)

In Questions 1–8 the answers are given as co-ordinates referred to axes through the bottom left-hand corner of the letter.

1. $(1\frac{3}{4}, 4\frac{3}{4})$. **2.** $(2\frac{3}{11}, 6)$. **3.** $(1\frac{8}{9}, 7\frac{1}{9})$. **4.** $(1, 7\frac{1}{4})$.
5. $(1\frac{8}{9}, 4\frac{8}{9})$. **6.** $(2\frac{7}{12}, 6)$. **7.** $(2\frac{1}{10}, 7)$. **8.** $(1, 7\frac{1}{3})$.
9. 1·45 m from other end. **10.** 7·5 mm from centre.
11. (50, 25) in mm referred to OA, OB. **12.** 46 mm from AB.
13. (8·52, 8·62) referred to missing corner.
14. (161, 81) referred to AB, AD. **15.** $(-6·05, -8·07)$ referred to OA, OB.
16. $(-1·21, -6·45)$ referred to OA and a perpendicular.
17. 18 mm from centre. **18.** (59, -15) in mm referred to OA, OB.

19. $\left(\dfrac{1000 - 70\pi}{20 - \pi}, 20\right)$ referred to AB, AD. **20.** 0·93 m.

21. $(\frac{10}{11}, \frac{6}{11}, \frac{2}{11})$ from centre of parcel. **22.** 2 : 3 : 5. **23.** 1 : 4 : 3.
24. $1\frac{1}{8}$ m from each outside face of cube P.
25. 1 m, $1\frac{1}{8}$m, $1\frac{1}{8}$ m from outside faces of cube P. **26.** 37, 11, 24 mm.

EXERCISE 15(c)

1. (4, 0). **2.** (4, 0). **3.** $(0, \frac{1}{3})$. **4.** $x = \dfrac{3n(n + 1)}{2(n^2 + n + 1)}, y = 0$; $(1\frac{1}{2}, 0)$.

5. (3·6, 0). **6.** $(3\frac{4}{7}, 0)$. **7.** $(\frac{3}{4}, \frac{3}{10})$. **8.** $(\frac{3}{4}, \frac{8}{9})$.

9. $x = \dfrac{2n}{n + 1}, y = \dfrac{n^5 - 1}{5n^3(n^2 - 1)}$; $(2, \frac{1}{5})$. **10.** $\frac{5}{9}l$. **11.** 0·282 m.

12. 25 mm from O. **13.** $100\sqrt{3} \approx 173$ mm. **15.** 1 cm from O.

16. 0·48 m. **17.** $\dfrac{1000}{3(8 - \pi)} \approx 69$ mm from AB. **18.** 70 mm. **19.** 3·28 mm.

20. 17·4 mm from larger face. **21.** 37·5 mm from base of pyramid.

22. 4 cm from surface of liquid. **23.** $\frac{1}{3}\sqrt{2}$. **24.** 50 mm. **25.** $\dfrac{135}{\pi} \approx 43$ mm.

26. $\dfrac{51h}{112}$ above base.

EXERCISE 15(d)

1. 57°. **2.** 4°. **3.** 9°. **5.** 36°. **6.** 5°. **7.** $\sin^{-1}\frac{1}{3}$.
8. $\frac{2}{15}a$ from centre, 54°. **9.** 31·2 mm, 64·1 mm. **10.** $\tan^{-1}\frac{2}{3}$.
11. $\tan^{-1}\frac{4}{3}$. **13.** $2r$. **14.** stable if $h < r$. **15.** <5 cm. **16.** 1050 mm².

EXERCISE 16(a)

2. 80 J; 4 m s⁻¹. **3.** 15 N. **4.** 0·25 m. **5.** 16 N. **6.** 1·25 m.
7. 0·05. **8.** 48 m; 75 km h⁻¹. **9.** 2400 m. **10.** 15 m.
11. 3·5 m s⁻¹. **12.** 5×10^6 N. **13.** 41·5 kN. **15.** 5 m s⁻¹. **16.** 20 m.
17. 10 m s⁻¹. **18.** 10·2 m s⁻¹. **19.** 10 m. **20.** 80 J. **21.** 1·5 m s⁻¹.

Page 234   EXERCISE 16(b)

1. 1.8×10^9 J. 2. 203 J. 3. 71 J; 8·4 m s⁻¹. 4. 588 J; 588 J.
5. 9·6 J. 6. 196 kJ; 6·3 m s⁻¹. 7. 34·8 J. 8. 1·7 J; 0·10 N. 9. 18 N.
10. 2·4 m s⁻¹. 11. 18·1 m s⁻¹. 12. 6 m s⁻¹. 13. 4·95 m s⁻¹.
14. 57·4 J; 4·8 m s⁻¹. 15. 48°. 16. 8 m s⁻¹. 17. 2·4 m s⁻¹. 18. 39°.
19. 2·8 m s⁻¹. 20. 4·9 m s⁻¹. 21. 2·8 m s⁻¹. 22. 0·15 m.

Page 238   EXERCISE 16(c)

1. 98 W. 2. 39 kW. 3. 10. 4. 590 W. 5. 22·4 s. 6. 22·5 kW.
7. 1125 kW. 8. 2500 N. 9. 9·6 MN. 10. 4·8 km h⁻¹. 11. 9 kW.
12. 240 W. 13. 7·5 kW. 14. 9·8 kW. 15. 238 W. 16. 3·6 MJ.
17. 409 kW. 18. 17·7 kW. 19. 1 in 9. 20. 1200 N; 34 km h⁻¹.
21. 96 km h⁻¹; 72 km h⁻¹. 22. 120 km h⁻¹. 23. 1560 kW. 24. 4000 N.
25. 1800 N. 26. 435 kW. 27. 30 s; 360 kW. 28. 0·2 m s⁻².
29. 2300 N; 9·2 kW. 30. 750 kW. 31. 30 m s⁻¹; 0·45 m s⁻².

Page 243   EXERCISE 16(d)

1. (i) 1125 N; (ii) 1562 N. 2. 6 m s⁻¹; 36 J. 3. (i) 1·2 kJ; (ii) 30 kJ.
4. 0·51 mJ; 0·09 mJ. 5. Both 0·3 m s⁻¹; 540 J. 6. Both 0·6 m s⁻¹; 0.
7. 1, 3 m s⁻¹. 8. (i) 1·815 MJ; (ii) 10 kN. 9. 216 kJ. 10. $\frac{1}{2}mu^2$.
11. 12·6 N s. 12. 404 m s⁻¹; 43°. 13. 4·2 m s⁻¹; 0·7 m s⁻¹; 13½°.
14. 44°. 15. 495 m s⁻¹. 16. 20 m. 17. 80 N; 160 W. 18. 40 kW.
19. 900 W; one-half. 20. 600 W. 21. 2·5 m s⁻¹; 2580 N. 22. 2·63 mm.

23. 11 m. 24. (i) Both 5 m s⁻¹; (ii) 3, 9 m s⁻¹. 25. $2\sqrt{\dfrac{EM}{M^2 - m^2}}$.

27. (i) 1·75 J; (ii) 1·25 N s at $\tilde{\omega}$ S of E. 125 N; 14 mm.
28. 130 N; S32°E; 0·29 m.

Page 253   EXERCISE 17(a)

1. 24 W. 2. 72%. 3. 110 N. 4. 10 l. 5. 24; 16; 67%.
6. Greater than 1930 N. 7. $\frac{1}{22}$, 4; 18·3; 73%. 8. 50, 0·2; 60; 62½%.
9. 10; 130 kg; 87%. 10. $F = 0.1\ W + 20$. 11. 280 N; 72 mm s⁻¹.
12. $800\pi \approx 2500$ N. 13. 10 N. 14. 13·3 N. 15. 24π J; 22·6 kN.
16. 2; (i) 299 N; (ii) 314 N. 17. 3, 4; 210 kg, 280 kg. 18. 95%.
19. 78 kg; 3·06; 76·5%. 20. $F = \frac{1}{4}W + 30$.
21. (d) 4, 3·88, 97%; (e) 8, 7·8, 93%; (f) 3, 2·88, 96%;
    (g) 7, 6·93, 99%; (h) 4, 4, 100%.
22. 32; 122 N; 38%. 25. (i) 20 N; (ii) 15·3 N. 26. 200 N; 200 W.

Page 260   EXERCISE 17(b)

1. 14%. 2. 40 N. 3. 0·38 N m. 4. 314 N. 5. 0·08 N m.
6. 10 : 1; 496 N m; 99·2%. 7. 96%; 99·6%. 8. 204 N m; 4·27 kW.
9. 1 : 7; 1 in 4·4, 1 in 2·5. 10. 1100 N. 11. 3140 N. 12. 256 N m.
13. 60 : 1; 106 Nm. 14. Just over 5; 8·25 N m. 15. 80; 50 N; 62½%.
16. 153 kg; 6·5 N. 17. 6400 N. 18. 70 N; 3·5 m s⁻¹. 19. 9·8 N m.

Page 264   MISCELLANEOUS EXERCISE D

1. 43° to direction of liner's motion, 2·6T.   **2.** 90 kJ; 70 kJ.
3. 54 km h^{-1}.   **4.** 200 s; 35 m s^{-1}.   **5.** $8\frac{1}{3}$ N.   **6.** 5 mm from centre.
7. 0·87 m s^{-1}; 39 mm.   **8.** 200 m; 27·5 kJ.   **9.** 80 N; 90 J.
10. 33·3 km h^{-1}, S65°W; 1.38 p.m.; 25·5 km.   **11.** 7·2 N, 46°.
12. sin^{-1} (0·064).   **13.** 0·73 J; 0·21 N s; 0·26 J; 0·38 N s; 3·8 N.
14. 0·2 m.   **15.** $(b - c \sin \theta)/(1 - \sin \theta)$.   **16.** 0·63 m; 52°.
17. (i) 2650 J; (ii) 675 J.   **18.** 89%; 75 W; 112 N.   **19.** 41°; 51 N.
20. (i) 30° to horizontal, 50 N; (ii) 44 N; 7° to vertical, 47 N.
21. 10 N; 0·12 N m.   **22.** 97 N, 25 N; 0·8 m s^{-1}.   **23.** 2 m s^{-1}; 18 kJ.
24. 0·58; 500, 200 N.   **25.** 45 N.   **26.** $OG = \frac{1}{4}OB$.
27. 6 m s^{-1}; 0·94 J; 15 ms.   **28.** 40π; 20%.   **29.** 0·1 m s^{-2}.
30. 250 N, about CD; 23 N; 273 N.
31. 2BZ, where Z is the mid-point of DC; tan^{-1} 2.
32. 120 kN; 1 MW; 45 km h^{-1}.   **33.** 1·5 m s^{-1}.   **34.** 72·5°.

35. $\frac{3}{4}a$; $\dfrac{W}{\sqrt{3}}$, $\dfrac{2W}{\sqrt{3}}$;   **36.** (i) 6·4 mm; (ii) 9·6 mm.   **37.** 14·8 kW.

38. 5; 4·4; 89%.   **39.** $\frac{4}{3}$; $\frac{4}{3}a$.   **40.** $\bar{\omega}$; $\frac{3}{4}$.
43. (i) $a \leqslant \mu g$; (ii) $\frac{1}{2}at^2(a - \mu g) \leqslant \mu g d$.   **44.** (i) 5 m; (ii) 15·8 m.
45. 49, 42, 66 mm.   **46.** 2330 N.   **47.** 150 N; 148·5 mm.
50. 7 s; 17·5 m.   **51.** 90° $- \frac{1}{2}(\alpha + \beta)$.   **52.** (i) $\frac{7}{24}$; (ii) $\frac{7}{15}$; (iii) $\frac{7}{9}$.
54. (i) 224 kW; (ii) 11·2 kN.   **55.** 42 N at 8° to horizontal; 210 N.

58. $\dfrac{2400 + x^2}{60 + 2x}$; 3·5 $< x <$ 68·5.

60. (i) $\dfrac{m - M \sin \alpha - M\mu \cos \alpha}{M + m} g$; (ii) $\dfrac{M \sin \alpha - m - M\mu \cos \alpha}{M + m} g$.